Written

D. A. LEE

First paperback edition November 2019

Panagiotis Lampridis - Book Design Stars

ISBN 978-1-9162726-0-6 (paperback)
ISBN 978-1-9162726-1-3 (eBook)
ISBN 978-1-9162726-4-4 (Golden Edition paperback)

Published by
Loving Creative Inspirational Publishing

www.dalee.co.uk

Golden Edition Paperback Printed and bound in Great Britain by
Clays Ltd, Elcograf S.p.A.

TABLE OF CONTENTS

Prologue   2

PART 1   20

CHAPTER ONE   21
– Dreams –   21
CHAPTER TWO   25
– Ashcroft –   25
CHAPTER THREE   32
– Raise Them Well –   32
CHAPTER FOUR   38
– The Grocery Store –   38
CHAPTER FIVE   50
- Babajee –   50
CHAPTER SIX   59
– Mosque –   59
CHAPTER SEVEN   69
– The Man with the Orange Beard –   69
CHAPTER EIGHT   77
– Fairy Stories –   77
CHAPTER NINE   86
– The Lady in the Fur Coat –   86
CHAPTER TEN   98
- School Dinners –   98
CHAPTER ELEVEN   110
– Lunchtime Specials –   110
CHAPTER TWELVE   118
– Eid and the Letter –   118
CHAPTER THIRTEEN   128
– Fight and Love –   128

CHAPTER FOURTEEN   137

– Trip to Bangladesh–   137

CHAPTER FIFTEEN   148

– Sacrifice–   148

CHAPTER SIXTEEN   160

– Shelley–   160

CHAPTER SEVENTEEN   173

– School Is Not for Girls –   173

CHAPTER EIGHTEEN   188

– Failing at School –   188

CHAPTER NINETEEN   200

– The Final Year –   200

CHAPTER TWENTY   211

– The Arranged Marriage –   211

CHAPTER TWENTY-ONE   222

- Surround Yourself with What You Believe In –   222

CHAPTER TWENTY-TWO   232

– Judgement Day –   232

CHAPTER TWENTY-THREE   240

– Suicide–   240

CHAPTER TWENTY-FOUR   251

– The Awakening –   251

CHAPTER TWENTY-FIVE   263

– The University of Life –   263

PART 2   271

CHAPTER TWENTY-SIX   272

– Love War –   272

CHAPTER TWENTY-SEVEN   283

– Love Conquers All –   283

CHAPTER TWENTY-EIGHT   294

– Love Lost –   294

CHAPTER TWENTY-NINE   310

– Empty –   310

CHAPTER THIRTY   325

– Searching for Mr Right –   325

CHAPTER THIRTY-ONE   338

– Telltale Signs–   338

CHAPTER THIRTY-TWO   351

– Rules of Engagement-   351

CHAPTER THIRTY-THREE   361

– The Proposal-   361

CHAPTER THIRTY-FOUR   379

– The Wedding –   379

CHAPTER THIRTY-FIVE   396

– Dead than Divorced–   396

CHAPTER THIRTY-SIX   412

– Purification –   412

CHAPTER THIRTY-SEVEN   428

– Letting Go–   428

CHAPTER THIRTY-EIGHT   450

– The Innocent Departed–   450

CHAPTER THIRTY-NINE   466

– The Return –   466

CHAPTER FORTY   482

– The Sign –   482

CHAPTER FORTY-ONE   496

– The Plan–   496

CHAPTER FORTY-TWO   516

– Breathing Light –   516

CHAPTER FORTY-THREE   529

– Perpetual–   529

CHAPTER FORTY-FOUR   542

– Confessions –   542

CHAPTER FORTY-FIVE   557

– Mamajee Speaks Out –   557

DEDICATION

To my friends and family, who gave me strength in the face of adversity; to my husband, who has guided and supported me throughout the years, you have been my inspiration to write; and to my children, who have taught me how boundless and unconditional love really is. It is because of you that I can aspire to be loving, creative and inspirational, always.

Everything comes to us that belongs to us if we create the capacity to receive it.

—Rabindranath Tagore

PROLOGUE

Tere were days when the one-mile walk from school felt endless, the heat rising from the rice fields and the sun high in the sky. Along the path, they could smell the soft, peaty, humid air, hear cowbells clinging to thin cattle as weary farmers stirred them along the riverbanks. Sometimes the pair side tracked a little, climbing trees, filling their dress skirts with sour cherries and guava along the river path, and in a contented giggle, they sat, devouring their pickings in the shade. These were timeless moments when only the faint azan from the nearby mosque prompted any urgency to scurry home before they got a scolding. Nanni would have frowned had she known, if not the rest of the family, had they been caught wandering aimlessly along the riverbanks with the luring glances of menfolk making their way to prayer.

It was on one of these days that she was stopped abruptly by someone in her path. The sun behind the silhouette beamed intensely on her doll-like complexion, making it difficult to see clearly. She tried to move out of his way, but the stern figure was inescapable. An elongated shadow cast over her along the river path as he slowly approached her.

From what she could see, he was unusually tall for a Bengali man, his long, chiselled face, pointed chin, a nose that stood high like a mountain nestled between two raised hills for cheekbones. Black hair neatly combed into a side parting. It seemed strange to Mamajee that he was wearing such heavy clothing. The sharp, tailored pin-striped suit and a collared shirt with tie looked uncomfortable as the sun baked the dirt path. He stopped just before the shadow cast over her face and stood a few feet away while puffing generously at a cigarette.

The man stared at Mamajee intensely, without even a passing glance at Laila, who stood firm to Mamajee's right.

"Where is your village?" he asked Mamajee, cocking his head for an answer.

"Saling Bazaar," she replied. Mamajee's face intensified with curiosity; thoughts raced around in her head for the trouble she might be in with the man, perhaps for picking sour cherries or for dawdling along the river path, where it was frowned upon for girls to be out at prayer times. She supposed.

"What is your father's name?" he demanded, with a steady and impatient stare. His voice sounded dusty, as if his throat was full of ashes.

"Abdul Salem," Mamajee replied, coyly looking down.

He nodded slowly, smirking and folding his arms, as though he knew something. He exhaled a long stream of smoke as if it had been pent up in a dragon's cave for years. He stood for a moment, assessing her, and then turned away, heading back to the bridge that met the river and main road.

Mamajee paused for a moment as Laila continued down the path, making her way home. She followed him with her eyes, curious, along the bridge to where he joined another man, who sat inside a parked blue Morris, waiting for him. The sun's glare on its roof made him barely visible to her. For a moment he paused, looked back at her from the open window as he started up the engine, then drove off, throwing out the cigarette butt as they pulled away.

*

Mamajee arrived home through the guest entrance, where Nana had lined coconut palms along the mosaic walkway. She usually came through the guest entrance when she was late, an attempt to go unnoticed by the frowning eyes of Nanni, who by now would have given them a lesson on the virtues of a woman. But Mamajee had somehow escaped unnoticed and made her way uneasily through the veranda to the water pump to wash her soiled feet and cherry-stained hands. The cooling water was an immediate relief to her sun-blazed skin. As she wiped her face, her attention was drawn to the faint whispers of conversations in the guest room. Curious, she peered through the veranda window to see who it was her father was speaking to.

"Salem Saheb, I know your daughter has not come of age, but the Saheb [*sir*] from London is not here for very long," came the voice of a man.

Nana was seated in a full bamboo armchair, looking down at the floor in thought. His body, skinny and frail, was gently propped up by a large cushion supporting his back. A hacking cough flared up, becoming a welcome relief to stall his decision or response to the man's proposition.

Mamajee listened intently from behind the fly net, peering through the hatch occasionally to conceal her presence.

The man had his back to her, his body leaning in, facing Nana. He continued to press Nana. "Do you want a good future for her, your daughter? If something happened, how could you forgive yourself, Salem Saheb?"

Mamajee became curious. *Were they talking about Laila?* she thought. "It can't be," she whispered to herself. "She's not old enough."

"Oh Lord!" Mamajee gasped as the thought dawned on her. *Laila? Would they want her to be married? How can they do this?* Laila was only a year and a half older than Mamajee. The thought seemed far removed from her. *How could a child of only fourteen make a wife?*

Mamajee slumped down on the cold stone surface, resting up against the outside wall. She thought about how she would miss the long afternoons together, when they would dress up in old sarees, winding them round so tight they would fall over each other in giggles. The tummy tickles, chasing each other around the pond. The way Laila always gave up her candy, even when she pined for it for herself. She thought about how she would cope if her sister went away. How Laila always braided her hair, and the dolls they made from offcuts of saree material.

"What are you doing there, sitting on the floor, child? You will get your dress dirty and catch a cold." Nanni looked unpardonably down at Mamajee, her voice whispering the words but her mouth not giving up the frown. It tamed into a thin line when she saw the man seated with Nana in the guest room.

"Come into the kitchen and start serving the tea, will you?" she said, ushering Mamajee down the hallway to the kitchen. "And put on your scarf! You should know better. Girls your age shouldn't be walking around with their bosoms on show!" She frowned, turning to walk in the direction of the kitchen.

Mamajee scowled back, following her. *As if I have anything to show off,* she thought.

"Is the man Baba's talking to here for Laila?" Mamajee asked uneasily, fearing Nanni may get angry for prying.

"No," she said, "not for Laila."

A sense of relief filled Mamajee's heart. *Thank God! Laila will be here with me, and I won't miss her!* she thought.

An inner smile glowed outwardly, and with a skip she reached for the cups in the cupboard. She placed the Chinese red-flowered cups in a pattern on a tea tray.

"Are there any biscuits, Ammajan?" she said as she laid sweetmeats and the teapot on the tray. Nanni didn't respond. She was busying herself around the kitchen, opening up cupboards and making sniffling noises. Her back turned away from Mamajee. Mamajee sensed some unease in Nanni's behaviour, how her saree veiled her face unnecessarily, as there were no men around to worry about modesty. She bent her head low, pretending to look for something on the ground, and Mamajee sensed some anxiety in the way she snuffled into the tail of her saree, taking in small, shallow breaths.

Mamajee inched nearer to where Nanni stood, peering over to look at her face.

"Ammajan, what is the matter? Why are you crying?" Mamajee pressed her hand against Nanni's elbow. Nanni took a deep breath, sniffling, wiping tears from wet cheeks that flowed faster than the monsoon rivers. Leaning against the cupboard, she shrank down into a heap on the drystone floor. Mamajee sat next to her, tentative, waiting for a response.

"Your baba was a good man, Eva, may Allah have mercy on his soul, and he did everything to keep you both healthy and alive, you and Laila. You were only three months old when we got the news. He was lucky, you know; he had months before the snake poison got the better of him. Still, we didn't know Allah had chosen what he willed, and I had no way to survive on my own with the two of you. Our future would have been difficult." Nanni's eyes gazed off into the distance as she continued.

"That was when your boro mama [*uncle*] made a quick decision about our future and brought us here; he found us somewhere safe and secure. Your new father looked after both of you like his own, dressed you, fed you and gave you a home." She paused, passing a hefty lump of air down her throat; it pulsed into her veil.

"Blessed I am by Allah for the life we have had here for so many years; that's why we are not here to judge what is written, Beti [*daughter*], only Allah knows what is written for us. I am only grateful to your boro mama in making sure I was safe, and now it's your turn, my little flower."

Mamajee looked perplexed. "My turn?" she said to Nanni. Nanni nodded, wiping tears from her neck. "Your father is not well, flower, and he needs to make sure you will always be okay, my love." She heaved as she pulled herself into a comfortable position. "And when girls reach a certain age, they have to leave their family and be looked after by another family. That's the way Allah has planned it."

"Another family? I don't want to go anywhere, Ammajan. I want to stay here with you."

Nanni said nothing.

"I want to be here with you," Mamajee continued, burying her face deep into Nanni's saree. "I don't want to be looked after by anyone else." She cried, coiling up close to Nanni, who sat despondently for a few minutes.

"Oh, my dear," Nanni sighed deeply, "this is what Allah intended for all of us, and you must obey Allah in everything you do, you see, child? Allah sees everything. The good, the bad, the past, the present and the future, even what you are doing now. Your whole life has been written. It is faith in Allah; it is this you submit to. Only Allah knows why this is written for you, but this is what has been written. Everything you do now, to obey Allah's will, will serve you in your next life, Beti. Do you see, my love?"

Mamajee thought about what this meant, why she had to leave to feel safe. She found in her the capacity to trust, to have faith, even though she did not comprehend what it meant. *What has Allah written?* It could only mean that she had to put her faith into something or someone powerful, someone who knew more than her own mother. The one she loved the most. It filled her with fear, knowing that Allah was watching, that she could be doing something wrong by Allah if she didn't follow his will. She knew she had to suppress it and resist her own needs as the tightness in her belly filled up from Nanni's words. She longed for time to freeze.

As she sat coiled up on the kitchen floor by Nanni's side, Mamajee knew that Nanni's tears meant she was helpless in responding to any plea; she was being subjected to a power higher than her. Mamajee knew she was a mother who had little choice in what Allah wanted or desired.

"Let me serve the guest," Nanni said, picking herself up off the floor. She wiped her tears with the end of her scarf. Then she pulled Mamajee up to her feet, passed the tea tray into her child's hands. Mamajee steadied her body from the strain on her arms as she made her way down the hallway.

She paced herself slowly, the teacups and spoons clattering on the tray, the mud floor cold and damp on her feet. She tried not to think about Nanni's teary face, which came in flashes in her mind, or the thought of what this meant.

Perhaps there is nothing to worry about. Maybe they have just come to have tea and just want to make sure I have beautiful things, the way Baba always buys nice things for me.

As she approached the door, she heard conversations between the men, slow and subdued, which fell silent as she entered. A man rose from his seat and smiled at her as she put the tray down. It was then that she caught a fleeting glance at him. The blood rushed to her face as she realised who it was. What did he want from her? Was it him? It looked like him. Had he followed her home?

The man smiled at her as he sat down, gesturing to her to take a seat. "Come, come, sit here," he said with uplifting praise. Nana remained seated in his chair, his arms loosely draping, chest dipping in and out with each heavy breath, his face grave, looking down at the coffee table in front of him.

"Have some tea, Rahman Saheb," Nana said, gargling his throat awkwardly. "This is my daughter Eva."

Mamajee looked over at Nana and then looked timidly down. She felt self-conscious and uneasy about being introduced. It was not normal for her father to introduce her in such a way.

The man looked at her, assessing her with his eyes and nodding his head in approval. "Eva? Eva, did you say?" the man said. "The 'one who cares, guards and protects', yes, it's a very nice name. Well, Salem Saheb, you know what my thoughts are on this. Now, you tell me, tell me what you want to do." Rahman Saheb leaned in to look at Nana, urging a response from him. The room fell silent again, with only the slight chink of a teacup as Rahman Saheb brought it to his lips, his eyes fixed on Nana for a response.

Nana's hands rested on the seat to steady himself. Mamajee took a small glimpse at Nana; the laboured breathing made a wheezing sound caught in the phlegm rising up in his throat. He lowered his gaze to the ground.

A long pause continued, which to Mamajee felt like decades of sitting silently. Her eyes, lowered to the floor, gave in to forming patterns with the mosaic tiles.

Nana looked out through the window; a mynah bird flew into the mango tree that Nana had planted years ago when Mamajee, Laila and Nanni had first arrived, to mark their marriage ceremony. His mind reflected on how it was the only wedding gift Nanni would accept. Her warm heart spared Nana any trouble, freeing him from the seething glances and the watchful, jealous eyes of Boro Ma, (Nana's first wife), who, on the day of their wedding, wouldn't even let Nanni bring her newborn and Laila into the house. Nanni wanted nothing more than shelter and security from Nana, but he could see the brooding jealousy as Boro Ma observed how he was falling for her. It wasn't uncommon for a man to have extra wives. No one could refute his reason: a young, beautiful, compassionate seventeen-year-old with two children. Her fair skin, face like a moonbeam, a ray of fresh light, her tenderness towards him in her voice. Boro Ma could offer none of this, evidently, her tired eyes, the emptiness that lay between years of trying. Seeing Nanni had presented him with things he yearned for and couldn't have. He knew it disgusted Boro Ma, even more so that Nanni made no demands, giving her less of a reason to detest her. Still, she had silently accepted. There was no ceremony of sorts, nor jewellery. Nanni wouldn't accept any of it. Just a simple exchange of vows was all that existed between the two of them, her brother as a witness. Nanni bit her lip as the vows were exchanged, monitoring the rage brooding in Boro Ma, as her newborn lay crying on the floor in the other room. It had long surpassed the morning feed as the sun climbed in the sky.

Laila tugged on Nanni's arm, wanting, needing. She sucked the end of the embroidered scarf Nanni had worn for the occasion, which bought her some time. So when pressed by Nana for an answer on what she wanted as a gift, she'd responded, "Just a tree for some shade and where we can hear the birds sing is all I ask for, nothing more. Somewhere secure and safe, that's all."

"I agree," he said faintly to the man. Mamajee glanced up from the corner of her scarf to see Nana's face and wondered what had been agreed in the long yet brief exchange between the two men.

"You can go now, Beti," said Nana.

Mamajee rose from her seat, eyes downward, unable to bring herself to look at the man staring back at her as she tiptoed out of the room. There was something tense that happened in that room, incomprehensible in her naive view of the world. The lingering odour of cigarettes in her scarf beckoned gasps of fresh air into her lungs. She looked out from the hallway window and saw Laila and the other girls in the courtyard, playing. They were building a small mud house for their rag dolls, smoothing the mounds of dirt around the sides with their hands. She sought nothing more than to go out and play. She was scampering down the hallway towards the main door when she was stopped in her tracks.

"Just where do you think you are going?" Nanni frowned, her face stern and cold. Mamajee saw an altered face now, one of complete detachment from her daughter.

"I want to go and play with Laila and Ameena," Mamajee implored.

"No. You will not be playing with them anymore; you have to stay indoors from now on. You are not to go out without my permission, do you understand? What will people say if you are seen running around outside? You need to be indoors, in your room. I want you to cover your head with a scarf from now on, and don't talk too loudly. Women are not supposed to be running around like a boy; people will shame you."

"Shame me? But I have always played outside?"

"Don't talk back," Nanni stormed. "When you leave us, you will have to listen to everything your other parents will tell you to do. You will have to sit and obey whatever their wishes are for you. You do not talk back; you sit quietly, and you answer with respect. Now, run along to your room and do as you are told."

Mamajee couldn't process it all. *Other parents?* she thought. She took a long last look at her friends and Laila in the courtyard and wondered what she had done to deserve the severity of Nanni's tone, the sharp words, Nanni's stony face.

As she sat there staring out of the bedroom window, she took in the view of the river, slightly blocked by the mango tree. She recollected how she and Laila frequently climbed out to pick ripened fruit, swaying in the shaded, densely tangled branches, laughing at the boatmen sailing past who couldn't see them hiding. Sometimes they would call out to people on the river path and giggle when they were unable to process where the sounds came from. It would always make Laila laugh when Mamajee used to make funny noises like birds and confuse them and other passers-by. The tree was a high lookout point for the odd car passing by the bridge beyond Nana's vast expanse of rice fields, which was always of great excitement to her and Laila. Cars were rarely seen, and the rumbling of an engine now and then would have them climbing up, catching their dress skirts, scuffing knees and grazing elbows. Now, as Mamajee looked out from that window, she thought about whether she would ever enjoy moments like that again.

*

Mamajee woke to the sound of people entering the house. A furore of loud noises and laughter travelled down the hallway to the kitchen. Nanni came rushing into the room.

"Eva, oh, Eva! Get your clothes and wear something nice, quickly! Some guests have arrived."

Mamajee contemplated. *Who could be arriving so early?* she thought. She put on a pressed shalwar kameez (Indian tunic), one that Nanni kept aside for when guests were visiting. It was pale blue with blueberry patterns all over the fabric. She tied her hair into a plait with a side parting and draped her hair with a light-blue crêpe chiffon scarf that matched the suit. She had forgotten all about the conversations from yesterday after school. Mamajee scurried down the hallway to the kitchen.

"There are some people here to see you," Nanni said. "Don't say too much; just stay quiet. I will do the talking, child."

"Get the tea on the stove for me, will you?" Nanni ordered, hurrying.

Mamajee looked perplexed. *People? Who wanted to see me?* she thought. "Why would they want to see me?" she asked Nanni, baffled.

Nanni didn't respond and continued on, opening up her grand cupboard, which stored her best cutlery and china, carefully lifting a tray out from the mirrored glass display case. She busily placed tea-cups on their saucers, wiping away the spillages from a gold-rimmed platter. A box of biscuits that the guests had brought was hurriedly opened and displayed delicately on china dessert plates.

Mamajee found it hard to make eye contact with Nanni, which aroused her suspicions more. She knew something was wrong. It felt unwarranted and precarious in Nanni's jitteriness, but Mamajee refrained from questioning in case it led to another snap remark. She relented in the thought that her mother loved her. After all, she knew best. Making her happy was the most important thing she could do right now, and to query anything would be disrespectful and insulting to her.

Nanni continued to busy herself. She peeled and sliced sweet mangoes, placing them on a gold-rimmed china plate. A large pot of rice pudding stood bubbling away on the mud stove. She reached over for more china from the grand cupboard, placing them all out on the bamboo table.

"What are you looking at, Eva? Can you help me?"

Mamajee rushed from one side of the kitchen to the other, trying to determine where she could assist, and failed in her efforts to support Nanni.

Nanni flustered, busying herself, reaching from cupboard to cupboard, pulling out spoons, saucers, sugar bowls. A box of sweet-meats was emptied out onto a platter in a pleasing display. Rice pudding was poured carefully into the centre of dessert bowls with a sprinkling of saffron and pistachios. She poured hot, frothy milk into a small milk jug and decanted a pot of hot brewed tea into a china teapot.

Suddenly sounds of footsteps came from the hallway, with a chuckling of laughter from an upbeat voice.

"Chachima, oh, Chachima," came the voice.

"Quick, Eva, cover your head and move into the other room," Nanni ushered Mamajee. She had just enough time to cover her head before a lady came through, dressed in a white-and-silver saree with star patterns embroidered along the hem. The veil of her saree was intricately laced with silver thread work that neatly rested on her head as if to not disturb the carefully combed centre parting and low-tied bun.

It was no ordinary day saree, Mamajee observed. It looked like something you would wear on a special occasion. She seemed relatively young, in her mid-twenties, but had broad hips and a full, voluptuous figure. There was an air of status about her, as if she was more knowledgeable and worldly than Nanni.

Mamajee tried to hide behind Nanni.

"Oh, is this your daughter, Chachima?" she said, peering over Nanni.

"Yes." Nanni smiled derisorily.

"She is very shy, Boyn [*sister*]."

She smiled lovingly at Mamajee.

"It is good that she is shy, Boyn," she said, looking approvingly at Mamajee. "Women shouldn't be open; they should hold everything within them." She smiled, nudging Mamajee a little with her elbow.

"Yes," Nanni agreed as she nodded, although the rest of her body seemed to disagree. It seemed frozen, stiff and devoid of joy.

"Come and sit at the table, Boyn," Nanni said, assisting her to a chair.

The woman sat down, politely smiling at Mamajee as Nanni poured the tea into a cup and served some sweetmeats.

"How old are you?" she asked Mamajee.

"Twelve years old," Mamajee said, turning to Nanni for assurance and permission.

"Hmm, has she bled yet?"

Nanni looked down at the floor. Mamajee looked puzzled. She wasn't entirely sure what they were talking about.

"Come here." The woman beckoned Mamajee, drawing her towards her. She inspected Mamajee's hands, nails, feet, scanning them for imperfections.

"She's very fair. No wonder the Londoni Saheb is so happy."

Nanni sat on a stool behind Mamajee, a faint smile in modest agreement. Mamajee felt awkward standing there as the woman inspected her with long, solitary looks.

"Let's go into the other room," the woman declared as she rose to her feet, guiding Mamajee towards the door into one of the bedrooms. There were crowds of people in the room, young and old women who had come to meet the guests. Some sat on chairs, the bed or on the floor. A large white bedsheet had been placed on the floor. In the centre of the room rested a black trunk, embossed in gold with matching ornate clasps and catches. Next to it were two smaller suitcases and a vanity box to match.

"Eva, come, Beti, come, sit here next to me on the floor," said the woman. Mamajee sat cross-legged, looking around at the people gazing back at her.

"This is what the Londoni Saheb has bought for you," the woman said, opening up the trunk.

Mamajee was shocked and laughed with joy. "Oh my!" she said, her palms covering her face. There in the box was the most beautiful deep-red and gold-embroidered saree. Flowers and vines intricately laced around the border, which sparkled in the rays of light seeping in through the window. There was a gasp of delight from the guests as the cloth was gently lifted and raised for everyone to see.

"Eva, this is just for you!" the woman continued, excited. Mamajee couldn't believe it; she laughed, overjoyed, clapping her hands with glee that something so beautiful was given to her. The woman brought out more things from the box. She placed a red patent sandal with a diamante buckle onto the ground, accompanied by a matching blouse and red petticoat for the saree. There were red glass bangles with white and gold dots. A make-up box with a vast array of colours. Mamajee's face beamed with delight. The younger girls her age sat excitedly edging nearer and nearer to the wondrous box of delights, peering over the top to get a second glimpse. More items came out: a white cotton saree for prayer times, ten different sarees, all with matching petticoats and blouses. Handbags, three different styles, a black patent leather one with a shiny gold clasp. A red cross-body-style shoulder bag in red and gold satin. The girls and Laila marvelled. Such gifts were rarely seen in the villages.

"You are so lucky, Eva," Laila said, smiling. Her comments, although generous, were laden with envy that she tried desperately to quash. Mamajee covered her mouth with her scarf and looked speechless.

Nanni peered in through the doorway, hiding one side of her face with her veil, her face neutral, her large round eyes looking at her daughter's flushed face as each item was lifted out of the box. A small tear formed and melted down the side of her high, rounded cheekbone and travelled to the crevice in her neck. She sniffled and beamed back a smile. Her fair face, like the sun cast over by a rain cloud. She knew what this meant; she knew that this was hard. This was a sacrifice but one that would be good for everyone.

Mamajee looked up at Nanni and smiled. She desperately wanted to go over to Nanni and show her all these things, but to her disappointment, Nanni turned and walked back into the kitchen. Then Mamajee's focus shifted back to the new clothes and items in the box.

The woman called out for Nanni as she returned with a tray of tea and sweetmeats.

"After tea, Chachima, please could you ask the women and girls to leave the room? I want to talk to Eva alone." Nanni gave a slow nod as she sat and sipped her tea.

"Eva, can we play with your sarees?" Laila said as she clapped her hands eagerly with excitement.

Mamajee clasped her hands and brought her shoulders in with excitement at the thought. "Yes, let's play with them after tea!"

The other women sat and smiled; some laughed, shaking their heads in amusement. Nanni sat calmly; there were few words, just the occasional nod as people commented on the finery that had been gifted to her daughter.

"Dear sisters, if you don't mind, please can you help in the kitchen? We have a lot of cooking and preparation to do." The girls departed the room, all except Nanni, Mamajee and Laila, who were asked to stay behind.

"Listen, Eva," the lady said, looking at her and holding both her hands. "All of these clothes and beautiful things are for you because you are special, because the Londoni Saheb wants you to wear them. Are you happy to accept?"

Mamajee couldn't believe it. Such beautiful gifts, even receiving *one* would have been a pleasure. She looked over at Laila, who giggled shyly back at the thought of trying them on. Mamajee nodded. "Yes, I do." She looked at Nanni, who didn't make eye contact and responded with a subdued smile.

"It is settled, then," said the lady, looking at Nanni and Mamajee with approval. "Laila, can you help Eva into her things? We will start the prayers soon after lunch."

Mamajee looked curiously at the lady, wondering what that meant, but Laila's excitement at dressing up distracted Mamajee from any other thoughts.

"Laila, will you get her ready?" repeated the woman.

"Yes, yes, yes!" said Laila. The girls excitedly unboxed the remaining items. Nanni and the woman looked over at the girls playing as they left the room to make a start on the food preparation.

In the kitchen, the women hurried around, cutting vegetables, peeling onions. The younger girls sorted the runner beans. Two large pots stood bubbling on the stove. One woman sat on a bamboo mat, slicing betel nuts with a betel nut slicer. Her mouth blood red from juices of the paan she had been chewing as she sat cross-legged, humming a ghazal. The other women instantly recognised it and joined in as they cooked merrily away. The cooking continued on for a couple of hours.

Meanwhile, Mamajee and Laila played happily in their room. Laila applied powder to Mamajee's face. It made her already fair complexion a pale cream colour. Mamajee winced as it stung a little when the powdered perfume caught her eye. Next, Laila drew out long eyeliner lines that whipped at the ends like two black threads. She applied lipstick onto her cheeks, rubbing it in, making it similar

to the rosy cheeks on her rag doll. Laila smiled pleasedly at her remarkable ability to turn Mamajee into a princess. Mamajee picked up
a hand mirror, turning her face to each side, and giggled.

"More red lipstick," she pointed out to Laila. Laila smiled and
looked for the red lipstick colour in the vanity box, applying it carefully around her lips.

"There," she said. "You look beautiful now."

Mamajee giggled again shyly at her, and the two girls laughed at
the pleasure it brought them.

"It is time to put the veil on, Eva," Laila said excitedly. Mamajee
blushed as she lifted the heavy veil onto her hair and pinned it in
place.

"Oh my!" Laila gasped. "You look like a beautiful rani."

The two girls danced around the room. Suddenly there was a
knock on the door, and it opened. The girls stopped dancing, calmly
sitting back on the floor to see who it was.

Nanni stood at the door with a platter laden with milk and sweetmeats. Her face seemed neutral, and there was a distance about it; it
seemed colourless. It confused Mamajee that Nanni had brought a
tray of food when there were no guests to serve in the room. The
milk came steaming in a small red Venetian glass decorated with
swirling gold patterns.

"Come and sit down for me on the cloth." Nanni spoke calmly
to her daughter.

Mamajee sat quietly down, smiling, while Laila knelt beside her.
Nanni joined her, the gold tray placed in front of Mamajee. She
looked down at the tray on the ground, puzzled. *Is all this for me?*
Mamajee thought. *It's as if I am a guest!* Mamajee laughed, directing
her amusement at Nanni, who seemed unresponsive and silent.
Mamajee's face scrunched a little at the absurdity of it all.

Then she looked up and gasped. Standing in front of her was
Mullah Saheb, her Arabic teacher. She wanted to run and hide with
embarrassment. It seemed obscene to be in his presence in this way.
Oh no, I am going to be in trouble, she thought. The thought horrified
her for missing lessons that morning. But Mullah Saheb didn't say a

word; he entered the room. There was no eye contact, as though Mamajee was unrecognisable. He joined them cross-legged on the floor, seating himself opposite her with the tray between them. He mumbled prayers as she continued to look down coyly with embarrassment.

"Okay, let's start," he said, clearing his throat. Boro Mama, Nanni's brother, came into the room and sat down beside Mullah Saheb. He continued to recite some prayers, and everyone joined in for the verse, entering the room with long, wailing notes. Mamajee became completely surrounded by people. She wanted to say something but was muted entirely by the loud offerings of prayer. She didn't fully understand nor dared to question what the prayers were for. Everybody raised their palms in worship and chanted the final auspicious verse from the Quran in harmony.

Mamajee glanced over at Nanni, who looked like she was breaking down in tears as she recited them, the words of Allah humbling her. When the prayer came to a close, Mullah Saheb turned to face Mamajee, who was looking down at the tray in front of her.

"By the grace of Allah, do you, Eva Fatima Khanom, daughter of Abdul Salem Hoque, accept this marriage? Say you agree."

Mamajee was speechless. She looked at Nanni, not knowing what this meant.

"Just say you agree," said Nanni, her face teary with the recital.

"I agree...?" she said, repeating the words questioningly. And no sooner had the words spilled out of her mouth than the whole room rose to their feet, and Mamajee was forced up by somebody behind to stand in prayer. Nanni was crying now in loud, aching sounds. Mamajee stood beside her, shocked, baffled and puzzled. Laila stood close by, quietly to her right, the bodies towering between them like swaying palm trees to the motion of prayer. She looked at Mamajee, also trying to make sense of it all.

Everyone walked slowly out, Mamajee being moved with the current of bodies through the hallway, where onlookers from the courtyard peered through the mesh windows. More people swarmed around the sides of the yard, trying to get a glimpse. Mamajee ambled as she took it all in. The swarm of bodies, the heat. The finality that came with her words became overwhelming. Just at that moment, Nanni broke down and fell to the ground, crying. The men gathered around Mamajee and placed her in a traditional bridal carriage.

"Mamajeejan!" Mamajee cried out to Nanni from the carriage. "No! Please!" Mamajee struggled. "Let me go! Don't let them take me, Mamajeejan! Mamajeejan, I don't want to go! Laila, help me! Somebody! Abba! Help me! Don't let me go!"

Mamajee screamed and cried for help, but nobody listened. She realised now, too late, that this was not a play wedding; this was it, her new life.

PART 1

CHAPTER ONE
- Dreams -

W hen I was about four years old, Mamajee and I would sit by the window, watching out on the rolling hills. We would watch the deep-green Pennines changing colour with the rising sun over the hilltops. The way those moody clouds covered the sky like a grey veil, shrouding the hills in darkness. Then a glimmer of orange and peach tones would break through, reflecting from the houses onto Mamajee's face as she talked endlessly about her childhood.

We would watch the planes fly over, beyond the hills, Mamajee's watery eyes glazed over with a vacant, fixed stare as each one passed over and out of sight.

"There goes another one," she would sigh, returning to the fireplace where we ate our breakfast of crisp buttered toast and strong-brewed tea.

I would watch her as she dipped the toast into the tea, soaking it in the cup, the juices from the bread dripping onto her chin occasionally as her mouth drew long breaths full of unspoken sentences. I watched that empty stare every morning, looking out of the window.

"Mamajee, where is Bangladesh?" I asked her one morning.

She sighed deeply between the morsels of bread and sips of tea.

"It's somewhere far, far away." She whispered the vowels with long breaths as if to send each word there.

"Farther than my school?"

"Much farther – you couldn't walk there. Oh, but it's a beautiful place. Always green, there are rice fields, and the sun shines until it sets in the sky, and the children laugh and play all day." A smile broke out on her lips, causing dimples in her cheeks and her eyes to sparkle as if by some miracle she was transported there. I smiled at the thought of being there.

"Can we go there?"

She rose up from the fireplace, slowly, almost dreamily walking to the window.

"That would be all I'd wish for," she said, shaking her head. "But it is not possible."

"Why, Mamajee? Why can't we go back?"

She breathed in as she looked up at the pale sky, the rolling towns across the Pennines, the stillness of it with the bare trees and shrubs that winter had now rendered lifeless across the landscape. A plane flew over, and her eyes followed it until it disappeared into a cloud. Her smile faded out, like sunbeams cast over by a rain cloud, as it passed out of sight.

"Oh, can we go there tomorrow?" I asked eagerly.

"No, not tomorrow." Her expression saddened.

"Why, Mamajee? Why can't we go?"

"Because…" She paused, distracted, shaking her head a little.

She remained with her thoughts, unresponsive as she leaned her head against the window, her breath fogging up a circle against the glass.

As she looked on through the window, she seemed suddenly distracted; her eyes were drawn to a light beam on the hill. A car had pulled up on the driveway of the white house that stood alone on the hill, surrounded by fields. From a distance, a man dressed in a suit could be seen entering that house. I saw Mamajee's face turn as grey as the clouds above us as she stared on closely. Then I saw tears that fell like raindrops from her face, gliding down from the crevices of her nose and dropping from the angles of her chin.

"Why are you crying, Mamajee?" I asked. I tried to swallow the buttered toast. I climbed up onto the windowsill to get a better view of what had saddened her.

She took deep breaths that fogged the window, and I saw her hands tremble.

"Because this is how it is written; everything is written this way. It was part of the grand plan. You, me, everything that has happened, everything that will happen, our entire existence, it is already written. We are only here to submit to Allah's will. It is Allah's wish, and we can't change what Allah has written for us." She seemed to tremble uncontrollably now, as if the words shook her to the core.

*

I have been looking back on that day for the last forty years of my life, reconciling how those very words have carved my existence page by page, chapter after chapter. How I had been lost in someone else's story, someone else's book, someone else's dream and someone else's life.

I relive that day, yearning for the innocence of it, before life meddled with my view from that window and before it meddled with hers. Before, when it was simple, and all I knew was Mamajee, the house and the rolling hills.

I look back on that day, rediscovering now what I already knew then, things you don't need words for, or a pen to spell it out with.

A child, which I was then, of four years only chooses to be loved; love in essence was happiness, and what made me happiest was to feel her love, feel it radiate like sunbeams farther than the hills. But something happened that day that changed all that. I have come to realise that while my dreams were to be loved and to please her, her dreams were far from where we stood; we may have shared the same view from that window, but that day was the first day I realised we certainly didn't share the same perspective.

I may have been four years old, but for the first time, something that Mamajee said disagreed with me. You see, I wasn't born for it all to be written for me. I was born to write it.

CHAPTER TWO

– *Ashcroft* –

Our house stood on a hilly part of Ashcroft, a small town that tinkered five miles east of the great city of Manchester. A city that, in Babajee's eyes, was five miles too far out of reach for ever visiting. The houses in our town sprawled out over the hills like salt and pepper over two green buns, and on clear days, when the sky was blue, I would count the number of hills before they reached the concrete buildings that lined the city skyline.

Back when the world went no farther than those hills, Ashcroft felt like a big place. I had summed my conclusion from the local newspaper, which regularly noted the number of copies it had printed, gasping at the idea that forty-five thousand copies were circulated to its residents every week. Distances also seemed great back then. The town centre, with its slow market stalls and shops, felt like miles away – ten minutes to be exact, farther than my little legs had ever journeyed on their own at that age.

The front two bedrooms of our house faced westward, with views of the Pennines, and while it may have suited a family of four back then, we were a family of six by the time I turned seven, two boys and two girls. We scaled down in size like a row of Russian dolls, a few years apart in age, and the four of us were packed in a double room like a can of sardines against each other in one bed widthways. The smaller box room was often occupied by a lodger of some description, often one of Babajee's workers from the restaurant or, more often than not, an "uncle" who was not really related at all. Mamajee sometimes felt embarrassed when people commented on the number of children we had and the lack of decent living arrangements, but Babajee refuted any claims. "We live in a house, one that I paid for with my own working hands, not this council scum money. I didn't land on Londoni soil to live off labour money."

Babajee had bought the house years before we moved in. He bragged to his close friends how he "didn't buy a terraced house; it was a semi-detached house with a garden surrounding it." With this claim alone, he elevated his status from what he considered working class. In Mamajee's eyes, though, it was an eyesore badly in need of repair. The frail, blue-painted window frames had peeled and crumbled away like puff pastry; there were gaping holes that the wind whistled through. The front door had lost a corner and even whined when it opened. Our living room was in a similar state of disrepair. Babajee bragged about Axminster carpets and Chesterfield sofas that he refused to replace, but in Mamajee's eyes, they had long had their day. She tried desperately to cover up the tears with large floral blankets or by placing rugs over areas that were left threadbare. And wherever she could, she added her own touch, with plastic flowers bought from the pound shop or with handmade crêpe paper flowers that she painstakingly put together in an effort to conceal the misery.

I knew we were different; most often the townspeople refrained from commenting, but I knew our neighbours had opinions. After all, we had the scruffiest house on the street. When I gazed across at their neatly manicured gardens, ours seemed like a jungle of thorns and rose bushes. The crumbling brick wall surrounding the garden had given itself away to brambles, wild flowers and our children battering it until the brickwork came loose. It was an eyesore that Babajee referred to as a "sight for sore eyes." I don't think he understood that phrase, until a neighbour walked past one day.

"When are the overhanging brambles to be cut back?" he said gruffly at Babajee, pointing at it with his walking stick.

Babajee smiled. "I know," Babajee said, nodding, with his thick accent. "It's a sight for sore eyes, isn't it?" he said, agreeing.

The man paused, with a rather confounded look from Babajee's response. "Well, it doesn't look like a 'sight for sore eyes' to me, but they will definitely be sore if they are not cut back away from the pavement, mind." He shook his head and ambled back along the road to where his own house stood, spotless, fleckless, with a scissor-trimmed lawn. Babajee smiled and waved as if he had just received a compliment.

I could tell the townspeople didn't like the way we dressed either, the way they glanced at Mamajee sideways. The way they stole glances at her brightly patterned sarees, or her bottle-green burka coat and scarf, the socks with sandals. Sometimes I wanted to explain to them that my clothes were clean, and it was only the years of hand-me-downs that had taken their toll on them.

It was pointless though. It wasn't that they were being rude. Most of the townspeople were Caucasian, and although they were never harsh or outwardly racist, an air of reservation lingered on the civility of our nature, and that begged us to question theirs.

We managed to avoid the harshness of those small-town stares, the whispers and silence as we walked back from the centre. Babajee made sure we weren't outside long enough, though it wasn't because of the townspeople. I discovered another reason why Mamajee and I especially weren't allowed to venture out much. It was against our religion.

"We are not allowed," Mamajee said one day as we sat eating tinned peaches at the windowsill and the TV blared in the background. My favourite programme was on, *Play School.*

"Why?" I said.

"It is forbidden, of course," she said. The same fixed glaze through the window as she ate. "A woman should not be seen out without a man, a husband or guardian."

"Is it because they need help crossing the road, like me?" I added, trying to fill in the blanks.

"No, that's not the reason; one day you will see why. A woman is a man's honour; she must respect his honour, and if we don't behave, then we will bring nothing but a bad name to everyone in the community."

"What about Karim? Is he allowed out?"

"He is," she said. "But right now, he cannot go without his Mamajee and Babajee – he is too young, like you."

I finished biting into the second half of my peach. My cheek puffed out with the large mouthful. Intrigued by my own eating habits, I was playfully watching and giggling at my own reflection through the window when my eyes refocused and were drawn to the street in front of me. I saw the neighbours' children come into view briefly as they hopped into their family car. I watched their carefree existence as they got themselves ready for a day out. A feeling of resentment rose inside me. I wanted that too, I thought, and as the thought crept in, I felt miles apart from them.

"Does that mean I can't play in the garden?" I asked Mamajee.

"Oh no, you are not to play in the garden. No, it's forbidden."

"But Karim and Masoud are able to?"

Mamajee's eyes grew wider. It infuriated her when I questioned or challenged anything.

"Yes, that's right, but you are a girl, and if you are going to be a decent one, then you better not refuse anything I say."

She got up, taking her bowl of half-eaten peaches, and placed it on the dining table.

I quieted my thoughts. I knew it would only lead to a shout or scorn. And as she moved on into the kitchen, I looked out, leaning against the window. The world outside felt distant and close all at the same time. The *Play School* show broke out into a song, and I diverted my attention from the window to the TV, where Big Ted and Jemima were dancing, and everyone looked happy.

Floella sat the dolls down. "Which window should we look out from today?" she asked the dolls cheerfully.

I watched intently, wondering which window Jemima would pick. I especially liked the square window, because it closely resembled our own living-room window.

She offered Jemima and Big Ted a choice: the square window, the round window or the arched window. I thought about the choices I would have made if I were Jemima. I could have almost wished that I was that doll for a day, just so that I had a choice, just so that I could choose.

To Floella's delight, Jemima the doll picked the round window. It tinkled magically, drawing me through the window to the tune of a harp as they transported us to the next part of the show, a documentary about ships. The film explained how ships worked, taking passengers across to faraway locations, how passengers stayed on the boat and looked out from their round cabin windows and how they slept and ate lunch there or went swimming in the ship's pool.

When the documentary finished, Floella came back to the audience. "Why don't you look out of the window and see what you can see?" She smiled, and the show rolled into song and credits.

With the world now only at my window, I spent my days indoors, watching my brothers play on the street. Often, I would let my imagination run wild.

I would stand at the windowsill of my ship's deck, the curtains my sails, the clouds rolling past above through heavy seas to our next destination. I was the captain and Mamajee was the cook, and we could be happy regardless. Soon it became my daily pastime.

I could see the rooftop of my school from there, nestled amongst the trees and stony terraces. I saw into English people's houses, the soft, clean furnishings, the coordinated colours of their carpets and walls. I watched them in their houses, enjoying their meals at the dinner table, not on the floor like we did. I saw how they took pride in their gardens, the pruning of plants, watering, clipping the grass neatly like a deep-pile carpet.

In the evening, I would sit by Babajee's side at my bedroom window after he'd carried out his daily prayers. Mamajee carried out dusk prayers in their own room. I liked that he picked my room though. I never questioned why he did, even though his own room had ample space to place three prayer mats side by side.

I looked at this act endearingly, as if it was because he liked being with me, and moreover, it offered promise for love and attention. I would sit beside him, watch him roll prayer beads in his hands, mumbling and chanting verses of the Quran under his breath as the sun descended behind the hills. We would watch the red lights of cars in the distance, flickering on and off as they slid in and out of our view between trees, the neighbours putting out their empty milk bottles for collection. We watched street lamps turning on and people drawing their curtains, sometimes with an odd stare back at us as they closed a door and withdrew out of sight. It didn't trouble Babajee if they thought it was uncouth. It was his window, his property he was looking out of, not theirs.

Beyond the first set of hills, the small white house stood isolated in a green, open field. You could see its brilliant white glow even when the dusky nights had blackened the hills into darkness. Babajee would watch it closely. His nimble fingers continued on rolling a string of prayer beads. I pretended to chant the same prayers, although I didn't know any verses of the Quran then, nor knew how to pray. I took pleasure in being in that moment and sharing his company. Something about him was softer, calmer. This was the only time in the day that I could be near him without being barked at with an order or being told off. He was unlike the man I was used to during the day, full of rage, the frown lines etched between his eyebrows, the hard exterior accompanied by his commands, complaints and daily gripes thrown at Mamajee or the rest of the family.

One summer night, as Babajee rolled his prayer beads, we sat watching the street lights becoming more vivid in the darkening sky, a tinge of orange circling each lamp, round like a row of lollipops along the street. Babajee hadn't moved much, his eyes glassy and fixed in his low rumblings of prayers catching under his breath. I sat listening to his melodic chants, the room darkening until we looked like two shadows, and my eyes weary with sleep, when unexpectedly Babajee's chants came to an abrupt stop. He raised his head and stared on at the hills, the sunset now only leaving a small mist of purple against the dark blue sky.

His eyes were centred on the white house at the top of the hill. By the dusky night, it now looked more grey than white. Occasionally it was illuminated by the flare of car lights passing by. He continued to watch in that direction. Suddenly the house light turned on. Babajee moved, shuffling himself on the bed, leaning in a little closer to the window.

"What is it, Babajee?" I asked.

He didn't answer as he looked on.

"It's a curse to look out at the sun; only pagans worship the sun." Mamajee's stony voice boomed in through the door behind us, startling Babajee a little. He sighed, rolling his topi and prayer beads into the prayer mat as he got up from the bed and left the room.

"It's time for dinner. What are you doing sitting here in the dark?" Mamajee asked, turning the bedroom light on. The stark light startled our eyes as they regained focus.

"Looking out of the window," I said, frightened that I was going to get into trouble.

"Why?" she commanded.

"I don't know," I said blankly.

"Come down immediately and help set up for dinner," she ordered.

I slipped off the bed as she looked out through the window, closing it and sweeping the curtains shut. I didn't want to raise any alarms. It seemed almost wrong in her eyes to be there, to wonder. Mamajee always had a way of turning things into condemnations. What seemed like the simplest of pleasures were against Allah's will in her eyes. It was forbidden.

And while my physical world became restricted, I learned that you could find out many things from looking out of windows. Here, I could look, watch and dream. I also learned that I wasn't the only one dreaming from that window. We all were.

CHAPTER THREE
– *Raise Them Well* –

O ver time it became apparent that the place Mamajee longed to go back to wasn't quite the paradise I had imagined it to be. In the summer of 1983, one of the most devastating floods ravaged entire villages, towns and districts of Bangladesh, submerging most of it ten feet deep in muddy monsoon water.

"Look, look, Eleanor. This is Bangladesh." Babajee's eyes gleamed, the glow of the TV illuminated on his fixated face.

"Turn up the volume," Babajee said, ushering Mamajee and pointing to the remote control. She promptly turned the volume up. I saw dark-skinned people crying, knee-high in water, and boats floating with hordes of children, men with rickshaws carting their families through mud and aerial views of vast green lands swamped with water.

Babajee sank into his seat as he lit up another cigarette, his face disappointed, wishing he could be there for them, that he could have recorded it, wishing it was on for a little longer. He scoured the TV screen, hopeful he may notice a familiar face in amongst the crowds yearning for food, shelter and water. Mamajee leaned into the TV set to listen, trying to break down the complicated English sentences narrated by the reporter. She refrained from asking too many questions as Babajee listened on.

"Why did we come here to die?" she cried. "We should be there with them." She sobbed, mopping her eyes with the edge of her veil, which wrapped tightly around her shoulders.

I sat next to her, leaning in to comfort her as she watched the many children with their palms up to the sky.

"That could have been us, you know. You and your brother were born there."

"Where, Mamajee?" I said.

"In one of those little mud houses, do you see? That is what Bangladeshi houses are like."

Babajee tutted, giving her a sideways stare to stop talking, at which point she stopped to give me an evil look, as if somehow it was my fault that Babajee was cross. Her mood suddenly hardened.

"I was born there?" I asked. I wanted to find out more, but before any further questions sprouted from my mouth, Mamajee drew a disapproving look that would lead me into more trouble than the question deserved an explanation for.

"What are you looking at?" she snapped. "Go get the paan tray."

I shuffled out of my corner of the sofa, which I'd managed so delicately to keep warm, like a hen nestled on an egg, savouring it from the prying eyes of my brother, who was ready to pounce on the spot the minute it became free. It was seen as a prime position because it was nearest to the warm fire and gave the best angle for the TV. We competed for it on a daily basis.

I climbed onto the hearth, with its raised stone setting. My six-year-old arms barely reached the shelf where the silver tray sat as Mamajee and Babajee's faces flickered blue against the TV set. I brought it back down circumspectly and placed the tray gently in front her on the coffee table. She leaned in to rummage through an assortment of small tin pots that filled the silver platter.

I watched closely at the process of preparing her delicacy like a religious ritual. Paan consumption was a favourite pastime in most Bangladeshi households, and it was indisputably eaten after every meal amongst the adults. Mamajee would first lay out the paan leaf in the palm of her hand. She would add choona, a white limestone paste, onto the centre with the chopped end of a wooden lollipop stick. Then came a sprinkle of sarda, dried tobacco leaf, which was placed on top of the choona. Thinly sliced betel nut was then added, with a slicer called a surta, an instrument of remarkable ornateness. Along its razor-sharp sides were engravings of paan vines and dancing princesses from the Mahal era. She then enriched the leaf with sprinkles of cumin seeds, fennel, kala jeera and dried coconut. A drop of rose paste and candied sweets that looked like toppings you would put on cupcakes would be drizzled for the finishing touches. If you were to ever see this delicacy eaten, you would have experienced a custom of its own. It was a favourite amongst Bengali housewives to bring their own trays and trinkets at dinner parties, adorned with flowers or intricate paan displays. The paan parcels themselves were folded into elaborate styles and concocted with different flavours and toppings. It often became a topic of conversation, like the weather, as the women sat amongst rugs and pillows in idle gossip. I watched her wrap it into a cone shape and devour it in one mouthful that swelled the side of her cheek like a balloon. For a few minutes, it rendered her speechless, given the size. Mamajee often found it a relaxant, the tobacco giving her an instant hit after each mouthful, her head swirling into the cushion on the back rest.

I tried to resume position on the seat. However, my brother had now shoved his way past and deviously sat there with a big grin at me.

"Hey, that's my seat! Mamajee, please tell him! He's stolen it!" I said, folding my arms crossly at him.

"It's not," Karim laughed. "Finders keepers, remember!"

"Hey, stop arguing, both of you," Mamajee said, rolling the paan to the other side of her mouth, her head swirling, her speech slurred from chewing.

"Move!" I said, pulling at his sleeve.

"Get off," Karim mocked.

"That's enough!" Mamajee barked, sitting up in her seat. "You should know better," she added, looking at me crossly. "A woman never argues with a man. If he wants to sit there, you should respect him!"

"Ha ha," he said, sniggering at me. "Obey my orders!" He smirked.

"Get off," I insisted, pulling him out of the seat.

"Leave him alone," Mamajee said, raising her voice, half spitting the red betel juice that had gathered in her mouth at me.

"Are you a man?" She looked me in the eye, bringing her face close to mine.

"No?" I said.

"Then you better sit on the floor – when a man is present, you give up your seat."

"That's enough!" Babajee said, turning up the volume.

"Look at these people; they are homeless, and here you are fighting for a seat on the sofa?"

I did as I was told, crawling back onto the rug while my brother sneered at me. I tried to overlook it, that Mamajee was right, focusing again on the television report where hordes of children gathered by a flooded riverbank, but I could no longer concentrate. I felt unsettled by Mamajee's response. *So what I'm not a man?* I thought. *How is it fair that he gets a seat?*

"We need to get these kids over there," Babajee said, lighting up another cigarette. "Give them some understanding of our culture, how to behave, bring them up like good, respectable people."

"Hmm," said Mamajee. "This is what happens when you come to this country. The children understand nothing about our culture, and before you know it, they will be like the English, walking around half-naked, being rude to their parents, and when they are old enough, they will leave the house; they won't even bother looking back once at us. It's what you came for though, isn't it, to be like the English?" Her comments antagonised Babajee at times, and if he was tempted to entertain them, they were often the ones that led to arguments, arguments that Babajee won by asserting his hand in the air threateningly or with new orders. I could feel the heat rising with the conversation exchange.

Babajee nodded his head slowly, readying his response.

"Oh, yes, yes, of course, that's absolutely true," he huffed. "And that's why I married an illiterate from the village, to teach them."

I sat on the rug by the fire, cuddling my knees up, half listening, part of me looking in the direction of the TV, part of me hoping it wouldn't boil into a horrifying and violent outburst.

"They can't even speak Bengali properly, let alone know how to be civilised and respectful," he retorted.

"Oh, I think we all know the reason why I am here, don't we? What happened? You couldn't find anyone else to spare you some honour then, could you? Had to marry an idiot from the village," Mamajee chided.

"Say one more word, haramzadi, and I will slice your mouth with that surta. Do you hear me?" His eyes intensified, more resolutely on actioning the threat. He stood up from his seated position. Mamajee continued to stare at the screen, chewing slowly on her remaining paan. Babajee moved slowly to the fireplace, slamming his cigarette case on the mantelpiece. The fire in his eyes would be enough to burn her alive.

"I will see how much idle gossip you can do after that."

"Send me back, then. Why keep me here?" Mamajee retorted, unfazed by the threat.

"Oh, yes, yes, that would be right. I know why you want to go back. It's a holiday for you, isn't it?" Babajee interjected.

"Hmm, holiday? You are turning these kids away from the straight and narrow path by coming here. You chose this path here, selfishly, to fulfil your own needs. Too blind to see anything but yourself. Maybe before you drag the civility of my name, you should take a look at yours."

Babajee made a sideways disapproving glance at her remark. But to my surprise, he didn't raise the stakes. For a moment I envisioned him picking up that surta and swiping it at her, or upending the table with everything on it. But he didn't. He stood quietly, looking down.

"It's your job to raise them," he finally said, asserting his remark with his index finger at her. His features sharpened as he looked at her apathetically, then continued. "Is it mine? Hey? Is it?"

He shook his head at her, then walked to the door, slamming it shut behind him.

Mamajee rose from the sofa. Chewing her paan emptily, she looked out of the window, at the hills setting in the dark evening sky. I'd seen that same look before, the plane passing over her, her mind elsewhere, distant, far from the TV's blare.

"Turn the TV off; it's prayer time. And, you..." She turned to look at me. "You better start listening to what I say. From now on, no girl who I raise will behave the way you do."

I remember the summer of 1983 not because of the devastating floods in Bangladesh but because, from that day onwards, Mamajee had decided things were going to change.

CHAPTER FOUR

– *The Grocery Store* –

"I t's about sacrifice, hmm, is it? Well, who's sacrificing what? Why can't we go back? You tell me why we are not going back... Tell me why!" Mamajee's face was full of anguish as she looked on at Babajee for an answer. He continued driving silently as if it didn't need answering. It was as though nothing he was going to explain would have mattered. We were on our way to the local grocery store after much persuasion by Mamajee. It was a dreary summer afternoon, and the streets along our route seemed empty of people, probably from the heavy downpour a few minutes before we had jumped in the Datsun.

"Islam," she continued, "means surrendering to the will of Allah. We can't live in this country if you want our children to stay on the right path."

Surrender. I thought about what that word meant. I saw how it made Babajee's face empty, expressionless as he drove down the darkening streets.

"Do you not see? My family, your family, they are dying out there. The house is damaged by the floods. You saw that news report; there are no crops to sell right now, all the farmland has been destroyed. Do something! All you are doing is sitting here, sitting here smoking and doing nothing." She turned to look out of her window, exasperated, drained, wishing that something would call him into action. Babajee continued as if the words were hitting an empty void. He pulled out a cigarette from the compartment near his driver's seat and lit it with the cigarette lighter.

Mamajee's eyes looked teary and in despair as the conversation hit a wall with Babajee. I could see her from my view of the side mirror. She thought silently as she stared out of her window.

"We can't, that's why. I can't get the paperwork to just go back, the passports and things, and I don't have time to explain all this to someone who won't understand."

Her face trembled, holding back tears, as Abba explained.

"We should make a sacrifice or raise money for the poor in that case," she sniffled. Her voice was trembling. Babajee looked on as he turned right off the main road and gave it some thought.

"With what? How?" he said.

"Well, how else? Feed the poor; you have family starving over there. If you won't go back, then feed them at least. Allah will bless you a million times over."

He thought about it as he rolled into a side street set amongst urban terraces that seemed to match the colour of the sky, gloomy and dismal. A blue-painted sign, "Aslam's Halal Supermarket", hung half-lit by an overhanging neon light that flickered down the narrow street. A bearded man could be seen near the window. In the front, some overripe bananas and sad-looking vegetables greeted customers by the doorway.

Mamajee looked on as some raggedy Bangladeshi children stepped out of a house. The boy kicked a ball around on the pavement; the girl had her hair covered over with a triangle scarf tied up to her chin. She wore trousers under a frilly pink dress and dived quickly back into the house upon Babajee's movement of the car door.

"See that girl? You should be covering your hair like that," Mamajee said, looking back at me. "We've come to this country to turn our children against our culture," Mamajee continued bitterly as she looked out.

"Wait in here," Babajee said, turning to Mamajee as he locked the car door.

"Why can't we come in?" She looked at him.

"Women don't go out shopping in our culture. Do you see women in there?"

"But you never get the right ingredients. There are so many things we don't have," Mamajee argued.

"Do you want people to talk about you? Is that what you want? To be shamed by the men in there?"

Mamajee watched him unresponsively as he left the whole family packed up inside the parked car, cigarette butt stamped out, simmering at the shop door, to take the weekly pick of what we ate for dinner.

It sometimes felt like hours while we were abandoned in the car, in the heat, baking, or most often in the cold, freezing. That day was no exception. I could tell we had been in there some time. The day had already darkened, and the shadows of the children grew longer by the dusky sunset peeking through a brooding rain cloud.

"We've missed the afternoon prayers; he's been in there that long," Mamajee declared to my brother and me in the back seat. "Look at him. Does he have any idea of the time he has spent in there? He doesn't let me in, because he's worried I might spend all his money, hmm, as if I'm going to run off with all his money."

My childlike mind began to wonder. "Mamajee," I said, "what is a sacrifice?"

Mamajee glanced at me. Her face saddened again.

"It's when you give something to Allah, something that is special."

"You mean, like a gift?"

"Yes. That way Allah will always be happy."

"Then why is Allah sad?"

"Because we have not been good, and Allah only likes good people."

"So is that why Babajee has to go into the shop? To buy him a gift so that he can be good again?"

"Your Babajee could never be a good person. I don't think Allah could ever forgive him."

"Why?" I asked.

She paused. "Because when you continue doing wrong, you can never be forgiven."

"What did he do wrong?" I asked. Mamajee didn't answer, and I watched her waiting with gritted teeth, toddler in her arms, anxiously hoping that he did come out with nappies, or milk or bread.

When he finally appeared, he loaded up the boot of the Datsun.

"What took you so long?" she snapped. "Why can't you just let me go into the shop?"

"Go on, go have a look. Do you see women in there?"

Mamajee ignored the rhetorical question that came with a long pause from Babajee looking on at her. She knew he was making a point of it.

"Did you get the milk?"

He started up the engine.

"What about the nappies?"

He lit up another cigarette without saying a word.

Mamajee huffed. It would mean another week of improvising for Mamajee, such as hand-washing terry cloths instead of using disposable nappies, or another day or two using powdered milk for tea instead of hot, frothy milk.

"You are getting too used to the good stuff here," Babajee said on the drive home when she tried to bring up another request for groceries.

"There are people in Bangladesh dying, and here you are complaining: you don't have this, you don't have that," he continued.

"Hmm, my point exactly. So then, why can't we just go back? Why are we dying to be here?" she fought back.

Babajee stared back at her. "Die here? Is that what you think this is? Dying?"

Mamajee bit her lip, turning to look out the window.

"You wouldn't even know what I am dying of," she said, looking to the hills.

"You don't even know what you have, do you?" Babajee said. "Hey?"

"I don't believe you do either," Mamajee remarked. "You don't think I have seen you turn your face to the West instead of to the East? Do you think I am blind?"

Babajee said nothing.

The clouds had broken up, and a plane shot over, probing the darkening sky like a slow shooting star as we waited at the traffic lights. Mamajee followed it as it passed out of sight. I saw her wiping her tears quietly. Babajee looked on at the distant hills, the orange lights slowly flickering with the melting crimson sky. The light from the white house turned on as the traffic light went green. Babajee stared on.

"Dusk prayers are almost over," Mamajee remarked insolently. "Can you get a move on?" Mamajee barked at Babajee.

A driver behind honked and startled him into action. He pulled away still looking at the white house. Then I saw him look at me through the rear-view mirror. That was when I caught a glimpse of a frightened man, one who had done something bad and was trying to please Allah.

*

Babajee waded past us as he dumped two plastic bags full of groceries in the kitchen.

"Make me a cup of tea, will you?" he called out to Mamajee from the hallway as he made his way upstairs.

"Hmm, yes, of course. What with?" Mamajee muttered under her breath.

I watched her despair as she pulled out the groceries from the bag in the kitchen.

"Mooli, again? Fish, broad beans, marrow, potatoes? What can I do with this?" she muttered under her breath. "Okay, at least he got the formula this time." She continued to process to herself. "We don't have any fresh meat this week." She sighed, looking up. "It will have to be chicken again."

It made me uneasy and disconcerted when I saw Mamajee fretting like this. That knot in your belly signalling danger, or some kind of tension arising.

I watched the way she puzzled over the ingredients, sniffling into her saree scarf.

"Okay, we can make mooli with the leftover meat, since your babajee likes mooli so much, hmm," she grumbled while pulling out a large marrow from the thin carrier bag. "And the marrow, ha," she said, holding it up and grinning at Babajee's pathetic purchase. "Well, I will use this to clobber him with." She smiled at her own humour. The tension lessened a little when she smiled.

I felt calm knowing that somehow she found a way to cope. On good days, she directed her attention elsewhere, away from Babajee's misgivings towards the kitchen. It was small and cold in there, with hardly any room for more than two people to move around in. The wooden cupboards were painted a pale blue and had years of finger marks dotted around their sides. The panes of glass were stubborn to slide, sticky and sealed by a greasy orange film accumulated from Mamajee's cooking, but in those cupboards were her secret ingredients, with which Mamajee transformed our mundane ingredients into magical meals: dried herbs, jars of pumpkin seeds, various lentils, beans and pulses, home-dried sliced lemons and orange peel. There were pickles of different types blended and preserved in Mamajee's favourite spices. Mamajee's pickles had become a favourite amongst our family friends, especially the apples or sour cherry pickles she made from her home-grown fruit trees in the garden. She would make everyone wait patiently for years before we could try any. Her finest pickles could only be enjoyed once they had been sealed for a couple of years. "They're not ready yet. You have to wait until the oils have blended with the spices before you can try it," she would say.

If there was one thing that gave her joy and satisfaction, it was her kitchen. She ran it like a small empire, and with it came superior quality. Mamajee never prepared food in the usual way that English wives did: she shook her head distastefully at knives. She chopped and cut vegetables with a dha, a self-standing, razor-sharp sword-like instrument shaped like a crescent moon, with a tail and legs; it reminded me of some kind of headless bird or maybe even a lizard arching backwards. To cut with the dha, Mamajee would sit perched on a small stool, crouching low to the ground. I would watch her in silent bewilderment as she swiftly chopped vegetables, descaled, gutted and beheaded fish, hacked a whole leg of lamb into small pieces, peeled fruit and vegetables so thin they would melt in your mouth; this was a beast of a contraption.

She washed the vegetables in bowls and colanders and brought them down to where the headless creature sat waiting on the ground, ready to slice whatever she fed it.

"Don't sit on the floor," she scolded. "You will get dirty and cold." She pushed over an empty yellow ghee bucket for me to sit on.

"Here," she commanded. "Sort through these broad beans; hold them up to the light for me. If there are any black spots, it means the ants have eaten them. Throw those out and put the good ones in the bowl."

I sometimes sensed Mamajee's isolation with Babajee's wall of stone-cold silence, and often, being in the kitchen gave her a sense of solidarity, away from him. I knew being there made a difference too. It kept her sane.

"He doesn't understand any of this, you know, what I have to do, what I have to put up with, day in, day out," she said, hacking away at a fish head, jabbing it down against the blade. I sensed the anger being taken out on it as she sliced through the middle of the fish and gutted it.

I gulped in disgust as blood and guts spilled out. Mamajee continued to complain as I crouched, silently sorting out the broad beans.

"How many men do you know who don't give their wives control of the groceries? Ha? You tell me. How many? Do you see the women next door having to put up with that? I don't even have milk to make tea. You know there's no bread for tomorrow's breakfast, you know, don't you? We will have to have cereal, and Allah knows," she cried, raising her hands in prayer and looking up at the ceiling. "What am I going to prepare for tomorrow's dinner?"

*

That evening, after hours of ranting and slaving over bubbling pots of curry, cleaning and clearing the kitchen, her loud voice echoed out through the hallway to the lounge room.

"Lay down the mat," she bellowed as she entered with a bubbling pot of curry.

"Rice is ready!" my brothers screamed from the living room, where they had been playing all evening.

Together they brought out the bamboo mat from behind the chest freezer, heaving it out with their little hands. Babajee sat there watching the news the whole time, even though he could see they were struggling. The clattering of plates prompted some urgency in him to wash and carry out the evening prayers upstairs.

Our regular family meals were always on the floor, where the bamboo mat was laid out in front of the fireplace. Babajee viewed it as a Sunnah (good Muslim etiquette) to eat on the floor. "The prophet Muhammed used to eat on the floor," he would explain.

It was questionable, though, to Mamajee what his real motives were for this. "Any excuse to not buy more chairs for the dining table, I would think, more like," Mamajee would say. Mamajee didn't protest too much at this, though: religion was her salvation, so anything that helped her to succeed religiously was always seen as a blessing. The mat was large enough to take up the middle space of the lounge area, teasing the fire as it descended softly to the floor.

Babajee joined us, gargling as he entered the room, drawing up his lungi folds as he seated himself in the prime position, by the fire.

Mamajee sat beside him, serving out the rice. He washed his hands in a warm bowl of water that she placed in front him.

"Pass it around," he said to her without eye contact. With his blessed hands now gracing the water, we all had the privilege to then wash ours. Mamajee passed the bowl around to the three of us, and we flocked around it like sparrows taking a dip in a puddle.

Mamajee had somehow rustled up a spread of food despite the meagre groceries she had furiously complained about. But Babajee only grimaced, shaking his head disapprovingly as he lifted the lid from each steaming pot.

"Hmm, chicken curry bhuna again. Why didn't you add more water? This will only last one meal."

Mamajee disregarded the comment, mixing up the children's rice plate. Her roasted masala with the aroma of cardamom and bay leaves was not something she would want to spoil with a pan full of hot water.

"Madras lamb," he continued, lifting another lid. "There's no aloo [*potatoes*]."

"You bought marrow, remember?" Mamajee added flatly.

He ignored the glare as he placed spoonfuls of the tender marrow onto his plate. He refrained from telling her how delicately it melted in his mouth as she watched him devour handfuls.

Babajee started first as always, his cheeks wallowing with every mouthful of rice. We didn't ever use knives, forks or spoons to eat. Babajee said it was Sunnah to eat with our hands. While he respected this tradition, ulterior motives always dawdled closely as if they were his bad cousin. "You always use less curry when you mix rice with your hands," he would say, and that meant less food, fewer groceries and less of his hard-earned money being wasted on feeding the family.

Mamajee sat watching. She didn't join in at mealtimes. It was culturally accepted that a woman's job was to serve at dinnertime and to eat only after the men had been served and finished eating. So, she would sit and watch us or serve another spoonful.

There were vegetables with fresh finger chillies, and shutki – a dried-fish broth with greens. She put small spoonfuls of curry onto our melamine plates, something Mamajee had proudly acquired with the help of another housewife who had recently paid a visit to Bangladesh. The crockery had a matching Bangladeshi theme, with floral vines around the rim. For years she had put up with a basic white tin set, which embarrassed her in front of guests. "We aren't that poor that we can't afford some nicer plates," she'd say. "People would think we are beggars if they saw us eating like this."

Babajee had said nothing, which typically meant Mamajee was right, and with that, she had taken the liberty of ordering them.

She waited for Babajee's orders.

"More water," he commanded, breathing in cold air from the spicy curry. She poured him a glass as he cleared his throat.

"Pass the salt," he said, shaking his head. "This curry is tasteless," he mumbled.

I could see it upset her as she stared on with pursed lips. "Well, you are still eating it, aren't you?"

He shook his head, antagonising her. "This is not good enough. Did you even learn how to cook?"

"No, I guess I didn't have time," she snapped curtly, looking towards the curtains.

"Ha! Time?" he said. "Did you want to make any other excuse for your inefficiencies?"

"Inefficiencies? Oh, maybe we should talk about them." Her face became stone cold.

"Quiet down, before I cut your tongue, haramzadi!" Babajee shouted.

We all sat quietly.

"You," he said to me, "go get the dha. Let me see what your mamajee wants to talk about today. Yes, how about I cut that conversation up into pieces. Let's start with slicing that tongue of yours."

I sat still, with my head down, pretending to ignore the comment.

The room fell quiet until only the flickers from the gas fire could be heard.

"Pass me that bowl of water," he ordered.

I moved it gently across, still looking down and refraining from eye contact. Babajee washed the curry from his hands.

"Pass me the cloth," he urged Mamajee.

She reached over the pot, handed him the towel.

Wiping his hands, he got up from his position, changed into his suit and headed to the restaurant.

Mamajee sat quietly. She fought back the tears.

"Mamajee," I said quietly, "why are you not eating?"

"Why?" she said. "Because of you. This is all because of you! Because of you, I am going to die here." She croaked into her scarf.

I looked nervously on, too scared to respond.

That night, by the dim light coming from the stairway, my brothers and I climbed into the double bed that Mamajee had set up widthways for us to sleep in, our cold feet dangling from the edge of the bed. Babajee frowned at the thought of heating the rooms all night, even when the gaping holes in the brittle, dry window frames had the wind whistling and howling through them. The three of us bundled up close, our bodies shivering as our cold feet touched. Settling in, we kicked each other and giggled, watching our breath fog up in the cold air, pretending we were smoking Babajee's cigarettes.

She took the book from me and tucked in the sheet.

"Mamajee," I said as I lay there, "I'm sorry."

"For what?"

"Because of what you said earlier."

She looked blankly at me.

"You said it was my fault that you would die here."

She said nothing, tucking in the cover.

"What's written is written," she said. "You can't change what has happened or what is destined for you." She turned out the hallway light.

"What's written? What does that mean, Mamajee?"

"It means you submit to Allah's wishes, and you accept what he has written for you."

"But then—"

"No more questions, do you hear me?"

And with that, the door closed. The light from the stairway hollowed into a thin line through the doorway into blackness.

"Written," I whispered to myself as I fell asleep.

CHAPTER FIVE
- *Babajee* -

There are always two sides to every story, Mamajee would say, and each one holds its own truth. You have to be careful which one you choose to believe in. I learned it was certainly true of Babajee: in some stories he shone, and in others he was dull and colourless.

Mamajee used to say his old age made him miserable; he was more than twenty years older than Mamajee, which meant that everything that interested her had long been done and buried in his past, like watching Bollywood films or eating ice cream or going to the park. It was hard to tell whether her words were emotional responses, laced in bitter fury and mistreatment, or whether Babajee was indeed of this disposition.

Like most Bangladeshi villagers, Babajee never had an official birth certificate, and Mamajee claimed that Babajee had increased her age on the passport by a few years. Needless to say, there was an obvious age difference between them.

Their wedding portrait epitomised their relationship perfectly. Mamajee, radiant, as fair as the moon, beautiful, yet sulky and childlike; and Babajee, serious looking, like a dark cloud of gloom. I often wondered what had possessed him to take the picture at a professional studio in the first place. His pointed features, lips pursed together into a thin line as if words were permanently being held back, a nose that rose up like a mountain, looking downwards into the camera with an intense frown. There was a wave of white hair combed to the side, giving an air of 1940s nostalgia to his rather conservative style and finely cut suit. His frown was a permanent feature. Even when there was something to laugh or smile about on TV, he would resist the urge to laugh in front of us by looking away.

It was only Babajee's friends that enjoyed the pleasure of his laughter, his nasal horn, as Mamajee would call it. Slapping his hands against his knees, the air filled with a toxic roar as they reminisced about a bygone era, the smoke lingering, floating around the living-room ceiling.

Mamajee usually ushered the boys upstairs so that his friends could talk and banter about business and politics, Babajee's restaurant and the good old days when they moved to Blighty, while she, too, withdrew to the kitchen, enlisting my hand in preparing tea and snacks for the guests.

Babajee's restaurant was the first Indian restaurant in Ashcroft. In its heyday, it was the life and soul of Indian cuisine. "People would queue outside to dine there," Babajee would say. He was revered amongst his regular diners, who included actors, comedians and distinguished businessmen, many of whom were pictured on his wall of fame at the restaurant. He had started his business with the help of his five friends, who he had met working in a cotton factory. "Your babajee," they would often tell me, "didn't know yes from no." They'd laugh. It got him in all kinds of trouble.

After spending years together working in this cotton factory, Babajee and his friends saved enough money to rent a property in the town centre. Together they turned the business into a success. Over the decades though, Babajee's partners all moved on, selling their shares until only Babajee had sole ownership of the business. It was his pride and joy, being a business owner, and he was never shy of bragging that he was a restaurateur. The truth was, it barely made ends meet.

"Business was slow," Babajee would say as he counted up the takings from the night before.

"What about that bundle of cash over there?" I would say.

"That's to pay for everything. The staff, the groceries, the bills, there isn't much left after that. Look." He would point to a thin bundle of tens and twenties.

Mamajee disagreed. "There are two sides to every coin, just as there are two sides to you."

Babajee would say nothing to that remark, and I sensed there was something she was antagonising him over that made him uneasy.

They often argued about money, the cost of groceries, the reluctance on Babajee's part to spend money on anything, the maintenance and repair costs to the house, the car and the unkempt garden that Mamajee couldn't get a dime from Babajee to invest in. And Babajee would argue back upon any such confrontation. "Yeah? Where's the money? I don't even have money to pay the bills, and here you are screaming out for luxuries."

I sometimes saw Babajee's point; we didn't have enough, I guess. I only knew this because I used to help him read the gas bills, electricity bills, telephone bills stating the amount due, some addressed from the court. I saw Babajee's face, the anxiety that came with every reminder, every red letter.

One morning I woke early, before the postman arrived, as I always did. There was a loud knock on the door. Two dark figures could be seen through the frosted window of the front door. I could hear Mamajee shuffling upstairs. "Get the door. Who is it?" she said wearily from the landing.

Two burly men stood looking at me with hardened faces. "Hello, love. Is your dad home?" said the first man.

"Yes, but he's asleep right now," I said, holding the door close as a cool gust of wind entered the hallway.

"Can we come in? There's something we need to talk to him about."

"Who is it?" Babajee said, wrapping his lungi around his waist and coming down the stairs.

"Good morning. Are you Mr Rabbani, sir?" asked the other man. "My name's Mr Burton. I am a High Court enforcement officer, and I have been issued a warrant for the removal of goods for failure to make a late payment. Can we come in?"

Babajee didn't hesitate. "Er, sure, please come in." Babajee addressed the men with a wide smile, though neither of them engaged or interacted with him.

They charged through into the living room and began pacing the floor, inspecting the property and jotting down notes onto a clipboard.

Babajee followed behind. I peered through the doorway.

"Are you aware of the notice sent to you from the magistrate, sir?" the man continued.

"No, I am not aware of this, my friend," Babajee said.

"There have been numerous notices issued for the payment of fifteen thousand pounds. Will you be making that payment today?" the officer said firmly.

"No, no, sir, I don't have any money, sir." Babajee chuckled, looking nervous. "You see, I have three children, and my business is suffering. I am not making any money, sir."

"Mr Rabbani, we are not interested in your excuses. The High Court has issued this warrant to remove goods if payment can't be made."

Babajee paused, his breathing deep. "Take a seat, gentlemen. Give me some time here." He coughed. "There are children in this house." He cleared his throat. "Let me see what I can do."

"Take your time, sir. In the meantime, we will continue with the inventory of goods." The men walked around, muttering to each other as they jotted further notes. Babajee came out to the hallway, where I had been standing, listening, observing. He looked at me with a pained expression, and as I searched his eyes, I saw the pressure, the fear that something indisputable and compromising was about to happen to us. Then it disappeared, as if the sun had burst through the clouds. His eyes lit up as if by looking at me something had revealed itself to him.

"Where's your mother?"

"She's upstairs," I said quietly.

Babajee went up, slowly, creeping his way up the stairs to find her. I sat quietly at the top of the stairs. I could hear them talking in low voices.

"Well, then, who else? Where can we find that kind of money? I don't have a penny."

"I would rather them take everything away," Mamajee cried. "How dare you insult me."

I then heard Babajee talking to someone on the phone upstairs, explaining what he needed.

"Please, I need it now … Yes, they are here now … Yes, mm-hmm … Today … Aha … Hmm … Yes … It's urgent. Please, if not for me, at least do this for her."

Mamajee passed me in the hallway, her face reddened from tears.

"What are you looking at? Sitting there eavesdropping, are you?" she said.

I sensed she hated me for something. Sensing that I was going to get a telling off, I immediately returned to my room. An hour went by. From my bedroom window, I could see the officers talking to Babajee outside on the street. The driver sat despondently in the removal van parked up on the pavement. Moments later a black sedan pulled up on the street. I couldn't see the driver. Babajee reached out to the car, leaned into the passenger window to speak to someone. A woman's hand appeared with an envelope, reaching out to pass it through the car window. Babajee nodded; he seemed to be grateful. The car drove off, and Babajee returned up the garden path, a reprieved look on his face. He caught a glimpse of me looking through the window, and his smile faded.

A little time later, after the officers and the removal van had left, I came downstairs. There was silence in the living room. Babajee had seated himself at the living-room sofa, expressionless. Mamajee was sat buried in her arms at the dining-room table. I stood by the door, watching my parents sit wordlessly. Then Mamajee broke down in tears. I could only imagine the tension from the tightening of my own. Seeing those men and that they were about to make us homeless would have had anyone upset. But her cries seemed deeper than that; the relief of clearing the debt had not offered her any respite.

*

The following day, Babajee's friends, all five of them, burst through the front door like a fiery volcano. Cigar ashes fell to the floor of the hallway as they greeted Babajee, slapping him merrily on his back as they made their way through to the living room. By default, we all knew the exit procedure. The boys took off upstairs, and Mamajee and I moved into the kitchen.

"Make some tea, will you?" Babajee called out to Mamajee through the wooden hatch. I gathered the tray and placed gold-rimmed cups that Mamajee used for guests onto it.

She had laid out almond biscuits onto matching gold-rimmed side plates and heated milk to make shawoi, a sweet vermicelli dish with sugar and cardamom.

"Take this in," she said, pouring herself a cup of tea from the pot before placing it on the tray. "Make sure you do your salaam when you walk in, do you understand? And put your scarf over your head, do you hear me?"

I nodded, lowering my head towards the tray as I strolled in. The men were in full-scale banter. Cigar swirls lingered in the air.

"Assalamualaikum," I said weakly at the door.

"Ooh my! It's Jane." They laughed and snickered as I walked in.

"The girl is just like her mother." They roared even louder as I brought the tray in with tea and biscuits.

"Hello, shundori [*beautiful*]. Can you speak Bengali?" they heckled.

I felt awkward not understanding the joke they were having at my expense. I saw Babajee tune out and stop joining in, his laugh fading out, drawing into his cigarette.

"How can you turn such beauty into a silly maid. I bet her mother would—"

"That's enough," Babajee said. "You always take it a step too far, Rahim."

"I am not the only one," he said, drawing out smoke into Babajee's face as he chuckled silently into his cigarette.

Sensing it had turned serious, I left the room, covering my head again with a scarf.

"What were they talking about?" Mamajee whispered as she sat on a low bucket in the kitchen.

"I don't know. They were calling me names and found it funny." I shrugged.

*

That night I was woken up from the heavy shudder of the back door closing. The door between the frame required extra force to close. It was 3 a.m., which meant that it must have been Babajee making his way back from the restaurant. I could hear him rustling, the living-room door creaking as he settled himself by the fireplace. With my sleep interrupted, I felt restless. I went downstairs to get a glass of water.

"What are you doing up?" Babajee said as I headed to the kitchen. He was sat cross-legged, reading his books. It was one of Babajee's favourite pastimes after a full night working in the restaurant. This seemed to be his time to relax in a world of books while everyone else was sleeping. I often saw him into the early hours of morning like this, volumes of Tagore, Chandra Bose and Nazrul Islam.

He began to read a passage to me.

My night has passed on the bed of sorrow, and my eyes are tired.
My heavy heart is not yet ready to meet morning with its crowded joys.
Draw a veil over his naked light, beckon aside from me this glaring
flash and dance of life. Let thy mantle of tender darkness cover me in
its folds, and cover my pain awhile from the pressure of the world.

"Such beautiful poetry," he said. "You should learn Bangla. You will find many answers to life's questions here."

"It sounds like a song, and a very sad one, Babajee. What does it mean?"

"It means there are times you will be sad, and it will feel very dark."

"You mean like at night?" I said.

"Yes, but this darkness is far more than at night. You feel it in your heart; you feel it all around you." He sighed.

"Have you felt like this, Babajee?"

He nodded apologetically.

I had never seen Babajee feel the need to apologise, and although it wasn't with words, something in his voice felt a fraction of remorse or something that I couldn't grasp or fathom.

"Once you have it, my dear," he sighed as he continued, "it never leaves you, and I pray that you never feel it."

He flicked through and read on.

The water in a vessel is sparkling;
The water in the sea is dark.
The small truth has words that are clear;
The great truth has great silence.

He nodded, agreeing with the verse. I saw his eyes gleam, the inner smile that it somehow released, the calmness that he felt alone in his thoughts.

"What does it all mean, Babajee?" I said.

"One day, you will understand, Beti."

I nodded, turning silently away, respecting his right for some distance.

"And, Eleanor," he said as I turned away.

I turned to face him, waiting for his words.

He fell silent again, searching for words. "Keep reading, and you will understand one day."

I didn't understand the poem, but it was the first time I saw the other side of Babajee, the side that shone, as Mamajee would say, and I longed to be closer to it.

CHAPTER SIX
- *Mosque* -

T hat summer, after the news of the floods and many complaints from Mamajee about our Western behaviour, Mamajee persuaded Babajee to send us both to the mosque.

"I don't want them turning into those pig-headed children across the street," she said, looking over our neighbours' children scornfully.

There was no discussion or warning about the day we would be sent there. It happened quite abruptly one afternoon while my brother Karim and I were sat watching cartoons, eating our afternoon tea, which comprised a bowl of Rice Krispies. I was sat listening to the crackles as the cereal popped in my mouth when I felt a hand slap me around the side of my head. "Did you hear me? No. Of course not. Allah's name always gets ignored around here." Mamajee looked at me militantly.

"Come on, up you get," Mamajee said, pulling me by the elbow away from the bowl of Rice Krispies. "You need to get changed."

"Where are we going?" I said, trying to swallow the last morsel of cereal.

"To the mosque," she said abruptly.

She took a pair of cotton trousers, pulled them up to my waist underneath my dress. I felt the tugs as she tied the drawstrings and tucked in my vest. She lowered a crinkled pale orange scarf over my head. It was one of Mamajee's old ones and long enough to wrap around my whole body as she looped it a few times around my neck. She pulled it tightly over my forehead, tucking my fringe into the scarf. I could see my reflection on the TV screen. I looked like a Russian doll, only the colour of a satsuma.

"Your hair mustn't be shown when you are in a mosque; you need to keep your hair covered. Otherwise, expect a beating," Mamajee said as if she knew it wouldn't be long before I made a mistake.

Babajee drove us that first day but, soon after, barely had time to pick us up and drop us there. My brother and I walked, normally, a mile and a half each way, hand in hand, crossing busy roads, past the bus station, across the old, war-torn high street that was now partly boarded up in the old factory area of Ashcroft.

We arrived at the mosque, an old stone building converted from a disused warehouse. The dark grey slabs that made up the archway to the front door looked cold, unwelcoming, arousing repentance even if you hadn't thought of sinning. The years of disregard to its exterior had given it to nature, and the dark walls wore a mossy complexion. The large windows were enclosed by steel mesh, guarding against anyone looking in or looking out. A large, makeshift sign hung over a set of heavy metallic doors, its presence overbearing, as if Allah was sitting inside, ready to feast on his sinners.

I looked up at this sight as we walked through the unwelcoming doors, wondering when our last day would be or how long before the end. Piles of shoes lined the entrance in a disarray of coloured patterns and sandals. There were shelves for people to put their shoes on, but they were hardly used, probably because the call to prayer was always a hurry, and touching shoes to put them away meant washing your hands again. As we entered the main mosque, a brisk chill awaited us. In my eyes back then, Allah, who everyone was fearful of, was a giant, gruff, bearded man who had no mercy on anyone. He hated women, and he relentlessly found flaws in everything we did.

My chest felt cold, and my shoulders tightened.

"Here, you can put your coat over on that hook over there," Babajee said, pointing at it with a raised eyebrow.

I clutched at my coat collar with the sheep wool lining to stop myself from crying.

The only comfort I had was the warmth of that coat, soft and snug; how the cold would nip through it if I took it off.

I shook my head, clutching to my coat tightly.

"The mullah will be coming in a minute," Babajee said, looking at me as though he was offering some comforting words.

I tried to hold back the thoughts, tried to stop myself from saying what I knew would land me in trouble with Babajee or just make him angry.

"I want to go home," I said. The tears now welling up, I tensed my eyes to stop blinking.

"Don't speak such nonsense," Babajee said quietly as he looked around.

A large man with an orange beard came striding up the entrance towards Babajee. He wore a beige cotton tunic, over it a brown knitted waistcoat.

"Assalamualaikum, Rabbani Saheb," the man greeted Babajee with a welcoming voice as he reached out his hand.

"Waalaikumsalam, Hafiz Saheb," Babajee responded to the man, who towered over him like a large wall.

He looked down at me sideways, as if he found it amusing that I was so small.

"Do you speak English, ha? English? Do you speak it?" He chuckled.

I nodded timidly. He grinned and, with a hearty laugh, patted me on the head a little. My neatly fitted scarf felt off-centre from my neck. I pulled it back in front of my face to conceal my fringe, as Mamajee had warned me earlier.

Hafiz Saheb bowed down to my height. "Do you know any Arr-abic, ha? Do you know it? Any Arrbi? The word of Allah, it is written in Arr-bic, you know?"

His voice was loud and upbeat, but his overbearing presence and attention to me made me want to crawl under Babajee's legs. I clung to Babajee's arm, hoping he might say something to draw his attention away from me. But the man peered down at me, his long beard only inches from my face, chuckling a little more intensely at me.

"No, my daughter, she knows nothing. I wanted to teach her, but I have no time, you know. It is better they come here."

"Of course, of course, inshallah. If Allah wills it, we can help turn them away from hellfire here," the man said reassuringly to Babajee.

"Come. Come with me," he said, moving us away. "Your babajee can go and get on with his work."

I wanted to cry as the man pulled my brother and me away.

Inside there were four rooms for the lessons. One room was set aside for boys of mixed ages. The second room was for girls under eleven, with some very young boys of nursery age. The third room was for older men who practised ibadah (a state of worship), and the final room was a large, red-carpeted hall used for communal prayers. It had a high ceiling, and although I didn't like being at the mosque, this was the only room that offered some comfort from where we were. The carpets felt soft on your feet, and it didn't feel so hollow and lifeless here as it did in the other rooms. Rows of tape marked the carpet where the men lined up for prayer. At the head of the hall was a large Arabic sign with the words "In the name of Allah" written in beautiful ancient calligraphy.

Hafiz Saheb walked me through the prayer hall.

"You," he said to me, his tone firmer now that Babajee had left. "You can go in this room. You, boy, you come with me."

This was the only time I recall not wanting to be alone without Karim. There was comfort in having siblings, that feeling that they might help if something went wrong.

I joined the second room, where around twenty girls of my age group sat on low wooden benches with slanted surfaces to rest their Arabic workbooks on. The girls were all around six, seven, eight, and some as old as nine. The boys were much younger. They sat quietly mumbling verses. Some looked up at me but then resumed the melodic chanting of the Arabic scripture, pointing at each word as they read along. I stood observing. The carpets were worn out here, threadbare in some places. I traced the spiral vines, making infinite floral patterns in my mind's eye as I sat waiting for the mullah.

The windows high up above my head were covered in steel mesh, and it wasn't easy to see out. Only the steeple of the church high up on the hill could be seen from where I stood. By now the children were talking, whispering, looking at me, and it was becoming noisy and a little rowdy. The younger ones had started to mess about with each other.

"Come and sit down here," bellowed a voice from the far corner. A man with a long white beard entered the room, carrying a three-metre pine slat. It was like something that was used for skirting boards or outdoor fences. Strangely, it was almost half the length of the classroom. I wondered what he was going to do with it as I sat slowly down at the prayer bench he pointed me to.

The noise of the children echoed with laughter and giggles as he resumed his seated position at a low school desk, the legs of which had been cut down low enough for kneeling. He rested his back against a green velvet cushion and observed the ruckus now being created by the children in the room. I could only sense a growing impatience in his expression as he watched on.

Suddenly, he smacked the thick plank of wood with a hard thrash against the surface of the low desk. "*Chuppaay!* Quiet!" he shouted. It was so loud that I felt the tremor resonate to the core of me, one that sent an echo that silenced the room. One of the younger boys that looked around four years old seemed to have continued prattling with another boy and was struck on his backside with this three-metre-long slat.

The children jolted again and sat still. Half-shaken, the boy immediately resumed position at his bench. I saw the fear as they cowered into their books back in their places. I could tell that this was a man you would not challenge or question whatever the request may be.

I sat quietly next to a girl who had her face down in the prayer book. The mullah then cleared his throat and began to read out the register.

"Shazia!" he called out.

"*Labbayk* [*I am here*]," came the answer from a girl in a navy coat.

"Fiza!"

"Labbayk," replied the girl sitting next to me. She smiled as she looked at me.

"Elno-o-o-orr," he croaked. There was no answer.

"Elno-o-orrr," he called again. Everyone looked at each other. Then they all turned to look at me. I realised he must have been calling for me. I just didn't recognise it from the pronunciation in the old man's voice.

He beckoned me over with a shorter piece of pine wood now firmly gripped in his hands. His eyes were fixed and stern.

I crawled out from the low bench and slowly came before him.

He said something, his mouth moving amongst the long beard, his elderly voice sounding muffled at first, but it became clearer that he was speaking in Urdu, a language I didn't understand. He repeated it impatiently again, and I looked around at the others to see whether anyone could help. I turned to look at him, as I seemed not to be getting any response from the children, who were looking at me in silence. *Am I in trouble?* I thought. I scoured my thoughts for an answer. *What if I can't answer and he hurts me with that stick for not responding to the register?*

He sounded pretty angry, whatever he said. He asked me then, in English, "Do you speak Urdu?"

I shook my head.

"Are you Bengali, ha?"

I nodded. "*Jee* [*Yes*]."

"Bengali!" the other girls laughed. I looked down, wondering why that had been funny when they didn't even know me.

"Hai!" Mullah Saheb shouted, ordering everyone to be quiet. "What is your name?" he said, looking at me snappishly.

"Eleanor," I said, my voice just about carrying the words and emptying them out of my mouth.

He looked confused, and then insulted. "Eleanor is not a Muslim name. Are you a Muslim?" he asked suspiciously.

"Yes," I said nervously.

The children continued to snigger in the background.

"Well, Elnoor will be your name here from now on. That is the correct pronunciation. Your name means 'light', and of course, your father has chosen well. Rabbani means 'divine'. You are in essence Divine Light. So, I expect you to answer the register with what next time?" He did not pause for an answer. "You will answer the register with 'Labbayk' from now on, understand?"

Relieved, I resumed my place at the prayer bench, where some of the girls moved away, holding their scarves over their nose.

"Urgh. She stinks," one girl laughed.

"Bengali people eat fish," another heckled.

For weeks my brothers and I put up with these torments. I endured countless attacks and sneers as we walked into the room. Sometimes they would kick my leg from behind or block my path coming into the room. I was isolated and out of place once again. I had already been told that I was disadvantaged for being a girl, and now I had learned that my identity was being further scrutinised, not because I was Muslim, but because I was a Bengali Muslim, and that had I been a Pakistani Muslim, maybe life would have weighed fairer.

I sat each afternoon that summer, learning Arabic and Urdu, watching the characters dancing on the paper. I memorised the letters, sang them out melodically to the threat of the mullah's wooden slat looming over each error in my pronunciation of words, in a language that was alien to me. It was expected that we were able to recite whole chapters of the Quran in Arabic from memory, and at the end of each week, Mullah Saheb would line us up against the wall as he marched along, listening to our recitations for any errors. I was terrified of what that wand could do: I'd seen children as young as five being whacked on the back with it, watched palms, face upward, be-

ing slashed and reddened over a mistake, and every utterance or er-
roneous word lurking with an agreeable punishment. My six-year-old
mind began to ask why.

One afternoon, just before evening prayers, I found Mamajee
busying herself in the kitchen. She had been sat crouched down on
the floor, gutting a large tilapia against the sharp edge of the dha. Her
face seemed calm, approachable.

"Mamajee?" I asked. "Why do we have to learn Arabic?"

"Because we have to. It's what our religion is."

"But why?" I pressed on.

Mamajee paused to look at me. It was as if what I had asked was
unconscionable and unreasonable. "Listen, there is no worse sin in a
person than asking such questions," she said. "There is nothing bigger than Allah; he sees everything, your past, your present and your
future, everything. You must obey Allah."

"In everything?" I said.

"Everything," she said with certainty. "Because everything is
written by him; the world is nothing, meaningless without Allah.
When you die, you will answer to no one but him, and if this is what
Allah asks, that we learn how to pray to him, then we must obey
him."

"But, Mamajee, I don't understand it. The words don't mean
anything."

"You don't have to, and it is all the more reason to trust Allah
and not question him."

Her voice was now raised and firm as if to stop me asking questions; it was a sin in itself, I would learn.

I tried to move on with that firm conclusion from Mamajee, to
not question, and began to focus my energy on learning. I concluded
that the quicker I learned how to read, the higher the possibility of
not having to go to the mosque anymore, that Mamajee and Babajee
would let me stay at home. I fought hard, even reading with Mamajee
at home in the evenings and on weekends. By the winter, I had mastered how to read Arabic and was reading the Quran, and shortly
after that, I had completed reading the whole Quran.

"Shabash, congratulations!" said Mullah Saheb one afternoon, his smile beaming through his long beard. "Those of you who complete the reading of the sacred Quran are awarded a special gift in Allah's eyes."

With his frail hands, he passed a parcel wrapped in a green silk cloth bag. It had a tie sewn on that wrapped around the parcel several times. There inside, blanketed between the green layers, was the sacred Quran.

I held it in my hands, its weight heavy in paper and precious in knowledge. Mamajee once told me that if anyone were to drop the noble and precious Quran, they had to pay a heavy price. From where it was dropped, the equivalent amount of food, wealth or clothing had to be given to the poor. The thought of dropping it made me nervous. I held it tight and placed it to my forehead and kissed it, as I was told to by Mullah Saheb. He then raised his palms up to Allah and read out a verse from the Quran. Everyone in the room raised their hands too in prayer as Mullah Saheb broke out into rapturous melody, the verses of the Quran euphoric and emotional, making the chants from the children louder.

After the melodic prayers of forgiveness, his voice softened into a low hum. Mullah Saheb wiped tears away from his shadowy eyelids with the palms of his hands and said, "My child, it is written by Allah; it is Allah's words, and I pray that you are guided by these words. I pray that you find peace in its guidance and you never leave the straight path. Allah knoweth all; he is wisest."

"Jee, Mullah Saheb." I nodded. I knew this already, of course, and was tempted to tell him that Mamajee had already passed on this message. I quietened my inner voice. If Allah was really watching, then he may hear this, so rising from the position where Mullah Saheb was seated, I went back to my bench to sit quietly on the carpet.

The children looked at me, some smiling at my achievements. It was unmistakable that most of the jeering of the last six months had now stopped. My achievements meant that I had somehow surpassed their knowledge and had elevated my status both with Mullah Saheb and the haters surrounding me.

"Mashallah, you are so clever," said one girl smiling at me. "What are you bringing for the celebration?"

"Celebration?"

She nodded. "Mashallah, God has willed it. You finished reading the Quran. You should be proud. Everyone celebrates that. They bring sweets or something to share when you have finished to mark the sacred completion, the Khatam."

I felt like a fraud: my motivation to finish reading the Quran was to somehow find a reason to not be here. The joy was only in leaving, to convince my family that I had done what they wanted me to do, Khatam – finished, the end. And now here I was being celebrated for fickle reasons by the same people who despised me. If Allah could see this, I could have only prayed he took note of how ugly it felt in every sense.

As I turned to look at the door where I would be leaving from, I felt that ugliness echo in my whole being. There, in the corner of that room, peering by the doorway, was the man with the orange beard. He looked at me and smiled, nodding as if agreeing to something. I smiled back as a child would, but it sickened me. It sickened me, because his smile made me awkward. I knew that smile had different intentions; it felt ugly. If only I had known how ugly things were going to get.

CHAPTER SEVEN

– The Man with the Orange Beard –

I couldn't wait to tell Mamajee and Babajee, as this might mean I could leave.

I held the Quran in my hand, holding it with both arms, cradling it close to my chest as I bent down, putting on my shoes hastily, my impatience increasing as I forced one foot into an unbuckled shoe and juggled the heavy book in the other hand. It was sinful to place the sacred Quran on the floor or somewhere impure. The other children had already put their shoes on and left through the entrance.

"Here, let me help you," came a voice from behind. I turned; there was the man with the orange beard, towering over me like a solid boulder. He bent over, grabbed my ankle and placed my foot inside the shoe. I felt ill at ease: no one had helped me with my shoes before except Mamajee, but that seemed a long time ago.

He grabbed the calf of my other leg. It felt strange, his index finger rising up beneath my pyjama bottoms. I moved back, slightly losing balance.

"So, you finished the Quran, did you, ha? You are a clever little girl, aren't you, ha?" He stroked the top of my head and caressed the sides of my face with his large hands. I wanted to cringe.

"Here," he whispered. "Give your uncle a kiss." His hands grabbed the back of my head as he pushed his face into mine. The wiry beard prickled my face. I tried to move away, but he had locked my head, moving me towards him. The smell of grease and sweat lingered on his chest as he drew me towards him. The impropriety froze me as he locked my head using his hands. He then opened his mouth, forcing his tongue into my throat.

I struggled to try to move from his tight grip as he brought me closer. He wrapped his arm around me. "You seem embarrassed. Ha, of your uncle? No need to be. You should be proud of your achievements." He laughed mockingly as he rubbed his large hand along my back. I could only crouch closer into a ball, the Quran nestled between my knees and belly.

I heard footsteps coming down the corridor. It was Mullah Saheb, and to my relief, the man with the orange beard let go.

"Assalamualaikum, Mullah Saheb," the man with the orange beard bellowed, rising up.

"Waalaikumsalam," Mullah Saheb greeted him.

I raced out, not looking back, trying to pretend nothing had happened, that there was no intention in his actions. I sat quietly in the car on the way home. *Maybe he was just trying to be friendly*, I thought, even though it had been overbearing and repulsive. *Maybe that is the way some uncles are; they just want to give their affection*. But it repulsed me. I wanted to wash my mouth, be distracted. I wanted to never see that man again.

"Babajee," I said.

"Ha, Beti."

"I finished my Khatam today," I exclaimed in the car, Karim glancing over a little jealously at me.

"Shabash, Beti! Well done," Babajee praised vacantly. His words sounded distant and unenthusiastic.

"And I don't want to go to mosque anymore."

I felt the car jolt as he changed gear.

"Why?" His eyes narrowed in the rear-view mirror.

"I can read the Quran now. I can do that at home."

"Being a Muslim is not that simple, you know. You have to practise it every day; it's a way of life. The Quran is not like reading a
book and being done with it. You have to read it all the time."

I could feel a deep sense of never getting out of this. By the time
I got out of the car, I was glad to be home, glad to be away from that
mosque, at least for now.

"Hey, did you hear?" Babajee called out to Mamajee from the
living room. She had been in the kitchen, cooking dinner, and was
busy placing dishes through the hatch.

"Eleanor completed her first Khatam today," Babajee declared,
looking surprised more than overjoyed as he took off his coat.
Mamajee looked despondently back. A wordless response often
meant she was somewhat pleased, but it wasn't worthy of acknowledgement through praise or smiles.

"Pass the pans through," she said to me calmly.

I moved them onto the floor, where she had already laid out the
bamboo mat.

"We should give something to the mosque, a donation to celebrate," she added.

The following day, I came home from school to find Mamajee
stirring two large pans of something. Her face puffed up as she blew
the steam away from the hot mixture lurking inside the drum. The
sweet smell of cardamom drifted up above the stove.

"What are you making, Mamajee?" I said, peering over to see it.

"In the name of Allah, you should always donate to the mosque
when you have received good blessings."

"Blessings for what?" I said. The word *mosque* conjured up a horrible image now.

"For reading and completing the Quran, of course." She continued stirring.

"I have prepared this sweet semolina to take with you today."

"Take where? I am not going to the mosque. I am not, I am not
going," I cried.

"Don't you talk to me like that, young lady; if you think that's
okay, you have got it wrong." Mamajee stopped what she was doing.

"I don't want to go," I said, folding my arms in protest.

"It is considered the work of the devil, not wanting to go to mosque. What do you think Mullah Saheb would think of you?"

"I don't want to. I don't want to go." I stamped my feet and shook them heavily.

"Why on earth not? Why are you being so stubborn?" she demanded irritably. I paused and felt embarrassed to say, or was it that I couldn't relate to that alien feeling and unease it gave me?

"There's a man there, and he is not very nice."

"You listen to me: you don't disrespect men. I don't want to hear you complaining and making excuses for your misbehaviour, do you hear me? If you did something wrong, you own up to it and say you are sorry."

I stood silently; I felt that there was nothing to come back with on that. Maybe I was wrong.

"Go on, go get your clothes on before you are late, and scrap that face. I tell you, if I see that behaviour again, there will be trouble." She looked stern. I sensed that if I pushed it, she might smack me with the wooden spoon she had firmly pointed at me.

Mamajee carved out clumps of the semolina and busily rounded them out into balls, placing each one into individual food bags. Babajee loaded up the car with the pans as I staggered and delayed over getting dressed. About the only comfort I found was that Babajee was driving us there today, the two pans of semolina clanging in the boot of the Datsun.

We drove silently, Babajee as usual not saying a word. I resisted leaving the car, stalling my attempt by pressing the door lock down.

"Come on, out you get," he said, beckoning impatiently. Babajee moved all the pans through the side entrance of the mosque, where the kitchen and storage room were.

At the mosque, the azan beckoned everyone to the prayer hall, where Mullah Saheb, who was leading the prayers, stood, eyes closed, melodically singing the calling to prayer. Babajee and the boys joined the far end, where the men lined the carpet. I followed the girls to the designated area at the back of the hall.

I was relieved the strange man with the orange beard was not visible amongst the congregation, and as I scoured the hundreds of men lined up in the prayer room, I felt pleased to spot Babajee and my two brothers at the far end. Mullah Saheb had commenced the prayers, and a residual burst of worshippers filed into position along the rows.

I felt a sense of release; I could almost take pleasure in giving out alms now as long as I could bury those thoughts in the ceremony. I continued peacefully, but just as everyone went down into kneeling position on the floor, I caught a glimpse of what had filled me with anxiety and trepidation all afternoon. There he was, standing at the doorway in front of me. He watched, looking intently at me with a smirk. I glanced but quickly bowed down, following the rest of the congregation in prayer. By the time I had got to kneeling position again, he was standing behind me.

I turned to see where Babajee and my brothers were, but they couldn't be seen.

The man pulled me up to a standing position.

"Hey, come here. You need to help me give out the alms in the kitchen."

The other girls looked at him. "We will help," they said keenly.

"No, you stay here," whispered the man. He grabbed my hand, guiding me to an empty room that led to the kitchen.

"Well," he said in a raised and relaxed voice. "You Bengalis are very generous, aren't you? Giving out donations to the mosque? Your dad must be good at sharing."

He pulled the pans to one side, from the kitchen counter to a large cold stove.

I stood quietly, away from him. I contemplated that his words were just being nice, but the undertone carried something different, and I deeply regretted where I was.

"Come here," he said. I inched one pace towards him, hoping that it was sufficient.

He moved towards me from the kitchen, pulling me into the empty room adjoining it. I tried to move backwards, but his arms were wrapped firmly around my shoulders. He lifted me up, one hand tucked under the arm and along my breastbone, and the other under my crotch, pinching and feeling it as he raised me to his head height. I wanted to move my face, but he had locked my head now, bringing his hand along my neck. He proceeded as he had done before, rubbing his beard and wet mouth against my face. I winced, squirmed, trying to break free from his grip. I felt embarrassed, awkward, ashamed. A part of me wanted to scream out to the prayer hall and hope that someone would see what he was doing. The other part wanted nobody to know. I winced, my eyes closed, trying not to breathe.

"Let me go," I pleaded quietly. As he breathed into my neck, his heavy and broad structure straddled on top of me, pressing me down with his weight on the floor. He tugged at my pyjama trousers, tied up by Mamajee with a hand-sewn ribbon.

"No," I cried, trying to push him away. He was kneeling now, his thigh over my thigh as he tried to untie the ribbon that was tightly knotted and was tearing the cotton pyjamas with his force.

The final prayers could be heard from the prayer room as the men raised their voices, chanting out to the call of Mullah Saheb's voice as I squirmed.

The man pushed my thigh away, as if he was tossing away some rubbish on the floor. Then he picked me up.

"Go on," he huffed. "Hey, your uncle loves you, you know that? Make sure you don't tell anyone about our secret. Do you hear?"

I covered my face and wiped my hair, tucking it into my scarf, as if somehow it would cover the rush of unspeakable thoughts. I hurried back to the prayer room. I could see Babajee and my brothers beyond the sea of worshippers now at kneeling positioning, focusing on their prayer to Allah.

As I sat down, gulping in air and shaking, trying to sink into the sea of normality presently observed by the congregation, I closed my eyes and begged under my breath. "Oh, please, Allah," I begged. "You got what you wanted now. You help me, help me, help me. I am sorry you don't like me, because if you did, you would help me find a way out."

But Allah wasn't there at that ceremony; he wasn't going to praise my accomplishments for reading his words in Arabic, the words that made the blood rush to the surface from every slash against my palm when recited erroneously. The same words that later earned me respect with the community, Mullah Saheb, Mamajee, Babajee and the class of heckling children. Allah wasn't going to be rewarding me for this. How could he when my only motive to learn had been to leave?

I have trouble recollecting how long I suffered this man's abuse. The memories are shattered into fragments of my childhood that belonged to a world where time, days and calendars served no purpose. But I counted each day until the summer returned. I only remember we had started school by the way the leaves were turning orange in the sun, prayer times were getting earlier, the long walks were getting darker and colder, and each day was met with morbid anxiety and unease. I passed the trees lining the streets with the hint of amber, the leaves falling down the path freely as the autumn winds swept them along the roadside each day, signalling that the end of summer was upon us. And as I watched with longing for time to stop, I could only wish that a gust of wind would take me with them. It was darker now on our walks to the mosque. I remember the cold lingering on my jacket, nipping against my cheekbones, my fingers buried deep in my pockets that never seemed to warm, but none of these was as harsh and unwelcoming as being greeted at the entrance of the mosque by the man who called himself "Uncle". Here I learned that what seemed like kindness in a person wasn't meant to be kind, that smiles weren't often delivering happiness or love, that a helping hand wasn't really there to help. Rather, they were intended for something else. He taunted me in ways nobody else could see. His hand arched over the door as I entered. The long, silent stares directed at me when I was reading gave rise to entrapment, persecution and intimidation. I couldn't put these into words. I couldn't read his signals, his intentions, but his presence was met with almighty resistence by my entire being. I felt my insides cry when the man ordered me to pack the benches away, excusing all the other children. "You're special. That's why I always ask you to help," he would say. "You are a good girl. You always listen," he often would say, declaring this in front of the class. It was met with jealous glances by the other girls when they heard him praise me, as if his words excluded them from high regard and elevated status. If only they knew what this exclusivity meant. If only they could see what I was experiencing when they all left, or when my brothers were ushered outside to wait in the cold. If only they saw how his hands lingered along my back and over my crotch. "Uncle's best girl," he'd say. Each day, my physical being felt what my mind couldn't express with words. It stayed on pressed lips that no amount of courage or pain could extrapolate correctly. There were no words in English, or in Bengali, for what my body grieved inside.

"I don't like that man," I would say to Mamajee, hoping that it would be enough to signal my distress.

"That's no excuse to not go to the mosque."

"I don't want to go," I would cry, stalling, delaying the exit from the door.

"Listen to me," she would say, pointing at me with her hands at her hips. "How can you pray to Allah if you don't know his language? Hmm? Tell me."

"I can read Arabic. I can read now," I would beg. My response was overruled.

"What you are saying is a sin against Allah, not wanting to go to the mosque. You don't go against Allah. You obey him, praise him and recite his name. That's what is written in the Quran: you submit to his will. Do you hear me?"

"But that man is not nice to me," I cried, howling and petrified.

She pulled the scarf around my face, ignoring my gripes.

"Go on, go get your bag before you are late."

Written, I thought emptily on my way to mosque. *But what are words if no one can hear them? What is a book if we can't seek its meaning? What is praise if the person worthy of it doesn't seem to care?* I had a choice. I could follow this and sit in a dark well of tears, or I could find a way out. I desperately needed to find one. *Find a way out*, I repeated to myself. *Find a way out.*

CHAPTER EIGHT
– *Fairy Stories* –

That winter felt like the longest I could remember. The days rolled into one by endless darkness, as though I had been running in a tunnel with no hope of light. When I woke, it was dark, and when I went home, it was dark. I looked forward to school because it was the brightest part of the day and where I paid homage to normality. At lunch I would often sit staring emptily at the hills, the bare, lifeless trees and the grey clouds casting shadows over the houses. I would watch the birds flying over, following them out as far as I could see. "One day I will fly over that hill like you," I would say to them. Unlike other children in my class, who thought being at school was boring, I relished school. It was a refuge away from the dark, undefinable reality that engulfed my life. My tormentor couldn't find me here. At school my horrors were diminished by the praise of my teachers, the orderly classrooms and the playfulness of my friends. Here I could forget about home, forces that felt unnatural to me and, most of all, that sickening place called mosque.

I prayed that the daylight hours never ceased, but as the sun set in the winter afternoons, blackening the skies into darkness, my fears came alive. My only focus now at the mosque was to avoid the man. I wore sandals with socks, even though the bitter winter nipped at my toes, just so that I could leave the hall faster. I passed the prayer room, diving behind my brother to pass up his remarks or praise. I would steer clear of eye contact, his sneer or his stifling glances as he pulled his beard, stroking it as he smiled at me. I tried to forget the way he watched as I put on my shoes. The way his hand stroked down my backside as I left the building. I sometimes convinced myself that he was just an uncle, that the gestures weren't harmful, but their vulgarity was too vivid to box away as unintentional. Like the way he brushed his beard against my face or when he tried to draw me into him to put his tongue into my mouth as my brother rushed off to the car.

When I arrived home, I felt imprisoned by the feeling of self-loathing. The imprints in my mind of his touch only brought disgust for my own body as I recalled the man's hand running down my thigh, his mocking laughter when I put away the benches. *I am the one to blame*, I thought. *I am letting him in, and when my mind takes over, my body gives up the fight.* I conceded it was easier to accept this as a thing that happened: I was powerless, and I had to detach and let go. I spent most of the time withdrawn from the commotion downstairs when we arrived home, the fights my brothers had amongst themselves, the shouts from Mamajee in the kitchen at the boys' conflicts as she prepared dinner.

I often sat quietly in my room, staring at the old calendar from 1971. One night, while everyone was busy downstairs, I had a thought. It wouldn't be long before it was my birthday month, February, although it was still a month away. I had circled the date on the calendar, 13 February, the day I was born. Mamajee always explained how unlucky I was to be born on that day. "Thirteen is an unlucky number," she'd say.

I tried to put myself somewhere better when I heard this, but her words planted a seed of doubt that year. *Maybe I was unlucky. Maybe Mamajee is right. Maybe that is why these things are happening. I was born unlucky. It explains why Mamajee hates me, why I don't get any presents for my birthday.*

On my seventh birthday, I woke up with a beaming smile. At least it was a school day, I thought. It's still a special day, even if I don't get presents, although I had hoped secretly that Mamajee may have slipped something under my pillow or that Babajee would have woken up to wish me a happy birthday.

It wasn't mentioned, and as I pulled my zipper up on my coat, I thought about the smallest things I could ask for on my birthday if I didn't get any presents.

"Mamajee," I said, "it's my birthday today. Can I stay at home and not go to the mosque? Please?"

She looked at me with a cold stare as if in disbelief that my birthday could warrant it. "How could you ask for something as callous as that? In Islam, we do not celebrate birthdays. It's a form of worshiping yourself instead of Allah. There are no signs of you changing, are there? You are a clear example of a disobedient and wayward child. This is what I came here to raise."

I could have cried. My heart pounded as if it were being pulled out on strings. Her words were too agonising for tears. I chose to block them, and as I walked out of that door, I felt myself harden like a solid mass of ice.

I slowly marched up the street, Mamajee behind me. The cold February breeze cut like shards of glass against my face. Each stride drew me nearer to the top of the road with a chill that stiffened my back. I saw Sydney, our neighbour who lived on the corner, stepping out through the door to collect his milk bottles. "Happy birthday," he said, smiling, peering out through his doorway as he entered. He deserved a smile, but I could only muster a half one before looking down.

"Hey, what's this?" he said, walking towards me, revealing a toothy grin and tightening his belt around his dressing gown.

Mamajee stood closely behind, bemused.

I stood silently.

"You can't be miserable on your birthday." He smiled as he peered down at me, the long grey strands of his comb-over pulling back in the wrong direction.

"I can," I said, sulking, my chin tucked into my coat collar.

"Well, why would you choose to be miserable on your birthday?"

"Because today is a bad day, and thirteen is an unlucky number, and I have to go to the mosque, and I wish I wasn't born!"

I ran, crying, as fast as I could through the churchyard, leaving Mamajee and my brother behind. They never came after me. The poor man stood, calling me back, but I was too upset to hear it. I ran so fast I collapsed in front of the gates breathless and crying. A black car pulled over, and a woman's voice from inside asked whether I was okay. Her words were gentle and reassuring, but I couldn't bear to respond and look back at her.

At school I burst into tears when the class sang happy birthday, and I had no appetite for a snack or lunch. I gazed despondently out of the classroom window, looking at the hills at class time, and I barely heard the questions my teacher asked me.

When I came home, I sat wearily at the dining table with a half-eaten bowl of cornflakes. I thought about hiding under the table or under my bed to go unnoticed, but I knew Mamajee would start her rant, which would only bring on another round of tears. Just then there was a knock on the door. I heard Mamajee answer it. I could hear the faint sounds of her talking to a man as I played with my sodden cornflakes, stirring the milk and tipping it from my spoon.

"Eleanor," Mamajee shouted down the hallway. "Come here a minute," she said, calling out to me as she rushed back to the kitchen. I walked reluctantly to the door, and there, standing with a beaming smile, was Sydney, our neighbour.

"I think you were in a bit of a rush this morning, weren't you?" he said, chuckling. The lines in his face deepened, making his eyes close until only two blue-grey beads sparkled through. He handed over a metallic silver-and-blue gift-wrapped parcel with a silent chuckle only old people know how to do so well.

"Happy birthday," he said again, with a toothy grin.

I started to cry.

"I don't want anything for my birthday," I sobbed, passing the parcel back into his hand, wiping the tears with my long, trailing dupatta.

The expression on his face was full of surprise at my response. He shuffled into the hallway, trying to find somewhere to place the parcel, before seating himself down on the stairs.

He turned to me as he half perched on a step. "Now, nobody chooses to cry on their birthday. What's with all the tears?"

Syd was the only one outside my family that I ever really knew, or that I felt had time for me. Every so often he would come to the house and just sit and play with us. Sometimes he would talk about the war or help us with homework. Sometimes we would read stories together, or he would pick my brothers up by their legs to empty their pockets while they giggled in a fit of laughter. But today we weren't going to be laughing. I was about to tell him something that I felt ashamed of and that could get me into even more trouble.

He waited for me to utter a word between the tears.

"I just ..."

The tears kept coming.

I could hear his breathing, the look of concern.

I breathed, gasping between tears. "I just want the man to go away ..."

Syd looked at me, his large eyebrows arching over his gleaming blue eyes like two grey rainbows. It was as though he had lost colour in his face.

Then Mamajee came in.

"What's the matter with you? Why are you crying?" she demanded as she pulled me away by the elbow. "You are going to be late, and here you are, telling tales."

Syd rose up from the staircase slowly. I saw the awkwardness: he didn't understand Mamajee's words in the Bengali tongue and watched silently.

He bent down to face me.

"Save it for later, okay. Just open it later; you'll see why," he whispered with a wink.

I remember his smile as he turned and waved. I remember it more because it was a second chance, a second chance at making a choice. In years to come, I would be grateful for that moment, but it would be years before I would realise its significance.

*

That afternoon, Babajee didn't have time to drop us at the mosque: he had to do the catering for the restaurant. My brother and I walked through the dark streets, passing busy roads and empty warehouse estates, our feet nipped by the cold, our fingers numb and frozen.

At the mosque, I parted ways with my brother and sat quietly at my bench.

There were fewer children that day in my room. I didn't mention my birthday. At least the man wasn't there; at least he hadn't been lingering over by the doorway. I didn't have to see the smirk on his face or the threat of him working his hands down my body while under the pretence of an uncle.

I felt a release of tension under my worried brow, and after prayers, Mullah Saheb excused our class early. It excited the other children, and we hurried into the hallway to put on our shoes. I saw the girls out but realised that my brother was still in the mosque, carrying out his prayers. Babajee would not be coming to pick us up today, and that meant I would have to wait until they had finished. I lamented: it was only 5.30 p.m., and he would not be finished until 6 p.m. I stood in the corridor, waiting, the cold air blowing through the doorway as men entered the mosque. By now all the men had gone inside and the prayers had begun. I was sat listening to the call to prayer quietly when the door opened.

There by the door, with a large grin, was the man with the orange beard.

*

"So," he said, walking steadily towards me. He smiled mockingly. I felt my body freeze, my legs lock together and my shoulders tighten.

"You waiting for me? For your uncle?" he laughed, mocking, smacking the side of his leg and looking away.

I looked down, hiding my face under my veil.

"Aw, it's a beautiful sight to see a girl your age being so shy of your uncle, but you don't need to be shy of me. I am your uncle, aren't I? Come, come with me. I will take you home."

I shook my head violently while my eyes fixed on the floor.

"Hey, what do you mean? You are not listening to your uncle. Hmm?"

I continued to stare down.

"Come, *chalo*," he said in Urdu. "Come with me."

I didn't look. I didn't want to see his face.

"Ha? Are you ignoring me?" he said, crouching down, peering into me, searching for an answer. I could see from the corner of my eye the stare of a man ready to turn into something else, regardless of my response. I remained quiet, knowing it wouldn't work for long. He placed his fat, sweaty fingers over my knee, sliding them up to my thigh. I flinched, trying to shrug his hand away. He paused. I felt a firm grip on my elbow as he pulled me towards him outside.

"No," I mumbled, frightened by the pressure he placed on my arm with his grip. I resisted raising my voice or causing alarm, in case it made him angry.

He pulled me towards the main doors. The cold air swept in, sliding my scarf off my head. *If only someone would come through the door*, I thought.

"Please, I have to wait for my brother," I pleaded with him.

"You don't want to wait in there with all these men, do you? Heh, that's what bad girls do: they hang about by the doorway, waiting for men to pick them up. If I had an opinion, I would be in my right mind to tell your father."

He tugged at my elbow, moving me firmly out into the car park.

"Here, come this way."

He pulled me into a dark passage where the mosque kept their bins. It was dark, and all I could see was the glimmer of light reflecting on the frosted cobblestones. The echo of his footsteps, crisp, gritty. He started humming something in Urdu.

"Don't worry," he said. "Uncle is not here to hurt you." He stopped midway through the tunnel and faced me in the dark, stroking my face.

"No." I heard my echo down the passageway. It resonated down the tunnel like a voice repeating itself several times. The answer was clear that this was not right, this was not something that I wanted. I realised I had a choice: I could accept whatever this man was going to do with me and let him torment me for the rest of my life, or I could pull on all the resources I had in me to fight back, even if it meant more danger.

"No! Someone, help me! Help me, help me!" I struggled. The voices repeated themselves through the tunnel as the man gripped me tighter.

I screamed so loud that my throat vibrated. The man let go. I ran, screaming really loud, repeatedly, as though I had discovered a new tool. He moved away.

I ran out of the tunnel, through the car park and out to the orange-lit street, screaming until I heard a familiar voice.

"Eleanor, Eleanor!" I heard the faint cry of a familiar voice. I turned in the direction of that voice, and there he was, standing with a surprised yet calm look. Syd.

I wrapped my arms around his coat.

"My goodness! Are you okay, child?" he said, looking at me.

"No. I want to go home," I said, frightened.

I was shivering, my heart beating in my chest.

"Well, that's what I am here for," he said, smiling, "to take you both home."

He put his arm around me as if he sensed something horrifying had happened, but he didn't press further. His gentle embrace and safety had given me all that I needed, and I could only be grateful that he was there. *Home*, I thought. I didn't look forward to that. But I was home in that moment, and I was safe again.

There were no recollections, celebrations or small tokens to celebrate my seventh birthday. Everyone ate silently around the fire on the bamboo mat, the TV blaring with the news as Babajee watched. I had resolved that was something I couldn't expect.

I washed my hands and crept silently upstairs to my cold room, only to find there, on the bed, was the gift from Syd, wrapped delicately in silver-and-blue wrapping paper. I smiled when I read the note: "To a very special little girl on her birthday, Eleanor. With love from someone who loves you dearly." I unwrapped the gift. Inside was a book titled *The Complete Book of Fairies*. But it seemed unusual: it was all handwritten, and the pictures and paintings were all beautifully painted with dainty fairies. On the first page were the words "This book is for you, Eleanor, so that one day you can harness your own magical powers and learn your own truth, write your own story, that which is your true power, your gift to the world." This really touched me. Somebody had written this, and it wasn't Syd's handwriting. I flicked through the pages, and I read that each fairy had magical powers, such as kindness and courage and honesty, and that these fairies were always around you to help you find your power. It made me glitter and sparkle inside to think of these things as magical. Somebody had given me this, and although I didn't know who it was from, I felt special, that I was significant. After all, this person had written a book and dedicated it especially to me. Today was a special day, not because it was my seventh birthday. I had learned something, that I could value myself even if the world around me didn't.

CHAPTER NINE

– *The Lady in the Fur Coat* –

The following afternoon, as I sat eating my bowl of cornflakes, I found Babajee standing by the door, his jacket on, keys jingling in his hand, finishing his last cigarette as he got himself ready to leave for the restaurant. He looked at me, contemplating. His eyes had a look of indecisiveness.

I thought about my response and what I would do if he told me that I would have to go to the mosque.

"Have you finished?" he said, eyeing my small bowl of cornflakes.

"No, and I am not going to the mosque, if that's what you mean," I said, looking down.

"No, you won't need to for now." He seemed to be talking quietly.

I was surprised and curious when he didn't object. I had prepared for a heated argument or to have been sent off to wear my headscarf by now. His behaviour seemed odd, softer and passive today. He must want something. We hardly ever spoke unless he wanted something, and generally, he only spoke softly when he was being careful not to arouse any suspicions in my younger siblings. They were busy playing with their cars on the living-room floor. I had barely got through two spoons of my cornflakes, in all honesty, but I lied and said, "Yes, I have finished. Are you going to the restaurant now, Babajee?"

He nodded as he drew the smoke in, coughing out clouds from his lungs. Then he cocked his head up softly, beckoning me to come over. We walked quietly through the door. I smiled smugly. The thought that Babajee was taking me, just me, somewhere, and that I had him all to myself, filled me with excitement and wonder. I hastily put on my coat and sneaked out through the kitchen door before Mamajee could breathe a word. Babajee silently walked out as Mamajee watched from the stove suspiciously.

It was cold in the car. My skirt barely covered my knees, and the seat leather felt sharp against the back of my legs. We drove through the town, past the main junction and, to my relief, not in the direction of the mosque, nor the market or the restaurant. I watched the frost sparkling under orange lamps along the pavement. The dark night sky and the cold stillness of the bare trees succumbed to the depth of winter. The only traces of autumn remained in a few loose leaves waiting to be taken away by a swift breeze.

"Where are we going, Babajee?" I asked, gritting my teeth as my spine shuddered with the cold. I pretended that I couldn't feel the chilly air from the fan blowing on my knees as the car began to warm up. I pressed my lips together, trying not to shiver, in case he changed his mind. He remained silent for a while, as if gathering his thoughts.

"Do you see all of this in the back of the car?" He reached his arm back to point to the boot of our rickety Datsun. It was piled high with boxes. "Business is slow, so you are going to help put those menus out on all the cars. Hopefully, more people will come with the help of my businesswoman over here."

"Yeah!" I said excitedly. Babajee chuckled. "I knew my businesswoman would be excited with that." He grinned, juggling his cigarette between his lips as he drove.

A sea of cars in the town centre car park glimmered in the lamplight, blackened by the night sky. "Put one of these sheets under each one of the windscreen wipers for me," Babajee said, standing there, lighting up another cigarette.

Car by car, stretching my little arms up to the windscreens, I placed each one under the wipers. Babajee stood smoking as the clouds of smoke whipped in curls around him. I went as far as my eye could see him, until he was a ghost under the lamplight amongst a ball of smoke. My sockless feet gave in to numbness as the frost nipped my toes, like critters climbing up the root of a tree. I regretted not wearing socks. I had absently, in my rush and excitement, slipped my shoes on without them. It was a selfish and mindless act. I knew if I had gone back into the living room to pick out socks from the sock drawer, it would have immediately alerted my brothers, who would have wanted to come.

My fingers were stiff now from the cold, the paper cutting at them as I tried to separate the menus from the pile in the box. I didn't mind though: I was helping Babajee now rather than being a hindrance. It gave my ego a boost knowing Babajee relied on me. By now I was far away from Babajee's car, and only a small cloud could be seen where Babajee was standing. I reached up to the windscreen of a long, black, stately looking sedan car. "Hello," came a gentle voice from behind.

I turned, jumping unexpectedly in the dark. I could barely see anyone at first, but then, in the light of the lamp, her face was illuminated like an angel. Her hair was fashioned in a bob, and she had a slim face, like Mamajee's. Her slight frame was wrapped in a large coat, low heels and scarf.

"Were you going to give me something?" she said, smiling, although a little nervously. Or was it the coldness that made her jittery? She moved a step closer, prompting me a little with her hands.

"Yes, my dad's restaurant menu," I said, giving her a flyer.

"Well, thank you very much. I will definitely be coming to your daddy's restaurant." She smiled at me, and there seemed to be a gleam in her eye, as if there was a lot to take in. "You ... are ... a ... little young to be out this late. Aren't you cold? Er, how old are you?" she asked awkwardly.

"I am seven. It was my birthday yesterday," I said.

She looked at me as though she were frozen, and I could only glean that it was in fact too cold to muster much conversation.

"Well ... happy birthday for yesterday," she said. She drew in air, and her breath exhaled in swirls above her. "And did you get anything ... nice for your birthday?"

"Yes, I got a strange book about fairies."

"Oh, why ... why would you say 'strange'?"

"I don't know. It was different, but I liked it."

"Good. Well, I hope that you will continue to enjoy it. You know fairies are magical, beautiful and have many great powers, don't you?"

I nodded.

I turned to see whether I could still see Babajee. It worried me that I might be getting into trouble because I was alone. "Is ... is your dad here?" she said.

"Yes, he is just over there, waiting for me," I said, shivering and pointing over at the smoke near the lamp post. She looked up into the distance and couldn't see who I was pointing at.

"Oh, well ... er ..." she said, hesitating, "let me walk you back to where your daddy's car is, then."

She took a few steps towards the car, then paused, as if overcome with emotion. She then removed her fur coat and wrapped it gently around me. "You seem a little cold, dear. Here, this will keep you warm." She sniffled, and her eyes seemed teary in the light as she knelt to face me. I recollect that moment with intense warmth as she wrapped the coat gently around me. The fragrance of her perfume lingered around the collar.

It was more than just physical warmth, though, that I felt. There was something more that, in my child's mind, I could not fathom about this moment. Something about it felt tender and gentle, and I could only equate it to a feeling of love. I felt loved. It was the kind of affection I saw at the school gates when other parents collected their children, the hugs and joy that I would see in their faces. I pined for it, and here I was, receiving it from a stranger.

Then she reached her hand out to mine and smiled, and I felt an enormous tingling from the softness and the warmth of her touch. I let my face brush a little against her soft, fur-lined coat, melting in its warmth as we walked on.

"You are a very good girl, helping your daddy out, aren't you? What are you going to be when you grow up?" she said softly.

"A businesswoman," I said, mimicking only what Babajee had said in the car before.

"A businesswoman!" She let out a small laugh; she seemed impressed by what was only a selfish need to please Babajee. She walked slowly through the rows of cars with me, the menu in her hand fluttering with the chilly breeze. "My, oh my," she said, looking around. "Did you do this all by yourself?"

I nodded sheepishly. Her eyes watery against the lamplight, she gasped and let out an exhale of air that circled above her now like dragon puffs.

"So, what is your name?" she asked, peering down at me.

"Eleanor," I said. I was afraid to ask hers in case it would be seen as rude or impolite.

She looked straight at me. "Eleanor," she said, repeating my name slowly and nodding.

Mamajee and Babajee had always taught me that it was rude to ask a senior what their name was, but I blurted out the question. "What is your name?"

"Mrs ... Mrs Abbots," she said abruptly, as if it were also strange to her for one to ask.

It was difficult to know with any certainty how long I had been away from Babajee. I could no longer feel my toes or my knees, and that normally meant it had been long enough. Babajee was now sitting in his car by the time the lady and I reached him.

"Excuse me ... sir," she said, tapping on the window. Babajee rolled down the window. She paused for what seemed like a minute, as if she was working out what to say. "Is this ... your daughter?" she asked awkwardly. She picked me up to show him. I felt the warmness of her long cashmere scarf, soft as a blanket against my knees, her embrace snug. I felt myself melting with her warmth. Nobody had ever held me like that, not even Mamajee, whose temper always guarded against any affection.

Babajee stubbed out his cigarette in the ashtray and pushed the door open to get out.

"Yes, this is my daughter. Has, er … she been any trouble?"

"No, no, not at all, but I thought I better bring her over in case you were looking for her." She smiled. Her eyes were more watery from the cold, and she seemed to be streaming tears. I leaned my head a little against her cashmere scarf, the cold air riding up my skirt from the way she was holding me, causing my upper legs to become bare.

"Thank you," he said, nodding at her as he opened the passenger door. She let me down, and I shuffled into my seat. I didn't want her to leave. I felt secure and wanted her to stay and was starting to feel teary.

She bent down to look at me. "Now, now, why are you crying?" she said.

"I want you to stay," I cried.

Babajee cringed, turning his head away. "Stop this nonsense," he said, embarrassed, edging to the door. "Take the coat off," Babajee mumbled to me with another unlit cigarette tipping at the side of his mouth. I pulled it off reluctantly, handing it back to the lady as I cried.

She looked at me sorrowfully. "Oh dear, what have I done? Here, take this instead from me," she said, taking the coat, pulling something out of her pocket. "Whenever you are feeling sad, just look at this, and remind yourself how beautiful and special you are." She placed it in my hand, but I was too busy looking at her beautiful face, her large eyes, the bobbed haircut, the soft scarf, taking in her fragrance.

"Thank you," I said, sniffling. Babajee stood silently behind the lady, wondering what she had said to calm me.

"All the best with your, er … business, sir," she said, stepping back awkwardly.

"Thank you," Babajee said, closing the door. He gazed on at her for a moment as if he was thinking of what to say.

I watched her walk away, her head down, the wind catching her hair under the lamplight, the silhouette of her darkening into the winter night, with only her coat above her ankles now visible. My face glazed now from tears, I tried to feel what the lady had put in my hands, but my fingers were too numb and cold to sense anything. Babajee then got in the car and started the engine.

We drove silently home. I tried warming my fingers so that I could feel what I was holding onto. It felt heavy. I slipped it into my coat pocket, together with my hands to warm them. Looking out of the window, I searched to see whether I could spot another glimpse of the lady, but there was no sign of her.

*

We arrived home to the blaring sounds of the TV, Mamajee frying something ferociously in the kitchen, the oil smell lingering through the hallway. Her face frowned, signalling I was in trouble. I stopped at the kitchen door as Babajee continued to walk on through to the lounge.

"Where have you been? It is so late." Her hands were on her hips. "Look at you? Is that what you wore on a cold night like this?"

I looked down at my bare knees, my sockless feet, with my shiny Mary Jane shoes.

"That's it! No rice for you tonight!" she yelled with one hand pointing at me. I could only see this as a cue to leave. I cried, running up the stairs to my shared bedroom. The rest of the family were downstairs in the living room. I flopped onto my bed, sinking into the warm blanket. I could hear Mamajee complaining at Babajee, plates clanging and spoons banging against pans. It was dinnertime. I could hear Babajee muttering things back, but his voice could barely be heard over Mamajee's overriding rage.

I wondered why Mamajee was cantankerous at me when all I was doing was trying to help. Billy, my cat, came over and jumped on the bed where I lay. He purred and sniffed my face. I started to cry. I stroked his fur, and we lay next to each other face to face. The touch of his soft fur made me recall the lady in the car park, the warmth of her scarf, the rose smell of her perfume. I stroked Billy, rekindling the moment I'd felt then of her warm hands.

Billy stretched his paw out onto my face. For a moment, I thought he was going to scratch me, but using the pads of his feet, he gently stroked my cheek, wiping my tears. I thought of it as a small miracle, how Billy, a cat, could give so generously. I immediately felt warmer and steadily calmer. It's that moment of stillness, when a tired body settles, only to feel on edge from the thunderous jolts of doors slamming downstairs.

Mamajee called from the kitchen. "Are you coming down or what?" The sound of her sharp voice echoed through the hallway, but all I could think of was that tender hug from a stranger. Each time I recollected it, the hunger pangs diminished, the cold defrosting into someplace warm, the tears now like sticky golden syrup clinging to my face. It was all too much for my physical seven-year-old body, but I slept in a dreamful bliss that night at the thought of that beautiful woman who had held me.

*

When I came back from school the following day, Babajee seemed very disappointed with me. I could feel it in his silence when I entered the room. His body language said it all as he sat on the rose-patterned rug by the fire, watching the news, choosing not to acknowledge me. I wondered what I may have done to displease him.

"Babajee, is there anything I can help you with today?" I said eagerly, edging slowly near him on the sofa, my legs not reaching the floor.

"Not anymore," he said gruffly. "You could have landed me in some trouble last night," he said, not turning to look at me.

"How?" I asked. He gave me a cold, silent stare as if it were obvious. "I thought I helped you though."

"Help? You helped me? Here," he said, pointing at a box full of menus. "You can have them all. I won't need them."

I looked at the remaining box of menus that I had not managed to distribute. He lit up another cigarette and continued staring at the TV silently. Somehow, I had failed at pleasing Babajee, and of course, I wouldn't be allowed to come with him again. I remember it being a devastating blow and feeling this aching sadness inside.

I thought about what the lady in the fur coat had said when she'd put something in my hand and told me to look at it when I was feeling sad. It prompted me to search my coat pocket. I rushed through the hallway, where my coat was. I searched the pockets. It was no longer there. I scoured the floor, the hallway and outside on the pavement. I had lost whatever it was that she had given me.

"What are you doing in the garden?" Mamajee said, peering out through the kitchen door.

"I can't find something," I said, scouring the cold, wet lawn.

"You shouldn't be in the garden. Get up from there," she said disapprovingly.

"I am looking for something," I said, hoping she would let me continue.

"Well, what is it?"

"Something that was in my pocket."

She seemed to be getting angrier with my explanation. "Well, it is Allah's will it is lost now. Allah didn't want you to have it. That is not what was written, is it? Now get up off the grass and come inside."

I stomped through the kitchen to the hallway and up the stairs, passing Mamajee, who continued stirring a pot on a stove. Babajee looked up through the living-room door, bemused at the thunderous sound of my feet echoing through the stairwell.

Lying on my bed and staring emptily at the ceiling, I repeated the joy of meeting that lady. How lovingly she had smiled. How tender her voice, how wonderful it had felt to hear someone say that I was special. It probably wasn't the words but a feeling that I was wrapped in love that lingered with every thought of her.

Maybe I will see her again, I thought. *She might even come to Babajee's restaurant like she said she would.* I cherished the thought and went downstairs to collect the only fragment of that evening I could save. A box full of menus. I used the blank side to draw pictures of her face. Her large brown eyes, the slim face, her gentle smile. On the back of those menus, I rewrote her words in puffy clouds: "You are special." I imagined what we would talk about when we next met. Sometimes I imagined her like a princess or a mum who took me shopping. It was an untouchable outlet that nobody knew about or could take from me. Not even Allah. Each afternoon, I drew pictures of this lady. I placed each one back in the box. I would slide the box back under my bed, where nobody could find it. I wrote her name next to the picture, Mrs Abbots, my teacher.

One afternoon that winter, I sat colouring on the back side of those sheets, my legs stretched out over my floral duvet. I perfected the tones to Mrs Abbots's beautiful pale pink spotted dress. The room grew darker with the dimming sun, making the pale colours fade into dark ash, and it became harder to depict. Babajee had wandered into my room. "It's prayer time," he said, turning on the light. He set his topi on his head, clutching his prayer mat as he shuffled the rug onto the floor.

"What are you drawing?" he said, peering over my shoulder. "It's always drawing or writing with you. What about mathematics or science? These are very important subjects, aren't they?" He picked up the paper, squinting to focus on it. I peered up to read his thoughts, hoping that he would be impressed, waiting pensively for a compliment or some praise for my work.

"Is this you?" he said.

"No. It's Mrs Abbots," I said, quite upset that he didn't recognise her from the detailed and meticulous portrayal.

"Mrs Abbots?" he said. "Who is Mrs Abbots?"

"You don't remember?" I said, surprised. "You know, the woman we saw at the car park when I was handing out the menus."

His face went cold, and as he tossed the picture down on the bed, I felt the incredible force of his palm hit the side of my face. He bent down, his grip tightening as he cupped my jaw, bringing me closer towards him. It was as if he was trying to get my firm attention as quietly as possible. I saw his eyes narrow disappointingly at me, how he peered down at me, the stern focus drawing out the severity of my actions.

"You listen to me," he said quietly, clasping my chin and intimately drawing his face closer to mine. His words were a rugged whisper caught by a hoarse cough. "Don't you dare mention that name or draw pictures of this woman or anyone again in this house. Do you hear me? It's considered haram, and … and we are not here on this earth to idolise women or men, for that matter."

"But, Babajee, I don't understand. I—"

"Don't do it, you understand?" he interrupted. There was the threat that he might explode if I asked any more questions.

I nodded slowly, and he eased off, letting go of my chin.

"Go on, get on with your prayers." His voice became a steady rumble, like molten lava.

I didn't understand the severity of drawing pictures of people. I had drawn pictures previously, and neither Mamajee nor Babajee had ever got angry or told me off for it. I vacated the room, peering behind to see my pictures and meet Babajee's fierce eyes.

I waited in the next room in the dark, listening to Babajee's chanting with the prayer beads as he gazed out of the window. I prayed that he wouldn't see my pictures or the box of menus on my bed. I didn't want him to throw them away. Somehow, I had made a little world of my own with those menus, and the thought that they could be destroyed in an instant worried me.

I heard Babajee clear his throat as the mellow rumbling of prayers under his breath came to a halt.

I only wished he would forgive me enough so that I could sit by his side again and watch out of the window with him, as we did most evenings. But that moment had been taken away by what had merely been my imagination in paper form. How could I have upset Babajee in such a way with that? I heard him slide off the bed, the prayer beads' soft jingle as he tossed them into the folds of his prayer mat. I prayed that he would walk past my bed and not look at the pictures I had drawn. I heard the shuffle of his feet on the carpet, his movements soft and slow, his long shadow elongated by the light coming from my room. I sat patiently waiting for him to leave the room. Then I heard him stop by my bed. I heard the rustle of the papers as he picked them up. *Oh*, I thought. *What if he rips them up? What if he burns them?*

Unusually, he put them gently back. There was no anger or outrage at them, no tossing of papers or throwing them in the bin. I caught a glimpse of Babajee as he vacated the room. His eyes gleamed as he turned on the hallway light. His face seemed subdued as if what he saw had brought out an emotion that my seven-year-old mind could not reconcile. It was not anger that I saw in Babajee's face. No, this was the face of a man who was deeply saddened by what I had done.

CHAPTER TEN
- *School Dinners* -

"Wake up. You will be late for school," Mamajee called out. I felt her drop something on my bed, close to my feet.

"Here, put this on quickly," she said.

I peered over the covers. A pink floral dress with a set of almost matching cotton trousers rested on the blanket above my feet.

"Be sure to put the trousers on underneath it."

I picked up the trousers, looking at them.

"These are pyjama trousers," I said, looking at her.

"Girls are not supposed to show their legs. I saw what you were wearing yesterday, that skirt, baring your legs. Put them on under your dress quickly and come downstairs. We are running late," Mamajee snapped.

"But, Mamajee, I don't want to. They will laugh at school if they see me wear pyjamas."

"I don't care what people think; showing your legs is haram. It's against our religion. Do you want to be a haramzadi?"

I wasn't sure what she meant by the word *haramzadi*, but Mamajee used it often to insult me. Later I was to find out that it meant "bastard child" or "child of a prostitute", which would have proven to be an insult to her too in any case. Only knowing that it must be something bad, I shook my head.

I remember the look on my teacher's face when she saw the heavy dress, the cardigan and the pyjama bottoms underneath.

"Are you supposed to be wearing those?" Mrs Wollingham remarked, peering through her spectacles.

"My mum says I have to wear them."

"I see," she said, nodding as if to reassure herself. "Go and take a seat, then, Eleanor."

I saw the way my classmates looked at me that day, as if I had come to the wrong party. As if it wasn't hard enough being the only brown kids in the school, or having names nobody else could pronounce properly. Eleanor, to them it was El-ay-nor; it wasn't Karim, it was Kar-em.

Mamajee now enforced a new set of religious rules that had to be applied in school. I was no longer allowed to show my legs during PE. It was against my religion, Mamajee told Mrs Wollingham with her broken English that day. She managed somehow to scrape a sentence together, pointing down at the PE kit. "No is skirt, only pyjama; no i-llowed dis one."

Mrs Wollingham nodded. I only wished she could have politely refused on my behalf so that I didn't have to run around with tracksuit bottoms underneath a skirt.

School meals were another rule breaker. Any meat or poultry had to be halal, and if it wasn't, it wasn't allowed on my plate. Lunch at school was a set meal comprised of a meat dish, vegetables and bread. It seemed an inconvenience to the dinner ladies as they removed the meat or chicken from my plate, huffing and shaking their heads that they had to make exceptions for me.

What they couldn't see was the isolation I felt from being an exception, not to mention how miserable it was to eat the dry mash and cold peas slapped in front of me. And as I mustered up the courage to roll the first unappetising, gravy-less spoonful in my mouth, I could only wonder whether God had made it only an exception for me. There were days I was sinfully tempted by an offer of sausage from Carl Hampson, my class partner.

"You can have mine," he once said. "It's not fair that we don't get to eat the same."

I shook my head. "I am not allowed. My mum says I will be burned in hell if God saw me eat P-I-G meat."

"What's P-I-G?" he said, prodding his fork down into another sausage.

"I am not even allowed to say it," I whispered. "My mum says he can hear every word, all the time, and if I say it, he will get angry."

He shrugged his shoulders and continued eating. "You can have my cake if you want. I don't like chocolate cake, anyway."

Mamajee caught on that we weren't eating properly, despite all my whining that I didn't want to eat mashed potatoes or boiled cabbage any longer. Yet it took only one complaint from my brother that he hated mashed potatoes for Mamajee to question whether it was worthwhile paying £2.50 a week for our lunch meals.

"All they are eating is mashed potatoes and vegetables," she complained to Babajee, who was neither listening nor paying attention as he devoured large handfuls of meat curry and steamed rice at dinner. "Why pay that much money for lunch when they can come home and eat?" Mamajee continued as Babajee gargled and mixed another plate full of vegetables and meat with warm rice. There was no eye contact, no response. I only hoped that he would not say no, that there were no reasons to refuse Mamajee's suggestion. "Look at him; you can see he is always tired when he gets home from school."

I wondered why it had only come to her attention now. Still, whatever motivated the decision was better than no decision, which worked in my favour.

"Can you write a letter to them and tell the teacher that they will not be eating school dinners anymore?" Mamajee watched Babajee as he ate another handful, slapping his tongue hungrily. She hoped that before the next bite, he might respond. "Well?" she said, still waiting.

"Well, what?" he said without looking at her.

"Will you write a note to the school? To tell them?"

"I will do no such thing. As if I have time for that," Babajee huffed.

"Well, what do you want to do? They can't go on like this."

He washed his hands in the finger bowl, wiped his mouth clean, splashing the warm water with his hands. "Pass me a towel," he said, continuing on as if no response was necessary.

Mamajee sat beside him with one knee folded up to her bosom. It was unsettling to watch her waiting for responses like this, and I could see it was becoming agonising for her.

He rose from his position on the rug, grunting and burping. Mamajee looked down wearily. She cleared the dish spoons, covered up the pan lids as he made his way out to the hallway and upstairs.

I sat quietly, watching her at first. She hadn't eaten yet, and that worried me now.

"Mamajee," I said, "are you going to eat?"

"Why does that worry you? It doesn't worry your father, does it? Oh, no, it doesn't worry him one bit, as long as he has his belly full of food; it doesn't matter if anyone else is starving. All I wanted was a letter," she said, exasperated, "to send to the school to tell them that you and Karim can have lunch at home, but that's too difficult, isn't it? If Allah had granted me that ability, I would have written it. I can barely speak English; I cannot read or write, and this imbecile of a man is not going to help me out, is he? Allah really doesn't have any mercy on me. I don't know what I have done wrong; all my life I have spent devoted to him, and I feel as if I have no bearing on his life. Dealing with your father is like burying yourself in the dirt: you may as well not exist."

She sobbed, looking into the dancing flame of the fire.

"I can write the letter," I said. I knew this idea was going to be torn up to shreds, but I wanted to help.

Mamajee turned to look at me.

"What did you just say?" She looked suspiciously at me. It was as if I had said something that was going to land me in deep water again.

"Oh, nothing," I replied, wanting to retract it in case it wasn't suitable. Mamajee looked at me.

"You can write?" she said, confused. Her furrowed brow caused wrinkles to appear on her forehead.

I nodded sheepishly, worrying whether the reaction from Mamajee's angry expression would be delivered in physical or mental form.

"If you can, you write it, then, and I will sign it." Her face lifted again, like a soft ray behind a rain cloud. It was only a thin smile, but her eyes loosened, her eyebrows unlocked.

I loved making Mamajee smile; there were only a few moments that I replay in my memory that filled me with immense pleasure.

She rose up from the mat, carrying with her two large pans into the kitchen. I followed her into the kitchen, carrying my plate, reaching up to the sink to wash my hands. For the first time, I didn't have to struggle: she carried me up to help me reach for the tap. That was a first.

I dried my hands quickly, the aroma of curry lingering on my fingertips as I wiped my face with a cloth. I then went back to the dining room, brought out my notebook and pen from the shelf and laid them out on the dining table.

Mamajee cleared the remaining dishes, piling them into the kitchen sink. She came back to the dining room. A calm expression of empowerment came from her pursed lips.

It felt good that I could help, that I could write a letter to my teacher. I wrote in my best seven-years-of-age English, the extended italic stems like the long stalks in the swaying rice fields.

"What do you want me to say, Mamajee?" I asked, as she wiped the table. Mamajee paused, trying to find the words in English.

"No school dinner; go home."

I wrote with long strokes instead:

Dear Mrs Wollingham,
My mum would like us to go home for dinners, so we will not be eating
school meals anymore.

Thank you.
Mrs Eva Rabbani.

Mamajee signed the note with big capital letters for a signature.

The following day at school, Mrs Wollingham read the note.

"Is this your writing?"

"Yes, miss, it's mine. My mum can't read or write in English, so she asked me to write it for her, and she signed it."

"Very well, that's fine," she said, peering down at me through her glasses. "Will she be coming to collect you at the school gates at lunchtime?"

"Yes, she will do." I nodded excitedly, although I wasn't completely sure.

Lunchtime soon became a hectic experience for Mamajee, and pickups became out of the question. In the spring, you could see the light-blue windowpanes of my bedroom peeking through the trees from the front porch of my school, where my brother and I would wait, and if she didn't come, we would make our way home together. But in the summer, the green leaves of the church field blocked the view almost entirely, less so when there was a faint rustle of the wind, which had the branches swaying, clearing the view. With three of us to feed and another on the way, it was another round of chaos adding to Mamajee's already full plate of household chores. She would try to keep the lunch menu as varied as possible: egg salad sandwiches with a teaspoon of mayonnaise, or breaded fish with hand-cut chips that required frying twice over. It was a race against the clock. The brothers running around, crying, tugging at her patterned nylon sarees, wanting to be carried or picked up, the refusals to eat, followed by a tantrum, the commotion of screaming, the cries, the woes and wants on the food choices. I watched the fights and squabbles over the TV channel and heard her voice becoming increasingly louder as she repeated requests to bring the plates through the hatch. I saw how she was at her wits' end, the deep breaths, the sudden loudness in her voice as she rushed us through eating. It must have been months that the luxury of home lunches lasted, months that seemed short-lived. I could only recollect it from the growing size of her belly or the number of times she complained of back problems.

"Eleanor," she said one day. "Get your notebook out." Her breathing was heavy, and she gritted her teeth with gasps. She rubbed her belly, sometimes her back. Her face, rounded at the jawline, had now lost the slim angles. "Tell your teacher you will have a packed lunch, starting tomorrow. You can make sandwiches for you and your brother, can't you?"

I nodded.

Dear Mrs Wollingham,
From now on, we will bring packed lunches.
Signed,
Mrs Eva Rabbani

I placed the note into my school bag, pleased as punch.

*

The following morning, I woke to find my three-year-old brother, Masoud, crying, his voice carrying up the stairway and now bellowing into my room.

"Mamajee!" he cried as he entered my room, searching for her.

"What is it?" I whispered.

The others were asleep, and I had hoped that his alarming wailing would not wake them.

"I want Mamajee!" he cried. He sucked his silk-lined blanket, sobbing into it.

"She is in her room. Go check."

I scrambled out of bed with half an eye open. It was five o'clock in the morning, and I could feel my head swaying with the tiredness from the sudden alarm.

I checked their room. Babajee was completely out, asleep, snoring with his head under the covers.

"Go back to bed," I whispered to my brother.

"I did a wee-wee in the bed," he said guiltily.

I looked down; his pyjamas were all wet through down the middle.

"Let's see if Mamajee is in the living room," I said, quietly helping him down the stairs.

The curtains were drawn in the living room, and sunlight seeped through the yellow floral patterns into the living area. Masoud clutched his blanket, and I could hear his cold, wet nose as he breathed through.

"She must be in the kitchen," I said, looking through the dining-room hatch.

But there was no one there. Mamajee kept most of the spare clothes in the sideboard drawer for my younger brothers. I wiped him down, peeled off the wet clothes and placed them in a carrier bag.

He stood, relieved that the smell and urine was being removed from him.

I gave him a set of dry underpants and placed him into a fresh pair of cotton pyjamas, then set him back upstairs into bed.

Where is Mamajee? I thought. *Why did Babajee not move once at the noise?*

"Here," I said. "You can sleep in my bed, since yours is wet." Masoud curled up, stroking his blanket as he comforted himself to sleep. I then pulled off the wet sheets from his single bed in Mamajee and Babajee's room and hauled them downstairs, cautious to not wake up Babajee. Disturbing him often meant a barrage of inappropriate curses in Bengali.

Exhausted, I climbed back into bed, wondering for a moment about Mamajee, where she was, but my weary eyes felt heavy, and I drifted into sleep before I could process anything further.

*

It felt as though it were only a snapshot that I had drifted into slumber when I heard the faint sound of my name being called, but it was unusual to hear.

"Eleanor, Eleanor. Aren't you supposed to be going to school?" Babajee's groggy voice called out.

I shot up. The time was 8.30 a.m. The sun felt bright in my room, as if it was all very late.

"Oh, I am late! We are late!" I said to Karim, who was sleeping on his side.

"Karim! Get up, get up!" I yelled.

He turned to look at the time as I shuffled out of the bed, half removing the covers from him.

"Where is Mamajee?" I called to Babajee from the hallway.

Babajee paused. "Your mamajee," he said, hesitating. "She's in the hospital. She's bringing back a baby girl."

"Oh?" I felt lost for words. It felt unnatural for Babajee to explain.

"Help me here. Get them ready if you can," Babajee said.

He lit up a cigarette as he went downstairs.

I didn't know what I was doing, or what to help with first. I washed my face, brushed my teeth. I helped Karim into his trousers and gave Masoud a toothbrush. I rubbed some cream into his face, trying to recollect the things Mamajee did.

I thundered down the stairs, grabbed some cornflakes and placed them into three bowls.

Masoud came downstairs and sat grumpily at the table.

"I don't want cornflakes, I want toast."

"We don't have time for toast; we are running late. Just eat up, will you?"

"No. I am not eating *any*thing!"

"Eat up!" Babajee raged. "You are going to be late if you don't finish it."

It felt strange seeing Babajee being up at that hour; it didn't suit him either, as he was also in a very bad mood. I could see in his eyes that he was already unfamiliar with this interim role and that he was losing his patience at the protest Masoud was displaying.

He glared at Masoud. "Are you going to eat the cereal, or am I going to have to send you somewhere else today, hmm?" Babajee said sternly.

Masoud had his arms folded, determined to continue with his strike against the cereal.

"Hey, son of a gun," Babajee said to Masoud, edging nearer. "Are you going to disobey me? Hey?"

"I am not eating—" And before he could finish his sentence, I saw Babajee reach out, grabbing him by the arm, and slam a hand against his face.

"No, Babajee!" I screamed. "No, let him go."

Babajee continued. "You son of a swine. You don't listen, just like your mother, you goddamn son of a swine."

Masoud screamed. Babajee threw his hand, slapping his back. He kicked him in his side, and my poor brother let out a piercing scream.

"No, Babajee, no more," I yelled, throwing myself in front of my brother.

I dragged Masoud away, holding him in the corner by the armchair near the door. Masoud's face was red from crying, his voice grizzly and vibrating with each yell from the pain. Babajee stood towering over him, looking at us both on the floor. I clambered away, walking us both towards the kitchen, away from Babajee's raging eyes.

"Listen, come on, don't cry. You are okay now. It will be okay. Here, let me wash your face," I said, clutching onto him. I was shaking and trying to steady myself at the same time. Masoud sobbed, trying to stop himself, gulping each breath down. I turned the tap, splashed some cold water onto his face. I poured him a cup of water. Babajee had gone back into the living room, and we could hear the grumblings of complaints about Masoud's behaviour being vented at Karim, who was now sitting quietly.

I found some biscuits in the cupboard. "Here," I said. "We don't have time for breakfast now, but you can have these on our way to school."

Karim sat quietly eating his cornflakes as if it had not fazed him in the slightest. Babajee stood by the fire as I walked past the living room. "Hey," he said, calling to Masoud. "Don't ever forget this. Do you hear me? You disobey me again, and there will be trouble." Masoud nodded.

We walked to school, the three of us together, in silence. Babajee hadn't seen us to the gate. The lollipop lady stood looking at us as she waited for the next set of traffic lights. I sensed that she knew, as she heard Masoud sobbing at the crossing, the biscuit still in his hand, his nose slightly runny. The tears had dried white streams along his cheeks. I put my arm around him and stroked his head. I wanted to cry too, for him. I knew he could be a brat, but he was only three; he didn't deserve the extreme punishment Babajee had resorted to from anger. I wished I could take it all away for him, hoped that he could forget it all when he got to the play area in his preschool. I hoped that he would move on from it, for his sake. I locked his spare hand in mine. "Don't worry about Babajee. Try to eat your biscuit, okay?" The three of us walked across the road when it was time to pass.

At school I was late for the register.

"Eleanor," Mrs Wollingham called out. I was expecting another round of shouting. "Can you come here a minute?"

I walked over to her desk, my head down to the ground, hoping that she wouldn't bite my head off.

"This note from your mother," she said, peering through her glasses at me.

I had trouble recollecting it but then looked down at the note I had left in my bag from the night before.

"You do know that you have to bring your packed lunch, and it's to be left in the canteen cupboard, don't you?"

"Erm, yes, miss."

"Very well." She nodded slowly and suggestively that I should go and place my lunch there.

I had forgotten all about lunch, and that my brother would also have nothing that day either. All because of my stupidity. Perhaps the dinner ladies might be nice to Karim if he mentioned he didn't have anything. I was in the junior part of the school, and this made it difficult to find out.

At lunch I sat by the tree in the playground, pretending that I had food with me. The wind rustled through the leaves as I looked out at the hills. There was a moment of peace, and I cried, bringing my knees into the fold of my dress.

It wasn't the hunger that broke me down, it was a deep sadness for my little brother, and the appalling rage he had been subjected to. I could still hear the piercing screams as I watched Babajee kick him on the floor. I wondered whether Babajee would have stopped if I hadn't pulled him away. The hunger now only served as a reminder of how it had all started that morning, how it didn't seem to be on Babajee's mind, getting us ready or making sure we were fed. I knew if Mamajee were there, he wouldn't have had to suffer, and maybe she would have packed our lunch. These were things Babajee didn't think about, and now, because of this, my brother and I would go without lunch.

"Help me, Allah, please." The tears wet two circles on my dress where my knees had been.

Just then a voice came through the railings.

"Are you okay?"

I looked up from my crouched position.

And there she was.

CHAPTER ELEVEN
- Lunchtime Specials -

T he breeze rustled the leaves and sounded like fresh running water. The sun glittered through the branches, leaving drops of golden shimmer on my dress. I could hear the faint sound of children playing in the distance, giving me a sense of comfort that I was near, but there was nothing more consoling than the sound of her voice, that sound, like the familiar feeling of warmth, of safety.

I wiped my tears. The woman paused for a while, as if she was putting her words together. She sat, perched uncomfortably on the root of a large sycamore tree.

"Jelly?" she said, awkwardly raising a jar, offering it to me.

I only wished my childhood would let me recollect more of these moments. I don't recall how the conversation started, but I remember how perplexed she looked when I declined.

"No, thank you. My teacher said I shouldn't take sweets from strangers."

She looked down at the pot; it seemed to have saddened her a little.

"Stranger. Er ... well, yes, that is true ... er ... but no, this one won't hurt you. You see, I am sitting behind the fence, so I can't possibly harm you from here." She smiled a half smile awkwardly, looking down at the pot of jelly in her hand. She seemed slightly taken aback by my comment. That then made me feel a little dreadful that I had refused such kindness. I was speechless. I couldn't put any words together and sat silently in wonder.

She wasn't a complete stranger, of course. I knew that. Why had I simply blurted out what years of conditioning had taught me to say on these occasions? I recollect, from a child's eye, how it hurt to see her saddened by my words, how I destroyed a perfect moment with them. That moment I had longed for in all the pictures I had created of her. Together in that moment was a perfect moment, in each other's company, the hills before us, the sun glistening through the leaves of the sycamore trees, the roots of which connected us through the dividing green iron gates between us. I had forgotten the tears, the sharp pangs of hunger. Seeing her, that face, how fair, how calm, clean and collected she looked, seeing that beautiful face had dissolved all the pain. It was no longer a figment of my imagination, the narrow, sharp jawline and the large hazel eyes. The way I had drawn a hundred times before, though she looked different in summer colours. Neat and pretty, in a jade-coloured floral dress that buttoned up like a shirt.

She leaned in through the gate with her hand reaching out.

"I normally bring jelly on sunny days like this," she said, sitting nearer to the gate. "Would you like to try some?"

I shook my head. "My mum says I can't have jelly."

She paused for a minute, looking at the jelly. "Why?" she said, looking down at the jar again. "All children like jelly."

I seemed to have made her sad again, as if I had offended her.

"It's not allowed in my religion."

"Oh? I see. So, why is it not allowed, may I ask?"

"It's got animal bones in it, that's why, and I am not allowed to have it, because of, well, it's not halal."

The woman nodded, perplexed and slightly revolted now by the thought, and she put the jar down.

"I see. So you can't eat anything with gelatine, of course, and it needs to be prepared, let's say, a certain way, doesn't it?" It was as though she had half concluded by some prior understanding of my religion.

I nodded.

"Well," she sighed, relieved that she may have understood me now. "I will just have to eat this all by myself later. I brought too much with me, anyway." She looked a little flustered, scouring the picnic blanket that she had laid near the tree. She placed the juicy red pot of half-eaten jelly to one side. Hunger made me salivate. I imagined the strawberry flavour melting in my mouth, as I held my head against the bars. I had had jelly once at home before, before Mamajee knew that gelatine was haram, meat that was not blessed by Allah to be eaten. I remember how she had thrown the pot from my hands, burying it in the waste bin when Khala (Mamajee's sister) had told her. Anything that had gelatine or animal fat had to be thrown away, including mints, sweets, cupcakes, shop-bought cakes; anything that I generally pined for was vetted immediately for its consumption to Allah's specification. It made me secretly resentful to Allah yet again, of the good things I missed out on, all the while terribly fearful that Allah was watching and could even hear what I was thinking.

"I do like jelly though," I added. My mouth watered as I swallowed. The pangs of hunger caused my tummy to rumble.

She looked at me and smiled. "And have you had your lunch?" she asked.

I shook my head. "I don't have any." I felt the tears coming through and began to cry.

"Oh dear, why not?" she said, leaning in, concerned now.

"I forgot it," I said, "and my brother's lunch too." Then the tears flooded out, and a lump formed in the back of my throat.

"Well, look, it can't be all that bad. Here, I have sandwiches and fruit; you don't have to think about being hungry. Have it, go on," she insisted, holding the food in her hands, reaching out through the bars.

I shook my head. I resisted, embarrassed, reluctant to accept her kindness.

"If you don't eat, you won't grow up big and strong." She smiled, waving a parcelled sandwich at me. I slowly took it, obligingly.

She smiled warmly. "Here, there is a napkin and some cake too, if you want it, and if you are still hungry, then there is, of course … jelly!" She smiled and giggled as if it were our secret.

I remember eating up the sandwiches, the bread melting on my tongue, buttery and soft. She looked away at the hills as I ate the last sandwich.

"Where do you live?" I asked her, my mouth filled with a sandwich.

"Do you see those hills over there?"

I nodded.

"Do you see the green patch and the small houses? Well, look beyond that patch of trees; my house is just over there."

"I like that house. I think it's my daddy's favourite too, as we always look for it. I wish I could live there." I smiled at the thought.

She smiled back as if it were the kindest thing I could have said to her. Then her smile faded as she looked down. "Well, maybe one day, when you are bigger and stronger, you will come and visit," she said, looking out at the hills and returning to face me with a smile.

I stopped smiling. I realised that Mamajee would never allow that.

"Oh no, now. Why such a long face?"

"My mamajee says that girls are not allowed out and that we have to stay at home."

The woman looked confused again. "And why is that, may I ask? What do you mean, you are not allowed out?" She looked perplexed.

"We are not allowed. Mamajee says it is written that way."

"Written?"

"Yes, written in the Quran; that's why I had to learn Arabic and go to that horrible mosque, so that I know what Allah has written."

"I see." Her voice trembled a little as she mustered a response. "Did you like going to the mosque?"

113

I looked back at her; for once, someone had asked. Someone wanted to know.

"No!" I shook my head ferociously. "I hope I never see that place again."

"Why? Why don't you like going?"

"There is a man, and he is not very nice to me, and I don't want to go there."

"What do you mean, he is not nice?"

"He keeps ..."

"Go on, tell me."

"He keeps ... kissing me, and it's horrible."

"Does this man hurt you?"

I shrugged, not knowing how it felt.

The woman looked down at the long blades of grass swaying in the breeze. Her face no longer radiated like the sun. It had lost colour.

"Listen, Eleanor, you have a choice. I want you to never feel like you can't make choices; choices mean nothing is ever written. You can choose to believe in something, or you can choose not to. You must choose what is right for you always; you must remember that always."

"What do you mean? How could that be, that I have a choice?" I replied, baffled.

"It means you can choose to not suffer and be afraid, you can choose to smile, you can choose what is best for you. You can choose to be happy, and you can even choose to eat the jelly."

"But Mamajee and Babajee won't like that." I shook my head.

The woman paused, looked down again emptily at the grass.

"I know," she said, nodding. "But ... to be who you really are inside takes courage, and you will have to find the courage to make the right choice for you."

"What is courage?"

She smiled. "Courage is finding the strength within you to do something that you are afraid of, to do something you believe in despite the anger, danger and disapproval of others. You see, there will be things you want to do in your life, and you will hear many voices telling you not to do them, because it is scary. But you mustn't be frightened, my dear child. New things you encounter will be frightening at first. But you mustn't be frightened of them. Fear is there to guide you, to make it certain that you are making the right step, and it will always feel right when it's the truth, no matter how many times someone tells you otherwise."

"But, then, how do you know? How do you know it's not dangerous?"

"Well, my dear, you, right now, right here, you have felt it. When you sat alone, you felt something, something true, something that you know deep inside is either right or wrong. When you cried, you felt it was because something was not right. When you are happy, you feel joy. Let that feeling be your guiding light. Think about the joy it will bring when you do something you believe in. Tell me something, what do you like doing the most? What are the things that bring you joy?"

"I love drawing."

"And has anyone told you that you shouldn't?"

I nodded. "Yes, my daddy, he told me. He told me not to draw pictures of people ... when I was drawing pictures of you."

She remained unresponsive to a look that seemed to render her speechless for a moment again as she swallowed the words. She nodded, reassuring herself as she continued. "Well, did it feel right to you, when your daddy said those things to you?"

I shook my head and began to feel the sensation, that there was a source of truth flowing inside me.

"You feel it; the truth is golden. It will appear and shine for a little while, but then your fears will shadow it. Keep that golden thought. Repeat it, whatever it is that feels true. Hold on to it, and you will find a way out."

She could see I didn't understand.

"Look. Do you see those stones there on the ground? Now, there are stones everywhere in the world, aren't there?"

I nodded.

"Now, if it were dark, would you be able to see those stones?"

I shook my head.

"No, you wouldn't. You may trip and fall, and it would be frightening if that happened, wouldn't it?"

I laughed, and she laughed too.

"Now, what if we were walking down the path one sunny day and you saw those stones lying on the path. Would you be afraid you would trip over them?"

"No," I said.

"And why would you not be frightened of them?"

"Because ... I can see them?"

"That's right. Because you can see the stones and you can avoid them. And what would you do if you see them?"

"I would jump over them like a bunny rabbit, and hop, hop, hop!" I said, smiling and giggling.

"That's right!" She smiled and laughed. "You would jump and hop over them. So next time you walk down that path, and you see those stones, just remember they are just stones. They will always be there, and they can't hurt you if you avoid them. Well, yes, indeed, if you walked into one, it would hurt, of course, or if you tripped over one, you would fall and hurt yourself. But if you see them, you can find ways around them, move them or even confront them. And you see, there will be many obstacles in your path, but you must not let them get in the way of where you are heading. Always listen to your own truth, that golden source that sets you on that journey to give you joy."

She paused. "Believe in that joy that helps you see that you don't have to be afraid of stones. Know that your golden source of truth will guide you to where you want to be, and, my dear, it takes courage to believe it. Courage is walking down that path, knowing that it frightens you because you know if you trip up, you might fall, but trusting that golden source of truth, of where you want to go, that it will take you somewhere much better, and that it's worth following it." She paused, looking down at the jar for a moment in thought.

When I look back at that moment, I recall knowing that I hadn't fully grasped her words, but seeing her that day was enough to fill me with the assurance that I was not alone in that journey, that someone could feel what I felt and understand me.

We both knew I was making difficult choices, that I was choosing a path I didn't believe in, and that deep inside it didn't feel right.

We both looked on at the hills for a moment, watching the long grass swaying in the warm breeze. Then the woman turned to look at me.

"If it were me," she said, leaning over a little towards me, "I would eat the jelly. Here, go on, have the jelly." She smiled, passing me the jar and a spoon.

I smiled eating it. There was a large release of the guilt conflicting in me, now coming to a resolution, and for a moment, it melted with her approval.

The bell rang, and children scurried out from the dining hall.

"I have to go," I said. "Will you come and see me tomorrow?" I asked.

"Of course, Eleanor." She smiled weakly.

I turned and made my way back to the playground.

The strawberry taste lingered in my mouth, and the feeling of happiness suffused my body. And then I stopped and thought. *She remembered me; she did recognise me, Mrs Abbots.* I turned back to find her, hoping that I might be able to ask her, but she had already gone.

CHAPTER TWELVE
– *Eid and the Letter* –

When it came to spending money, Babajee was as tight with his wallet as he was with his lips. And this I learned only from the incessant complaints Mamajee made to Babajee on things that needed fixing, and Babajee's lack of interest in supporting these requests, because we didn't have enough money. "Money?" she would say. "We have money for cigarettes. Why don't you tell us the real truth? It's not money, it's that you are a tight-fisted old man who has no care or interest for his family."

I often sensed there was some truth to her words when Babajee remained tight-lipped and walked out of the room door, slamming it shut. Sometimes I wondered why he didn't care. It was often left to Mamajee, who, heedful of the costs, patched things up where she could. The sofa with the large tears and gaping holes was fashionably covered up with towels and blankets, giving it a patchwork of colours most idle housewives would laugh and scoff at. Carpets so badly worn by the door and almost threadbare were patched over by Mamajee with a rug that irritatingly wedged the door at most attempts to open it. Bills that never got paid on time by Babajee, despite the red-letter reminders and calls from creditors that filled Mamajee with dread, she knew that any hint towards Babajee about paying them meant further procrastination. Babajee would wait, call after call, reminder after reminder, until the day came when we sat in darkness by the candlelight or the flicker of the flame, without the TV, the blankets tucked around our toes. It was Mamajee who always sat quietly while the kids mucked around, making shadows by the candlelight, and I would silently sit with her, watching her face glisten with tears. Survival for Mamajee meant finding ways to circumvent Babajee. It was a light-bulb moment for Mamajee when she discovered I could read and write; I could now fill out forms and write cheques for bills.

And while Mamajee's patience was arguably tested, there were two occasions in the year when Mamajee wouldn't endure any parsimonious behaviour from Babajee: the two festivals of Eid. Celebrated by Muslims all over the world, Eid is as much fanfare and celebration for Muslims as Christmas is to Christians. I would watch Babajee, much to his reluctance to part with the wad of notes tucked into his back pocket, grudgingly oblige.

"Oh, Eid, what a joyous occasion!" Mamajee would say, her brown eyes sparkling as she fussed over the plans, and I could see she took pleasure in watching Babajee's bemused face turn ashen from the thought of costs. It was his sense of pride, though, that often drove him to the perils of being penniless. The opinions of the community of Muslims in Ashcroft forced him to entertain his wife's ostentatious requests.

For Mamajee, it was the long fasting month of Ramadan that brought her the most excitement and anticipation for Eid. In those early years, I witnessed Ramadan during the hottest and longest days of the year in England. The fast was observed from the first glimpse of daylight and ended at the last glimmer of the sun as it set. In the summer of that year, Mamajee and Babajee began their fast as early as three in the morning, without food or drink and with little sleep until ten at night, when the long, hot summer day finally came to an end. It was exhausting for Mamajee, her body slow, lifeless from dehydration. Babajee became irritable from the lack of food, and often the smallest and most mindless detail warranted his need to spark arguments where tempers would flare towards Mamajee. I could only pray that the suffering could be over for both of them, and it was without wonder how they fervently waited for the big day to arrive.

You could always tell Mamajee was excited about Eid by the way she worried. It wasn't like worrying about gas bills or where she would find spare change to buy the extra bottle of milk. For Mamajee, it was in persuading Babajee to take us shopping for groceries and festive treats, such as sweetmeats, vermicelli, coconut and mango, and not to mention Eid clothes. It was customary practice to bathe and wear new clothes on Eid, and for Mamajee, this was the only time in the new year that Babajee would spare some thought into indulging Mamajee with a saree. It was just as thrilling for us too, the children. Mamajee would have us fitted in new clothes, and our shoes, tattered by a year's wear and tear, would finally be replaced.

One afternoon before Eid, we all piled into the Datsun for our annual shopping trip to Wilmslow Road, an area long established as the Curry Mile of Manchester and where the thriving Asian community of Manchester had access to halal groceries, Indian clothing, Tupperware, and much sought-after knick-knacks at low prices. It was Mamajee's only place to buy sarees and to choose more traditional children's clothes for the occasion. Mamajee appeared ever more spritely as the women at the saree shop sprawled out saree after saree in an endless array of colours.

"Oh, look at this one. That is beautiful," Mamajee gushed as she picked up a green silk saree with hand-stitched embroidery across the hemline. She gave Babajee a quick glance to see whether there was any hint of approval. Babajee sat despondently, with gritted teeth, looking away with fearful glances at what he might have to fork out for these garments. Then he sauntered outside, where he lit up cigarette after cigarette. I was happy that Mamajee was slightly immune to this behaviour, although mindful and reserved in her choice or price.

"What about you?" Mamajee said, after making her choice of saree. She turned to a long rack of frilled chiffon dresses in pinks, yellows and blues.

I shrugged awkwardly, embarrassed that for once Mamajee was giving me an opportunity to choose.

"Go on," she said, smiling. "Have a look. It's the only time your babajee will let you buy something."

I contemplated as I stroked the chiffon dresses along the rack. The cool fabric shimmered iridescently in the sunlight. The sequins reflecting on the ceiling glistened like a myriad of stars. I found myself smothered in the sense of approval.

"I really like the yellow one," I said, smiling. She placed it against me to see whether it fitted well.

"Well, this is the right size. Go try it on." I put the dress on, and even Babajee smiled when he came back into the shop as I turned and danced around. It was only then that the delight and magic of Eid became realised.

For the boys, Mamajee chose the kurta pyjamas and mirrored waistcoats and caps to wear to the mosque, and while Babajee could not be persuaded into buying anything for himself, he remained tight-lipped for once about the costs.

After dinner the night before Eid, Mamajee and I sat in the kitchen, making all kinds of food for the following day's Eid celebration. There were freshly made samosas, both sweet coconut with cardamom and savoury lamb-and-potato ones. Mamajee had prepared and marinated chicken tandoori, pilau rice scented with cloves and bay leaves. There was sweet rice with raisins, sprinkled with almonds and pistachios, and four or five types of curry that she had spent hours earlier that afternoon preparing. I watched her frantically pace around the kitchen from one stove to the next, a mixture of enthusiasm and excitement in her tone. "What do I need to do next? What do I do? What was I doing?" she muttered to herself as she rushed around.

After the evening prayers, Mamajee took us all up to our rooms to see whether we could see the new moon. The clear night sky, darkening a shade of crimson over the hills. "Can you see it anywhere?" she said. "Eid can only be confirmed by the sighting of the new moon." We all searched the sky, and finally Mamajee spotted it. "Look, look, Eleanor! Look, everyone! Can you see?" Babajee joined us at the window as the boys bounced on the bed. "Look, over there," she said, pointing up at the sky. "Look, do you see? Eid Mubarak, everyone!" Mamajee cheered excitedly. But as she turned, she noticed Babajee wasn't looking in that direction at all. He seemed more interested in the hills.

"Eid Mubarak!" I said to Mamajee excitedly back. "Does that mean we can wear our new clothes tomorrow, Mamajee?"

She remained unresponsive, as if the moment had disappeared completely and left the room without saying a word.

Later that evening, Mamajee came into our room to settle us into bed. The boys excitedly continued bouncing on the bed, while I gazed at my new dress hanging up by the door. Mamajee looked out at the night sky as she closed the window.

"Mamajee, what time do we have to wake up tomorrow?" I asked.

"I don't know," she said absently. "Depends if it is Allah's will that we celebrate."

"But I thought you said if we see the new moon, then it means we celebrate it," I said inquisitively.

"Yes, well, sometimes … not everyone wants to."

"Well, I want to," I said, pouting.

She remained silent as she closed the curtains.

"You will need to wake early. No messing around now; get some rest."

*

In the morning, I woke with a big smile. My new dress hung up against the door reminded me that today was a special day: it was Eid. I looked across to my brothers, who were still fast asleep, and excitedly crept downstairs before any of my siblings woke to gain first dibs on the children's TV channel. But this Saturday was somewhat different.

Babajee was sat there by the fire, reading his favourite literature, and at the same time had taken over the TV with his favourite programme, the morning news. I was at a loss as to what to do with myself. I sat there, dismally looking at the flickers of muted TV news bulletins while he sat reading quietly, occasionally clearing his throat. I inched myself closer to the remote control by his side, hoping he wouldn't notice from his fixation with his book, but just as I moved nearer, he held his hand over the remote control, flicked his eyelids up to look at me from behind his reading glasses.

"Where's your mamajee?" he asked, unperturbed, turning to the next page while his other hand rested on the remote control. I stopped in my knelt position, outmanoeuvred and edging away to my place back on the couch.

"She's asleep," I said, disappointed.

"She is still sleeping? Go wake her up," he ordered. "Doesn't she know the boys have to do the morning prayers at the mosque today?" He continued reading. Babajee resented Mamajee having any luxuries, such as rest; it was as though she was married only to serve him. He lacked any empathy when Mamajee complained about being tired, even if she had been attending to the children the whole night, including my sister, who was a newborn baby and needed feeding. I looked at the time; it was only seven-thirty in the morning. I shuffled my way off the sofa and thought about how best I could do this without upsetting her. I crept up to her room; she was dead to the world, it seemed. Her long locks were like twisted waves and ribbons draping on the bed.

I leaned over, nearer to her ear. "Mamajee," I whispered, "Babajee is calling for you downstairs."

"Mmm," she mumbled sleepily. "I'm coming. Go on, go get yourself ready," she said.

I crept back downstairs to make myself some breakfast, a bowl of cold milk and cornflakes. I sat eating on a small stool in the kitchen, my feet tingling from the stony-cold floor, sending goose pimples along my skin. But something else had ignited all my senses. A rush of excitement filled my body and heated my insides like an iron kiln. I could see from the blur of the frost-patterned glass in the doorway that the postman had arrived and was busy shuffling letters through our letter box.

I hopscotched across the hallway. My mind rushed ahead with promises that there was something for me, although this was highly unlikely.

I pulled the letters through, each one, as the postman pushed them through from the other side. I giggled as he smiled through the letter box at me. I shuffled through the letters, scanning through the names in the hope that one would be for me, and noticed one had a special stamp, "By Airmail", and was enveloped in thin, blue, wafery paper, as though it would melt on wet palms. It was addressed to both Mamajee and Babajee. On the back, it read my uncle's name, Mr Muhammed Miah, the long strokes penning my grandfather's village. I felt pleased as punch; this was what I needed to make Babajee and Mamajee happy again, to see their faces glow behind the blue paper like the paper-blue skies they longed to be under once again in Bangladesh.

I turned the whining handle of the living-room door, which yearned for some oiling. Babajee continued to sit by the flickering fire, reading his book. This was sure to make him beam; any letter from Bangladesh would.

"Babajee, there is a letter here from Mama." Bearing good news, I smiled in the hope that he might smile back at me.

He peered from behind his glasses, looking up at the envelope as he silently took it in his hands. He reached up for the paperknife, idle on the mantel, and slid through the letter, unravelling the thin paper out with his fingertips. He read silently, looking up and down as though he was inspecting it, and placing the book down by the fireside. Then he stood up as though he was restless and moved away from the fireside to his favourite armchair.

"Where's your mamajee?" he said firmly. "I asked you to get her, and she is still sleeping." His eyes became fireballs of fury, as if he would burn up from the rage inside him at his request not being fulfilled. I had entertained a thought that he would be pleased with a letter from Bangladesh. These were things that he had delighted over in the past but on this occasion had little effect.

I ran upstairs, skipping up two of them at a time. Mamajee was in the bathroom, bathing her face with warm water. Her saree was loose against her body. "Mamajee, Babajee is calling for you down-stairs," I said.

I think she must have known that when the second order had been made, it meant she was also being warned. "Okay, I am coming down," she said with a frown, her voice dry and coarse.

I sat back in the kitchen, where my cereal had now become a cold, soggy mess. Delaying the need to throw it away, I looked down, stirring it. Mamajee's heavy footsteps thundered downstairs to the corridor. She peered into the living room, and I followed her there, wanting to catch her joyfulness at seeing the letter.

"Mamajee," I said, reaching out for the letter. "This is from Mama." I smiled at her.

Babajee sat there in the chair, smoking away despondently.

Mamajee opened the letter and read it out loud.

Dear Dulabhai [Brother-in-law] and Afa [Sister],
May Allah bless you and your family, and I hope that everyone is in the best of health.
We have terrible news from the village. Babajee (may his body rest in peace) passed away suddenly at night. We don't know the reason for his sudden death; Allah is wise and knoweth all as to why such a tragedy should befall us. Boro Ma [Babajee's first wife] has taken care of the funeral arrangements. By the time you read this letter, he may already be lying in rest. Ammajan and Boro Ma are arguing a lot. It is mainly over the household arrangements, and they say that Amma-jan should not be entitled to any rights to the household affairs because of Ammajan's previous marriage to your real father. Because of this, Ammajan is always afraid to add to her sad loss, as with all of us, about Babajee passing away. It is unfair Ammajan should be treated in this way. I wish you could help make Boro Ma understand that Ammajan is still married to our late father and that she should be entitled to live in the family home.
Pray for us. Give my love to the children.
Muhammed

She gasped inwardly, covered her head, grabbed her dupatta over her mouth. I saw her crumble to the ground, curling into a shell on the living-room floor, her cries low, contained between her aching grief. I was out of my depth: the seven-year-old me had little understanding of loss, especially in the family. I reached over, touched her to comfort her, kneeling by her side. I looked over at Babajee, beckoning him to help. He was sitting in his favourite spot, the armchair, very still, unresponsive to Mamajee's emotional grief.

His posture seemed relaxed, his arms comfortably on the armrests, his chin downward, unperturbed by the crying, the groaning and anguish pouring from his grief-stricken wife. I wondered why he had not shown any response, but then I saw his eyes. Well, what can I say about those eyes? The fixed stare, the redness lined around the whites. If I had known what it meant, I would have stopped time. If then, and only then, I had known what he felt, what this was going to mean for Mamajee, what this was going to mean for me, then maybe, just maybe, our lives could have changed course and the world would have been a different place.

Within a few seconds, I saw a side of Babajee that I had dreaded. He rose up to his feet from the armchair, his chest heaving, his teeth grinding. He kicked the coffee table upward, knocking the breakfast and tea onto the floor, the contents being thrown across the carpet. Mamajee looked up from her crouched position on the floor, her face moist with sweat and tears.

"You child of a swine!" he yelled out loud, towering over her. He grabbed her hair, lifting her to an upright position and abruptly pushing her down to the ground.

"Oh my! Lord, help me!" Mamajee screamed. "He is going to kill me!"

Her cries came from the pit of her stomach, thick and raspy as the air sucked out of her lungs with his incessant kicks into her stomach. I saw Mamajee cower into a shell, trying to protect herself as he proceeded to attack from the side. I felt my seven-year-old body freeze with shock and fear.

"No, Babajee!" I shouted, trying to push him away as he raised his hands to pound her on her back. He was relentless and pushed me back with his leg.

"No!" I crawled back, trying my best to cover her body from further attack. Mamajee was looking more limp and lifeless, and I started panicking and crying.

"Babajee, stop, please! Stop, Babajee!" I cried.

He eventually stopped. Heaving furiously, he took a step back from her lifeless, limp body on the floor. My body trembled; it felt like years had passed me with each pounding fist. Mamajee lay silent, her arms and body red. There were marks on her neck, blood scraped across her forehead. Her hair, unlocked from the bun she had tied it into, sprawled out like a tangled black web across the carpet.

He stood looking down at her, grunting, panting for breath but with little remorse for the state he now had his wife in.

I sat whimpering next to Mamajee quietly, holding back tears, preventing any arousal that could elicit another reaction.

Babajee's face looked livid; torches of red fury emblazoned in his eyes, his body rigid and fully charged.

"You and your scumbag family are all liars! He's not even your real father! Liars, all of you are liars!" he said, pointing down at Mamajee. "And you!" he continued, pointing at her, as though he was summoning her death. "There will be no mercy on your shameless, filthy existence. I knew it. I knew the day I set foot near that bridge that you and your family should not be trusted. Now look where I am, hey? Look where I am!"

He heaved, looking down at her in disgust at the wreckage as though he was a passer-by observing a bag full of rubbish. It was a look that lacked remorse for what he had done, of pure entitlement, detached and with no accountability. I saw a look as though he didn't recognise the body on the floor and as if it were no longer his problem. I silently watched as he made his way to the door, slamming it in a way that made the house tremor, the window frames shudder and Mamajee's precious china rattle in its showcase.

CHAPTER THIRTEEN

– Fight and Love –

The rest of the day was unbearably intense, as though the house were made of dark stone walls. It felt cold and isolating. I didn't recognise it as a day for celebration, a day that held so many promises of happiness as a family. My dress remained hung up by the bedroom door. Babajee had taken Karim to the mosque for Eid prayers, leaving my younger brother to entertain himself in the living area. I heard the door slam as if he were making it known that he was leaving. I came downstairs and watched Mamajee from the doorway, trying my best to stay out of her way and at the same time anxious and worried that she might think that I was callous for not being there. I wanted to be there, of course, but her words were like the jagged edge of a bread knife being used to cut meat, sharp, blunt and inappropriate, and she took it out on me in ways that hurt.

"This was all because of you: you gave him that letter … I do all this for you, and this is how you pay me back, ha? … All you want to do is please your babajee; did you ever consider me?"

There were no comebacks, nothing I could say to help, to put things right or to make her feel better. It hurt that she didn't feel the love I had for her in the tough times, and even in the good, I hadn't proven my worth enough. At least that's what it felt like in my child's mind. I didn't long just for her to love me, I longed for her to see that I loved her. I watched her as she buttered toast and strong-brewed tea in the kitchen. She stirred the tea pan emptily, her hair still a bedraggled and tangled mess made into a bun, her eyes dark, with two deep grey circles and dewy with tears. She had marks on her head that had turned into a bruise. I noticed scratch marks on her arm and a red mark on her neck. I stood speechless, petrified that anything I might say would deserve a harsh snap remark.

She didn't look at me, although I felt she knew I was there as she continued on hobbling her way past me, through the hallway and into the living room to where my brother sat watching cartoons on TV.

He hadn't really noticed Mamajee's face, as he was preoccupied with the cartoon being played. Mamajee knelt by the coffee table and placed the tea-and-toast tray down, heaving with pain as she positioned the tray in the centre.

"Eat," she barked, ordering Masoud to come to the table. I edged nearer to the coffee table. My brother continued to misbehave and not listen to Mamajee's call to come and eat.

"I said, eat!" Her voice was loud and full of rage. I jumped and ushered my younger brother to the table. He glanced at Mamajee and could see there was something not right as he rolled his legs around to face the food on the coffee table.

"This is what I have sacrificed my blood, sweat and tears for? This is why I almost died? These kids, these kids will never appreciate me. They will never appreciate what I do for them. Even if I died, they wouldn't care."

She started crying, and the tears just kept rolling.

Masoud looked down, holding onto his toast, trying to fathom the severity of his actions. I sat next to Mamajee, pretending to nibble at the end of a piece of toast while Mamajee continued with her rant at the difficulties she faced with Babajee and the unfortunate, self-pitying circumstances she had been put through.

"I am leaving," she declared. "There is nothing anyone will say to me, because this is the truth; it's all because of you I am dying here," she said, looking at me.

I felt sick with pain. I couldn't fathom which bit hurt to hear the most, her leaving or being blamed for all of this, but if I was to choose, it was because she was leaving. I would have been happy to take the blame. If handing over that letter had caused so much pain, yes, then it was my fault. Yes, be mean. Yes, I deserved it. But nothing could be worse than Mamajee leaving us. I burst into a breathless cry. The toast had turned into a large lump in my throat, and from the tears, I could barely breathe or speak. I curled up in a ball, kneeling into her saree. "I am sorry," I said in English.

I started to feel sorry for myself. How could she not want to stay? It was selfish, I thought, selfish that she could detach from us so easily, that her impulses urged her to leave us, my baby sister, my two young brothers and, most importantly, me. I cried inside at the insignificance of us in the matter and my stupidity in the need to thrill and excite Babajee with a letter that was supposed to bring glad tidings and that had now led us all to suffer the consequences.

"Don't leave us, Mamajee. Please, please, don't leave us," I begged, the magnitude of my offence deepening with every plea. The words "I'm sorry!" lumped in my throat. "It's my fault. I shouldn't have given Babajee the letter. I'm sorry." Tears and snot had gathered all over my face as I sobbed, making it harder to breathe. I gasped for air between syllables. She sat motionlessly and said nothing. Her face bore no emotion or reaction as she stared vacantly on. Masoud said nothing as he quietly looked on.

"Mamajee," I said, crying, "I am sorry. Please, can you stay? Please don't leave us." The words muffled into her saree as I repeated them over and over. "I don't want you to leave. I don't want you to." I curled into a ball by her knee.

She seemed unyielding, hardened like stone. My words were impenetrable.

"Do you see what I put up with? I put up with this for you. Do you think I would be here if it weren't for that? All my life your father has abused me, taken from me, and I have tried, tried so hard to accept his misgivings, and what? My misgivings are what? That I was born from another father, not the one who raised me? Tell me, how is it wrong?" She continued talking to me in tears as if I knew the answer. "Money, that is the reason he is angry. He thought he was marrying into wealth, into inheritance. I suited his selfish needs: in marrying me, he could cover up his past mistakes with some promise of wealth." She looked on emptily. "And all the time, I have been told that all of this was written, this life of mine. That is all it is, they said. You might get hurt, you might get bitten, but all you will learn is all this was written. Written, that is what I am, and you are," she said bitterly.

Masoud sat still and silent, holding onto his toast. For a moment I could almost feel the air thick with silence. I didn't know what all this meant, but she was talking now at least. I could sense her calming as her body relaxed a little next to me.

I remember how even my three-year-old brother felt the depth of my pain and the consequences for them. Mamajee thought as I continued to sob into her saree. I can remember her distinct fragrance, the light cucumber smell of her saree, how it choked me up to think it was the last time she would be here. How I refused to concede defeat to the decision she was making.

The minutes crept into what felt like hours. My body refused to budge from her side; my mind refused it. I heard the ad breaks from the cartoons on the TV, crouched in my state of bereavement and melancholy. Masoud was now back to rolling cars on the carpet with the sound of music and animated voices from the TV set low in the background. I was far removed from what once was such a pleasure, to be the first to get the remote control, to choose the channel. I couldn't participate in that; it was a world distant from me now. I felt the TV flicker, the light illuminating in hues of blue and yellow through my eyelids.

Mamajee continued to brood over things as she stared on expressionlessly. I closed my eyes, focusing on the aftermath. I could feel my face warm against her saree as I lay curled up.

"If you want me to stay, then you better not refuse anything I ask of you. After all, this is the only reason I am here," she said finally.

I turned to look at her. "I am not here for anyone else, you know. I am here just for you. You are the reason I am here. So that you are looked after, that you will get married into a respectable home and people won't look at you like you are from a broken home. There is nothing for me here, do you know that? There is nothing else for me here. There was a promise that one day this man might care, may see what I have left behind to be here. I gave him all of this unconditionally, but I know that I don't feel this in return. He sees me as the dishonourable one, but it never occurred to him what a cruel decision he made to bring me here. I have no future, no care and no wants for this man. I won't ask anything else other than you listen to me, learn to be the good Muslim daughter that I am expected to raise. If you do that, if you keep my face from being shamed and you can make sure you adhere to those rules, then I will stay."

I looked at her, tears of happiness and complete relief. It seemed such a small ask for what could have been a huge loss for all of us. I nodded, sniffling and teary. Mamajee looked on, staring through the window. Her eyes glazed over, dry and emotionless. A look of emptying disbelief of what her life had become. Little did I know, years from now, what those promises would mean. How they would be put to use. How they would etch out my life from that point onwards. I reflected on what that lady Mrs Abbots said at the gates: in every moment, there is only one golden truth, and you need to honour it. I had to honour that truth that I needed Mamajee, and as any child might, I didn't want to lose that love for the world.

It was tense in the house for a while, but on the outside, nothing looked that obviously different. Mamajee continued to wash, clean and cook. She spent the afternoons in the kitchen, making curries with potatoes and rice with coconut. She didn't trouble Babajee with any additional grocery requests and avoided him at any cost. It meant that Mamajee barely came into the living room, sometimes even when my sister was crying. It would often mean that I got yelled at, because she expected me to take care of her and hold the baby and help as best as I could. Often, I would hear bangs and wooden spoons clanging against pans as she took her frustrations out in the kitchen. I knew she was furious, her mind occupied by trauma, anger. I could sense it all with each distinct sound. Sometimes I covered my ears. The guilt was my struggle: it was entirely my fault that she was still here. She was suffering because of me.

Often her rage erupted more when Babajee was in the living room. He seemed to have built some resilience to those echoing sounds; it didn't seem to faze him as he stared emptily on, smoking away the afternoons in front of the TV with the roll-up cigarettes Mamajee continued to make for him. It seemed inconsequential, how insignificant she was. I doubt it played on his conscience at all as Mamajee lay almost lifeless on the floor. I am sure in his head he was entitled to behave that way; she deserved it. Those blows to her head and her belly had all been because of her behaviour, not Babajee's. The only time I had Babajee's attention was when he needed something.

"Hey, Eleanor," he would say sullenly without making eye contact. "Go get me a glass of water." And in the hope that it would impress him, that he would smile, I would run to the kitchen, climb onto the sink surface with my legs and reach out for a glass. Then I would turn the tap on carefully so that it didn't splash on my dress and I didn't overfill the glass, all the time with hostile stares from Mamajee behind me, watching venomously. It angered her when she saw me helping him with something.

At dinnertime this intensity continued. Mamajee would silently lay out the mat on the floor, and everyone sat around, with Babajee at his crown seat by the fire. Mamajee would serve up the curry and rice. We all ate in silence, occasionally disturbed by Babajee's grunts and belches as he ate. We all knew the rules, even the youngest of us would sit there quietly. All the while, Mamajee would sit, attentively, to see whether the kids were eating, behaving or needing more food.

I was wrought with a deep sense of guilt and fear between these two colliding forces. I served nothing more than a wall to throw bullets at, and each one I took, I blamed myself. I absorbed it. I took it all as my fault entirely. After all, the truth was that this had happened because of me.

*

When I woke on Monday, I felt the warmth of my pillow, curled into my tummy. I was thankful for it being a school day and that I could escape the nuances of home life.

I looked out from my classroom window and wondered when I would see Mrs Abbots again. It rained for a few days following that weekend, the clouds thick like a mass of concrete covering the sky over the hills, the downpour laying streams along the window as though the heavens were also feeling my sorrow.

I waited every lunchtime in the rain, sitting under a tree for shelter, refusing to go inside when the teachers called. I thought about her on my walk home from school, passing through the churchyard and the stony mud path. I watched the light catching those stones: "There will be many obstacles in your path, but you must not let them get in the way of where you are heading."

As I crossed the road, I saw Syd.

"Hello, miserable," he shouted as he stood at his garden gate. "What's with the long face?"

I tried to stay quiet.

"I saw your mum before. Is everything okay at home?"

I nodded. But I knew he knew.

Then, the one lunchtime, as I sat there between the trees, I heard the crisp sound of footsteps, the rustle of leaves and that beautiful voice from behind the gate.

"You can see it, you know, everywhere," she said, smiling.

I turned to look at her, puzzled.

"What?"

"Love, love is everywhere."

She placed her wicker basket by the tree as she sat herself down on a large tree root and gazed admiringly on at the hills.

I looked at her again. "I don't know what you mean."

She pulled her hand through the gate. "Pass me your hand."

She took my hand, held my finger over a pattern on the ground. "Do you see it? It's a heart."

She smiled, looking around. "Do you know that love is in everything, everywhere, all around you and inside you?"

I shook my head.

"Look for yourself; can you see any hearts anywhere? Look, keep looking."

I searched, scouring around me.

"You must search for love in everything, even in the smallest stone. You will find it, but you should never stop searching for love."

I didn't know what she meant, but then, as she was talking, I found a soft grey stone. It was shaped in a heart.

"Look, I found one."

I handed it to her; she put it gently in my palms. "Now do you see the magic of love? You will always be loved if you open your heart to feel it. It will be there for you, as long as you seek it, as long as you will it."

That afternoon, on my way back home, I saw what Mrs Abbots meant.

I saw the heart etched out from a stone wall. I looked down at the floor and saw pebbles shaped like hearts. It was in a pool of water and in the shapes of leaves. Suddenly I didn't feel so alone. The world was not such a lonely, loveless place after all.

If I couldn't find love at home, I could survive by finding it in everything else. I would collect stones shaped like hearts and place them in a box, along with petals and leaves shaped like hearts, and I would spend my lunchtimes at the gates, listening to Mrs Abbots's stories. She often named the birds that came and perched on the trees.

"That one is Frederick," she would say. "He's always late for lunch." As she threw some bread out to the birds, it made me giggle, thinking how many funny names they had. Frederick, Gertrude, Mavis, Mindy. She would talk to them as if they were talking back. "Now you listen here, Gertrude," she would say. "I have told you before that cheese is out of the question. You will only get a sore tummy from eating it." Her commentary would tickle me pink.

She would hand me matchboxes and task me with filling them up with the smallest things I could find, and then we would count them up and see who had the most the next time we met. One day, when I had collected the most, she said, "You see, the best things come in small packages. You can have a lot, even with the smallest things. You can still be happy."

I spent the summer healing with these little treasures. Her words distracted me from home, the arguments, fights, bickering, blame and guilt that I was being exposed to. Each time, I distracted myself, looking for a stone or something that looked like love. And by the end of the summer term, I had collected a lot of hearts, petals, stones, leaves, ribbons, paper hearts and confetti, and placed them in a box, wrapped in a floral cloth. One lunchtime I presented them to Mrs Abbots. "I wanted to give you something, Mrs Abbots; I made it for you." I could sense how touched she was when she opened the wooden box, holding back tears.

"I am glad you can see so much love around you. You really do see the beauty of the world now, don't you?"

I nodded.

"Do you want to know something? Do you know that each time you give love like this, it will always come back to you someday?"

I nodded. *One day*, I thought, *perhaps if I continue loving my parents, they might see it; it might come back one day.* At least that was what I still hoped.

CHAPTER FOURTEEN
– *Trip to Bangladesh*–

"Eleanor, bring those shoes over here, and put those things in that bag! Do I look like I have four pairs of hands?" Mamajee announced rhetorically. I passed her the items and then made myself useful by sitting on the large suitcase so that she could zip it closed, although, being as light as I was, I wasn't of much use. Her expression was full of panic, panting for breath as she bent over to find some more things to squeeze into the suitcase. There were clothes piled high near the suitcase, queuing up to be loaded, and I wondered how this was all going to fit in.

The bedroom had turned into a market. Countless items had to go into these suitcases. Children's toys, vitamin C tablets, bulk packs of paracetamol, family-sized tubs of Vaseline and Vick's VapoRub.

"What is all this stuff, Mamajee? Do we need to take all of this?" I observed as she stuffed more clothes into the sides.

"Oh, most of this is not for you; you'll see more of these clothes when you get back," she said, folding away my new white cardigan. "These things are for the poor children, you know, like the ones you saw on the TV, only these children are not just poor children, they are your own cousins and family."

I pictured them now, the ones she ached for as she watched the news, the children with the large brown bellies and thin limbs who would sorrowfully look back at us, crying, yearning.

My parents had collected many items over the years to take with them to Bangladesh, and it was all locked inside this chest. I couldn't wait to see what was inside. The lid was a little awkward to open. I sat marvelling, leaning over the chest with my hands resting on my knees as she tugged at the clasps at each side, which had almost welded together over the years. I helped her with the other side of the lid, and we both opened it together. Inside the chest was a large green embroidered blanket with a gold fringe hemmed around the side. "This is an expensive blanket," Mamajee explained, holding it carefully in her hands. She put it down gently. Then she lifted out a china set. "This was given to us by your aunt as a wedding present," she said, surprised how she had forgotten all about it.

I sensed these were moments she had longed for all these years; she could finally return to her country, to her birthplace. All these years I had watched and listened to stories as we sat by the fire at breakfast, how with each passing plane she shed tears, or craved the delicious fruit that you couldn't buy in our supermarkets in Ashcroft. How she melted in the memories of swimming in the deep rivers and ponds, and most of all, I listened to her cries, that if it weren't for me, she would still be living there and in a happier place.

Finally, we were going to board that plane my parents had longed for. I wondered what it was going to be like in Bangladesh. Was it really going to be as hot as they described? It was August in Ashcroft, and the weather was only just warm enough to walk outside without a sweater. I had imagined swimming pools and gushing waterfalls and had already piled high a collection of lilos and armbands to use out there. That night I slept facing the calendar Mamajee had left in the room. I looked at the endless rice fields in the pictures and imagined that I would be there soon, playing with the children in the villages and swimming in clear blue waters.

*

In the morning, I opened my blurry eyes to the same calendar, dated back from 1971. The rice field looked greener in the picture now as a thin ray of sun hit one side of the field. I could hear Mamajee coming up the stairs, stamping her feet heavily onto each step, her flip-flops making a flapping sound as she made her way up the last step, creaking as she made her final heaving ascent to the top. I closed my eyes again, pretending to be asleep. If she saw me awake in bed, it was most probable that I would get a telling off.

"Are you still not up?" she said, her voice shrill and harsh as she peered into the room.

"Hmm?" I groaned, rustling the covers a little.

"Come on now, up! Up you get. We don't have a lot of time, and the minicab will be here soon," she said with a brisk tone as she pulled the sheets away. "The minicab will be here soon," she repeated, "and we still haven't had breakfast. Come on, there is much to do." She paced across the room, heaving as she peeled the curtains open and opened the window to let in some fresh air.

I rose from the bed. "What should I wear?" I asked.

"You can wear your new dress with pyjamas, of course, the one I put on the staircase balcony … and make sure you tie your hair in a plait, none of this leaving-your-hair-down nonsense." She walked out of the room, leaving the door wide open. I sat in bed for a minute, recollecting the moments; I had thought so much of this day to come. I edged my feet down to the floor, scouring it for my slippers and quickly shuffling them onto my feet to make my way to the bathroom. This was the last time I would be brushing my teeth in England, I thought. This was the last time I would be having a shower using hot and cold taps in our bathroom. Of course, we would only be going for a few weeks, I said to myself, as school started in September.

I rushed my way through the cleansing process, knowing that Mamajee was clicking her way to the kitchen downstairs with her flips-flops. It always made me nervous, as I was ever so conscious she needed me in the kitchen. I changed into my new dress. White with purple berries printed all over it. It had a silk ribbon criss-crossed down the front to form a small waistcoat that was sewn onto the dress. Then I went down the stairs boisterously, alerting Mamajee to avoid another frown from not assisting promptly. I passed the pile of toast through the hatch and peeled the shells off four boiled eggs. Mamajee poured strongly brewed tea into a jug and added frothy, boiled milk to make a dark brown mixture. She handed it carefully to me to take over to the table.

Babajee came down the stairs. His entrance, earmarked with a clearing of the throat, which was his way of asking, "Is the food ready?" He pulled out a prayer mat from a shelf belonging to a wide mahogany showcase and proceeded to place it on the floor in front of him. He placed a cap on his head and surrendered to Allah, his lips reciting the verses underneath his breath as he clasped his hands in front of his chest and prostrated his thin, frail body to face Mecca.

It still amazed me that my father prayed. He never used to, until a couple of years back, when one day he came back home after receiving a letter that his older brother was very ill in Bangladesh. My uncle had begged my father to come back to Bangladesh and visit him. He had been aching to catch a glimpse of all of us for years. My father had spent too much time deliberating over whether to go, until it was too late. Another letter came through, bearing bad news that his brother had passed away. I will never forget the day he came home, opening the living-room door slowly. His face, lost in dismay. He quietly changed into a lungi, placed a velvet prayer mat in front of the fire, facing it eastwards, and collapsed into a pile in prayer. His shoulders hunched as he knelt and bowed over. I could hear the faint cries as he buried his face in the floor. Mamajee had come into the room from the kitchen and stood and watched. She also began to cry, knowing the pain he was going through. I had stood and watched in awe, not knowing what to do or what to make of it all. I had never seen Babajee cry, and I had never seen him pray.

Today I watched him pray, praying that he would never make the same mistake again. Babajee had booked the tickets immediately, this time without any deliberation, upon hearing that his second brother was now also very ill in Bangladesh. Mamajee called my brothers downstairs, who were now fully clothed in matching outfits. She always dressed the two boys in the same coordinated outfits. They marched downstairs with their white shirts tucked into some beige chinos and a neat patterned sweater for the bus journey to the airport. Their hair was always Brylcreemed neatly and combed with a side parting.

Babajee finished his prayers, and everyone gathered round the table to collect their cup of tea and crisp buttered toast. Mamajee handed out rolled parcels of toast with a mixture of crumbled boiled egg for us to eat while they brought the heavy chest down from the bedroom. She then cleared away the breakfast table hastily as my father opened the door to the middle-aged, red-faced driver who had arrived to take us to the airport. I watched his bewilderment upon seeing the luggage as he carted each item back to the vehicle. We had two family-sized suitcases, four smaller ones, a treasure chest, eight holdalls, one assigned to each of us.

"By heck," the driver said. "How long are ya goin' for?"

Even my four-year-old sister was assigned an oversized bag to carry. Fortunately, she had help, as she couldn't even drag it off the floor. My father picked her up, resting her on one side of his hip and propping her on a seat inside the people carrier. Her short hair had been cutely tied up into a fountain shape on her head with a bobble. She sat happily in her seat. We all clambered in and sat down quietly. Soon we would be on our way, I thought, on our way to the country that Mamajee craved to fly back to as she watched each passing plane soar through the skies above.

*

The air was thick and humid. I walked down the stairs from what smelled like the armpit of the plane to a lingering, palpable smell of body odour. A waft of warm air grabbed at my dress as I walked down the stairs hot and sticky. In the distance, I saw people standing in rows, waiting for their families. Our journey was not yet over: we had another flight to catch before we greeted our own family and relatives. The sun blazed in its early morning skies. It felt strange getting off that plane, and I couldn't believe I was here. In the distance, green lands lay abundant, like the scenes in the news reports. There was a lot of commotion as we climbed into a minibus to take us to the terminal. Ground staff shouted and moved people into the busy minibuses that had no air conditioning, and the heat grew more intense as people crowded close inside. Mamajee stood counting the heads, watching us all. She hadn't slept much. I could tell from her mouth. Her lips were dry and sealed, her eyes closing together constantly as she peeled them apart.

When we arrived in Sylhet, another round of chaos followed. At the arrival gates, strange people with dark faces stood and shouted for us. I couldn't process the commotion upon our arrival as they stood with their arms reaching out for us. One of them grabbed hold of Masoud, my youngest brother, and lifted him up from behind the gate. Karim suddenly grabbed his leg in sheer panic that a stranger was going to run off with him. Babajee grabbed Karim's shoulder quickly.

"It is okay, Karim, don't worry!" He smiled with delight. It was one of my uncle's sons, Ali Akbar, who had come to meet us at the airport. Babajee recognised him as being the youngest of the sons from the picture and was pleased to see him. Ali ruffled Masoud's hair, his cute dimples deepening with his smile. Babajee introduced us. "This is your cousin. Now greet him to his feet." Bowing at the feet was a traditional greeting that was observed to elders and seniors. It felt awkward doing this to a complete stranger.

Ali Akbar didn't feel awkward; he was quite happy to stand there waiting for us to bow at his feet. I kowtowed down and touched his feet. He seemed pleased with our traditional etiquette and manners. "They are good children, aren't they?" he said, nodding at Babajee, his bright teeth and dark, glistening skin beaming back at me as I rose to my feet. "Waalaikumsalam, my sister. You have grown now. Do you remember me, your 'brother'?"

I drew a blank, shaking my head, trying to make the connection. I summed up that he seemed friendly enough though.

"Come, come," he said, ushering us to the exit, where more dark-skinned people reached out to us. At first I thought they were more relatives, until a head peered in front of me.

"Please, Londonis, please, just a few pennies, and I will pray a world of peace and happiness for you."

Ali Akbar gently guarded us and moved him away, directing us to where a rusty white minibus was parked and waiting. Mamajee did a round of headcount checks before the door slid shut. We were all in, slowly being pulled away from a crowd of hands reaching into the minibus.

The journey was unfamiliar. This was the first time I had been on a plane or out of the country, and at times it felt surreal, as though I was dreaming, my sense of reality further removed by heat, warm air and the sudden jolting of the vehicle as it challenged itself over bumps. From out of the window, I saw people dressed in sarongs, holding onto baskets, selling food. I saw mud huts surrounded by rice fields, similar to the calendars my dad bought from the Bengali grocery shops. I saw bare-skinned toddlers with their mothers, cradled in their sarees, and fields of bright green rice stalks, the colour so vivid it left imprints on my eyelids when I blinked. The roads were dry and cracked, and the sun-baked mud kicked up clouds behind the car as we plugged along through the small towns. We stopped in many towns that heaved with traffic and congestion, and each time we stopped, the heat in our un-air-conditioned minivan slowly grew more intense and thicker. I felt no sense of respite from the electric fan Mamajee had purchased from the pound shop near the market. Weary from the heat and jolting, I had laid my head against a window when a sudden voice yelled out.

"Dear, oh, dear sister," came a voice from outside the minibus. I jolted and raised my head away from the window. It was a man selling sour apples neatly carved into a flower design and propped on a stick. I turned to look at Mamajee sitting next to me.

"Do you want some?" she asked. She bought a few for all of us, and we devoured them within seconds, until there was nothing left of them but sticks. I looked at her again, holding up the stick, wondering what to do with it. "Just throw it outside," she said. "This is Bangladesh, not London anymore!"

Hesitantly, I did as she ordered, cringing at my disregard in throwing the bamboo stick out into the muddy village market, where we happened to have stopped. I cowered into my seat at my inappropriate behaviour, but to my surprise, Mamajee roared with laughter at my reaction. It seemed she was in her element here and that these were trivial matters.

I drifted in and out of sleep on the journey, with the wind blowing warm air through the window. It was difficult to determine how long it would take before we arrived at Babajee's village. It felt as though we had been driving for hours. The minibus suddenly came to a halt, awakening us with the sudden thrust of the door sliding open. A cool breeze drifted in that offered a wave of respite and enticed me to leave the hot, sweaty vehicle.

I stepped out onto a patch of grass. Before us was a sea or a lake. It was so large I couldn't gauge it, and I had trouble making sense of what we were doing waiting here.

"Can you see over there?" Ali Akbar smiled as he pointed. There, on the other side of the river, stood a crowd of people lining up on the banks. "Sister, this is your family; they have been waiting all day for your arrival." He smiled excitedly.

I gasped at the thought and, at the same time, was baffled by the idea that so many people were our family. There must have been hundreds of people waving at us along the banks excitedly.

We were helped into a boat, along with our luggage, by a village boatman. I saw children cheering and running; some shouted, "They are here!" as we gradually made it over to the other side of the river. From a distance, they looked like termites in an endless march along the bank. Their thin brown limbs and round faces, running back and forth excitedly.

By the time we reached the bank, the sun was settling into the evening sky. A soft orange haze silhouetted the palm trees. The air was still warm and humid despite dusk approaching. Our clothes sticking to our skin from the sweltering heat of the car now accompanied the wretched smell of body odour and a swampish stench of the river. Crowds of people gathered by excitedly along the muddy bank. Some reached out to help us with our bags and lift us from the boat. The others stared on excitedly, the whites of their eyes and teeth more intensified by the golden sun. The air was ecstatic with smiles, joy, impatience, people yelling at others to move out of the way. Mamajee gave one of the women a hug and wept into her shoulder intensely. Twelve years Mamajee had waited, moment after moment recollected as planes soared through the sky.

Now before me, looking down from the banks, were the people she talked about, unrecognisable; even the introductions became a blur of names. I didn't have much time to process the links, introductions and explanations that Mamajee was giving me on the cousin, Uncle, whose brother was married to a girl whose son or daughter had come to greet us.

It was getting dark, and we were being moved by the crowd in the direction of the village. My father's house was one of the grandest in the village. It had a white masonry finish with an east and west wing built in a C shape and housed his two brothers and their families. It was one storey in height, with a clay tiled roof. Directly opposite the house was a barn that housed the chicken pen and two cows. It was like a communal fridge for eggs, meat, chicken and dairy products.

Upon arriving in the courtyard, Chachima, Babajee's sister-in-law, delivered fresh, warm milk for us, but to her dismay, none of us would drink it. Milk was such a treat in Bangladesh even the young were not privy to a glass, and here we were, squandering the opportunity. Accustomed to a more luxurious life in London, milk consumption was just another forced intake and an instant repellent of joy.

To the left of the barn was a small mud hut, about the size of a single bedroom. It belonged to Babajee's brother, who he had not talked about and I didn't know much about. The house was now occupied by his wife, who everyone called Fagol Chachi, meaning "Mad Aunt". Indeed, she had become mentally disturbed; she was looked after by Shelley, her oldest daughter, and her son, Rahman.

The commotion continued through the entrance of the village as the welcoming party guided us in. We were well guarded by Ali Akbar, who had two of our suitcases, occasionally using them to barricade us from the scuffle of people reaching out their hands to touch our hair or faces. We found ourselves in the centre of the courtyard with the house stood before us. A few of the villagers lingered by their doorways as we entered the house. I could hear Babajee, his voice upbeat with excitement, talking to someone, telling them about the journey. Mamajee was engrossed in conversation with another lady, in a blue cotton saree, and the pair seemed to be chattering and crying with excitement. Another girl, dressed in an orange shalwar kameez with a red dupatta pinned across her front, had us, the children, seated in a bedroom. She brought over a tray of cold lemon drinks. People surrounded us in every direction, staring, looking at us intently, touching our skin in bewilderment. Their eyes glowed in the dusk, with only a dim silhouette of their bodies peeking through the doors and entranceways.

Then came the call to prayer, something I recalled only hearing inside a mosque, and a sound I rarely heard in real life. "Oh, it's ma-ghrib prayers; we must go," I heard someone say. The men left to join the prayers; the women went back to their homes, and some still lingered for a few minutes before we were finally alone.

That night we had dinner by a kerosene lamp propped on a dining table that struggled to have four people around it. We took it in turns to be seated: the boys and men first, followed by the women and girls. Chachima, Babajee's sister-in-law, now a widow, had cooked a small spread of beef curry, chicken and three vegetable dishes. I had no appetite for any of it. The heat, smell and tiredness from two days of travelling had my head jolting back and forth.

After dinner my brothers made their way behind a mosquito net that Mamajee had pulled down. We were sleeping in the same room we'd eaten in, and the musty smell of curry lingered throughout.

"Look at her," said Chachima. "She is a beauty, isn't she?" I heard her say, the words amid the swaying slumber.

Mamajee didn't acknowledge Chachima's comment.

"Go on," Mamajee said sternly to me, "you best get to sleep," as if the compliment irritated her.

I rolled to face them, tucking my pillow in to rest my head, I couldn't help but notice the way they both stared. The light from the kerosene lamp behind them, lifting the whites of their eyes with a gleam as if something pleased them.

"Make sure you cover your head with a scarf tomorrow," Mamajee said before turning her back to move Chachima on from her lingering gaze at me.

It was the first time I had heard Mamajee make such a request to cover up, other than when I attended mosque, and it was then I sensed things were changing.

CHAPTER FIFTEEN
- Sacrifice-

I woke that first morning to the sound of chickens brooding and clucking underneath the wooden bed. A thick blanket of heat swept over my face in waves.

I crept out of bed onto the mud floor, sweeping my feet around for slippers. It was a strange experience, waking up in another country, and I sat perched on the bed, taking in the room. The windows weren't like the ones at home: there was no glass sealed into the panes, just a set of iron bars and bamboo shutters that guarded us against the outside world. I looked out from the metal-barred window. The view from the bedroom looked onto the courtyard where small mud houses belonging to my relatives stood. The houses were about the size of two double bedrooms. It was hard to believe these huts would contain whole families, one room for the kitchen and the other for eating, living, sleeping and praying. I looked out onto the courtyard, where the women from the village continued their daily chores, carrying their children on their hips, tending to their chickens, sorting out grains of rice or washing dishes at the pump.

After breakfast, which consisted of dry, sweet rusks and strong-brewed tea in petite china cups, Ali Akbar took us out to show us around the village. We learned a lot from him about the village through his passive commentary. He showed us where the toilets were – the fact that it was just a hole in the ground out in the bush a short walk from the house didn't need emphasising. "Just make sure you go before it gets dark," he said. "There are no lights in the jungle, and there are snakes out there sometimes, so you have to be careful." We all shuddered at the thought.

We then passed a pond where women from the village giggled coyly at the sight of us. "How are you, Londonis?" they said from behind their veils as they continued washing their clothes.

"You can wash and have a bath here," Ali Akbar said, pointing at me. "Make sure you bring your spares though," he said, looking at me. I immediately understood what he meant. The women never took their clothes off when they washed; they scrubbed themselves from underneath their garments or when submerged inside the pond. He then showed us the water pump, where more women stood waiting with pitchers of water. "Everyone gets their water in the morning because they will need it for cooking and washing, and that is why it is busy now. Remember, you will also need the water from the pump for visiting the toilet." I calculated in my head the logistics required to just visit the toilet here: there weren't such luxuries as toilet paper, and you took a pitcher of water to wash before you headed there, which meant it would, to my dismay, take around ten minutes for every trip.

He then showed us the kitchen, where there were no taps or sinks, as we would have at home, just another hole in the ground for lighting fires. Surrounding the hole were stones where a large steel pot rested. It was odd that there were no cupboards or ingredients anywhere. A pot of salt, sugar and dried milk was propped on a shelf above the stove.

"Where are all the ingredients?" I asked him.

He laughed. "We have a bazaar. Everything is bought fresh here, no need to store anything apart from what's in that shed over there." He pointed out through that window. "Come, let me show you," he said, beckoning us out through the kitchen door.

The four of us followed him out to a house made of mud, topped with a thatched straw roof. He opened the door, and the immediate stench of manure came from inside. "This is where we keep our livestock. This is Lackey, my cow, and this is her baby calf." We stroked her down. To the right, in a smaller pen, were a brood of chickens that Ali Akbar scattered seeds at. "If you ever need milk or eggs, you know where to come." He smiled tenderly at Lackey as he stroked her down.

"How old is she?" I asked.

"Not sure," he said. "Probably a few years old. I found her stuck in the flood water last year. The water was above her legs, and she had been caught there for a couple of hours. I managed to drag her out from the mud, through the long grass. We weren't sure where she came from, but she is here now. That's why she is called Lackey, because she is lucky," he said, smiling.

"She is indeed," I said, stroking her.

I found it odd that he was my first cousin: he was twenty years older than me. I put it down to the huge age gap between Babajee and his late brother, and hence why we were almost a generation apart. He was tall and thin and had unkempt hair that stood on end. He had a thin face and a dark moustache that covered his upper lip. A striking resemblance of Babajee could be seen in him. His high cheekbones were parcelled around with taut and dark sun-baked skin, which made the whites of his eyes glow like two moons in the night.

Ali Akbar spent most of his day running errands to the village market, fishing, hauling logs for the fire or helping with the farming of rice and vegetables for the family, but he always had time for us, even at the despair and growl of Chachima, the voice of order in the village.

It seemed to come as a great joy to him when we arrived, that these chores could be abandoned on short notice so that the honourable London VIPs were chaperoned from place to place. Ali Akbar took us on boating trips, where we rowed down the river and along the banks, where we were greeted by villagers who seemed baffled by us Western folks, as we marvelled over their daily fishing chores. My brothers enjoyed fishing with a bamboo stick, thread and a small, fine hook. Ali Akbar showed them how to hook the rice bait and the signal for when a fish might have hooked onto the bait. He took us to the ice-cream stall along the banks, which at first instance excited us, but to our disappointment, it wasn't anything like ice cream, more like dried milk in frozen water. Nevertheless, the two-mile walk and the merciless sun burning a hole into our backs was enough to make us gulp the whole thing down without any deliberation.

Ali Akbar showed us how to grab chickens and put them back in the pens, how to milk Lackey but not take too much of it, as she needed milk for her baby too. He took pride showing us Lackey and her new baby cow standing inches away. He would pat her and stroke her coarse hair down until it was smooth. He would take her to the field, where her baby would graze and drink water from the stream. In the afternoon, he would take us to the village pond, where we could dip our toes in the cool water and take our British toys for a paddle.

What we really liked about Ali Akbar was that he avidly looked after us, batting away flies and mosquitoes when they came anywhere near our vicinity. When we wanted a treat from the village market, he always spared some change for lollies. Ali Akbar would carry my four-year-old sister on his back, even on the hottest days, when the sweat beads would mound up on his forehead. He made every effort to play with my two brothers, teasing, play fights and climbing up trees to pick fruit. Ali Akbar even helped us on our boat trips and made sure our feet didn't touch the muddy banks by hauling us from the boat and onto a dry patch of land so as not to spoil our Western clothes. He would bring back fruit that was a rarity in London, such as jackfruit, goji berries, sour cherries and amra, which tasted like a fusion of apple and mango. He looked out for us, like an older brother, and we felt safe under his protection during the day.

While our days were filled with adventures, Mamajee and Babajee had a busy agenda. The village house had fallen into a state of disrepair over the thirteen years of Babajee's absence; it had been left neglected. The flood marks were waist-high against the masonry paint. The roof had slats missing and broken joints that were now worn down and brittle. There were land deeds and letters to be sent for legal threats of possession that had been outstanding with the courts. Babajee also wanted to make sure that the gravestones were clearly marked for where his mother and father had been laid to rest.

*

The east and west wing rooms were joined by the living room. It seemed cramped and small, mainly due to the oversized bed that had been brought to accommodate extra sleeping arrangements.

Babajee paused to look around, and his face showed little sign of any real connection to the room and the possessions within it. He stood on the dirt floor, hands behind his back, inspecting the room, scouring over it with his eyes fixed and head in motion. A large dark wooden armoire overshadowed a corner. It had faded in colour midway up, and the side panels had warped and curled at the lower edges.

"It looks like it was damaged by the floods at some point," Babajee said, peering over closely at the legs.

A matching dressing table with an oval glass mirror had also been through the same turmoil. Above it was an assortment of black-and-white photos in faded dark wooden frames. A picture of Babajee leaning against a sixties Morris, wearing a dark tailored suit, his hair combed to a side parting. Another with a dark-haired English woman in a field; they were both laughing. It was a rare expression to see on Babajee's face, and I wondered for a moment what had brought him so much joy in that moment. To the left, a tired wooden table stood propped against a barred window. It was supposedly a dining table for four, but two of the chairs were missing. "This used to be my desk when I was at school; it's very old now."

I was surprised that Babajee had noticed me in the room and, secondly, that he had volunteered to share his thoughts. I felt a surge of excitement rushing to my head that it might open up the opportunity to understand him more. "What were you studying?" I asked softly.

He shot me a glance, which I thought was going to be a scolding about asking him anything. He looked down at the mud floor, nodding his head in disbelief. "Study?" he said. "Study?" he repeated as if it baffled him to think of it as such. A wry smile illuminated his face. "I was planning to be someone great," said Babajee. "I worked tirelessly every night by the light of that very kerosene lamp. It was here that I read the writings of the greatest literary prize-winners, where I learned about Darwin and the natural sciences." His eyes glowed with wonder as he walked through his past.

"And then what happened, Babajee?" I asked.

His smile faded, as if his vision of it all was slowly disappearing into the reality of where he stood. We both turned, distracted by a shuffling of flips-flops. Mamajee came into the room. She stopped to look around, and she seemed her usual breathless self, her hair dishevelled with small strands standing up from the humidity.

"We ought to organise an offering to Allah in light of Boro Bhai's [elder brother] passing. We should do it promptly and feed the poor." Mamajee held her breath with a short pause of silence to hear a response from Babajee. His hands still behind his back, he looked up and down, his face grief-stricken, his breathing heavier, as if age and cigarettes were taking liberties with his throat. He nodded in agreement.

*

The days seemed to roll into one now; there weren't any clocks in the village, and people carried out their day to a different beat. We knew it was morning, for example, because the hens started clucking; I could tell it was wash time by the sound of gushing water from the communal pump; I knew that breakfast was being made by the smell of the mud stove being lit by the village women in the morning. We were prompted to pray by the calling of the azan by the local mosque. It may have been days or weeks that had passed, and we were now dancing to the rhythm of routine, of life here. And while the sounds gave each moment a call to carry out another daily task, there was only one sound that would echo in my memory of Bangladesh in years to come. It was waking up to the sound of Lackey's bell and her mooing with her calf. It was a divine sound and something that would live with me for the rest of my life.

One morning I woke to this sound as if her bell was an alarm clock calling for me to rise. I smiled as I opened the shutter and watched her calf suckling from her as Ali Akbar washed her muddy legs down. I watched how he took particular care of her, batting the flies off her twitching body with a soft-bristled brush.

It was the day of the remembrance ceremony to mark my late uncle's passing, and while it is normally a sombre occasion, it seemed to come with such merriment from the people of the village.

That morning the women of the village started the day by brewing strong black tea with cinnamon and cloves; the more privileged Londonis were able to enjoy the luxury of stewed tea leaves brewed with powdered milk.

The women laid out banana leaves across the courtyard. There were large baskets woven from coconut leaves for placing steamed rice. In the kitchen, the older women fussed over which pots to cook the curries in, while the men sat smoking and drinking tea in the guest house. The younger boys were ushered around with various errands: some carried large bags of rice, and others came back with pitchers of water from the communal pump. It was a hot and humid morning, and I watched the fuss from the shade of the veranda, propped up against a crooked bench, the heat rising from the thatched roofs of mud huts as the sun rose higher.

More people arrived at the village, having learned about the Londonis who had recently arrived and the auspicious ceremony they had been invited to. They gazed at us as though they had never seen something so rare. The younger women stood grinding rice into flour, using a large wooden pole that stood about six feet tall, which they dropped with both hands clasped around it into a wooden mortar over and over, pounding the rice until it had turned to flour. They sang folk songs to cheer themselves through the exhausting labour it required in the soaring heat. A couple of hours later, they had ground enough flour to make chapattis for the entire village. Some flour was taken away by other women to make star-shaped dumplings, snacks and rice cakes. The village felt energised. The women seemed more exhilarated than exhausted. The fragrance of the wood burning to charcoal, steamed coconut rice dumplings and sweet samosas filled the kitchen and travelled out to the courtyard, where poor children sat eagle-eyed and wide-bellied as their mouths watered over the food preparation. Some even begged for a piece of the rice crust or a bowl of the rice starch. Much to their disappointment, the looks from Chachima were enough to startle and steer them back to the courtyard, where they were asked to sit.

By now the afternoon sun hovered above the house, sweltering its inhabitants. The men inside the guest house moved out to the shade, where the rustling of palm trees gave to a light breeze and offered some respite. The children had been waiting anxiously now for an hour, and their feeble sounds meant hunger was deep in their malnourished bellies. Their poor mothers and fathers stood patiently behind them, their eyes scrunched together by the sun on their faces and in anticipation of the food to be served.

I had little understanding of the rituals of ceremonies in Bangladesh. At home, when Mamajee and Babajee gave thanks to Allah and provided an offering to the poor, Mamajee would cook large steaming pots of buttery, sweet semolina fragranced with cloves and bay leaves. It would then be turned into soft, warm balls of dough and given out at the mosque. My brothers and I would groan with displeasure at the sight of these delicacies. It was forbidden to throw them away, and Mamajee would curse us with sideways glances, which normally meant trouble if we dared attempt disposing of any. Life in the village, though, was different; the excitement could be equated to a Western wedding. The village people were upbeat, happy and full of life, as though they were attending a party, and the food, smells and atmosphere gave remembrance a new meaning. That, indeed, remembrance is a celebration of life. But all of this meaning was suddenly lost when I realised the real reason they were waiting in the courtyard, the real reason the food hadn't yet been served, and what I was about to hear and witness that day came with consequences and repercussions that I would be battling in years to come from now.

It was the sound that woke me into life every morning: the sound of Lackey's bell. The children scuffled around excitedly upon hearing that sound, and the adults moved around to form an entrance to the courtyard as Ali Akbar walked her through to the tinkling of her bell and the eager smiles and blessings to Allah from onlookers. His face was grey, long and deeply troubled as he held onto Lackey, the rope tied around her neck.

The villagers looked on as the bell on her neck rocked and jingled slowly with every stride. Ali Akbar looked down, his hand resting on her neck and the other holding onto the rope tied around her neck. She was brought to the centre of the courtyard. The children sat anxiously on the steps. A mullah came and sat on a wooden chair with armrests that had been placed at the head of the courtyard. He cleared his throat and began to chant. The men reached out their arms in prayer, and the women covered their heads with their saree veils. More people had gathered round the side of the courtyard now, and those that couldn't find space peered through the hatches and the doorways. As the prayers began, Chacha, an uncle by some distant relation to Babajee, brought a large noose-style knife. Lackey stood patiently next to Ali Akbar. Her head cocked up and down. Ali Akbar's face looked lifeless and empty, as though someone had taken the soul out of him. I watched, dreading the thought of what would happen next as Chacha approached Lackey. Ali Akbar held onto Lackey tightly while Chacha moved closer to her neck. Lackey's eyes were round, glossy and full of life, oblivious to the next event that would terminate it. The prayers from the mullah became louder, and the villagers chanted with him. "Allahu akbar, Allahu akbar, in the name of Allah." Chacha then swiped her neck with one clean sweep. Lackey groaned and fell to the floor. The last tinkling sound of her bell could be heard as blood gushed out from her throat into a large well that was dug into the floor. Her legs jolted; her eyes closed.

Ali Akbar looked down at Lackey as the blood continued to pour out into the mud well. He breathed in gulps of air, hands slicing through his hair at the atrocity he held himself accountable for. He walked backwards, stepping away, while the other men entered into the circle to start skinning and dicing.

I followed Ali Akbar, who walked away, heading to the stable where Lackey's lonely calf stood grazing some hay. Ali Akbar sniffled as he stroked her. I looked on from the barn door, speechless.

"Why?" I said. I could see that if I pressed any further, the wall of pain he was made of would shatter to pieces.

"Sometimes there are sacrifices everyone has to make," he said, looking at me tearily and insistently. "We are all here for a reason, aren't we? It is Allah's will; it was written that way."

*

Later that afternoon I watched the children and families fill their bellies with a sacrifice that I couldn't bear to look at. The meat portions were wrapped in banana leaves, to be taken away while the women finished clearing up and made a fresh round of black cardamom tea served with rice dumplings and coconut samosas. I sat quietly on the veranda beside the kitchen and watched the continuation of life around me.

I could hear the laughs and giggles from inside the kitchen as the women finally finished their lunch after a long day of entertaining and service. Mamajee and Chachima were now the last ones eating in the kitchen, and the other women had moved on to the washing and clearing activities. Mamajee had her back to me and was most probably unaware of me sat outside by the kitchen. They were, much to my displeasure, talking about the sacrifice.

"What a feast it was!" said Mamajee, tucking into more beef curry. "A million thanks to Allah for the blessing of eating well."

Chachima smiled. "This is all I wish for, blessings for you and your children. No one could ever dream that Allah would grant us the day when you would come back and we would feast so auspiciously and give so generously." Chachima's head bowed down, her palms resting on the bamboo mat where they were both sat together. She covered her head with the saree veil, and then her dark, rubbery hands reached up to Allah and sighed. "Allah allowed us this sacrifice, for you and your family."

"And we could not have done this without you." Mamajee smiled gratefully back. "Every day, I say to Allah that as long as we can raise them well, that they pray five times a day and that they do not stray from the straight path, it is all I ask for." Mamajee shook her head.

"I feel your pain, and this is all I pray for too." Chachima's voice sounded mousy quiet as she said it, and I thought for a moment that she might be crying. "How old is she now?" asked Chachima.

Mamajee replied back, "She will be twelve in February."

Chachima looked down, shaking her head. "Girls this age will start getting into all sorts of trouble soon. You should think about her future."

"I know," Mamajee agreed with a pained expression. "I don't want to keep her through her school. What is the point? She will only be married soon anyhow," Mamajee said dismissively. "It is better to be married when you are young and fresh. What is a woman going to do with an education when all one needs to do is have kids?"

"He does remember though, doesn't he? What was written down all those years ago?" Chachima asked.

Mamajee hesitated. "Oh, yes, of course, but her father would want her to finish school, though, first. You know, if I had it my way, you know what I would be doing, don't you? But the man wants me to burn in hell a little longer," she said grievingly. "I just want to be rid of this sin that I am carrying. The longer you leave this, the longer you will burn in hell. He doesn't see that though, does he?" Mamajee said profusely.

"Hmm, well, that's a few years away, then, isn't it?" Chachima said, disappointed.

"Ali Akbar will be thirty-five by then. Nevertheless, it will still be a good age, but you can't have us waiting too long. He's getting too old," Mamajee agreed, and nodded her head with approval. "Let's see. He's a good boy, I know," assured Mamajee.

"Yes, you see that, I hope," barked Chachima, "after everything my son has done for you and your family. He has sacrificed his whole life here for you. Tending the animals, the farmland, he even sacrificed his cherished cow. What would he not do?"

Mamajee paused, looking down. "You are right, Ali Akbar has been looking after everything here; he's sacrificed a lot, and what I give to you in return is only a small sacrifice, of course."

"Good, I am glad we are settled on this. Allah has given his blessings." Chachima smiled, offering Mamajee another spoonful of curry.

I thought of this moment as though my whole life flashed before my eyes, and in this vision, I saw the life ahead of me. I felt a sickening feeling. I thought about what it would be like to be married, living in Bangladesh, in the heat, with the restrictions. I pictured being with Ali Akbar, tending fields, him bringing home fish and vegetables to cook. I shuddered at the thought of a wedding day when I would be dressed as a bride and Ali Akbar holding my hand. My stomach wrenched at the idea of being man and wife, sleeping together. The thought of him being a brother figure, and then his dark hands on my body, gazing at me with his moonlike eyes, and his moustache prickling against my face. I crumbled onto the mud floor as I recalled that sickening moment Lackey had fallen to the ground, the last tinkling sound of that bell and Ali Akbar's words: "Sometimes there are sacrifices everyone has to make. We are all here for a reason, aren't we? It is Allah's will; it was written that way."

CHAPTER SIXTEEN
– *Shelley*–

I lay on the mat as the cool wind whispered in through the veranda window. I listened to the boatmen singing their songs as they cast the net, the gurgle and cries from distant children walking along the riverside. I heard the chatter of housewives busily fussing as they carried on with their life, and in the moment of calmness, I also felt a moment of madness. Maybe I could run; maybe I could get on a boat and sail out from here. I thought about how I could get a telephone card and call Mrs Abbots or one of the neighbours to help. I thought of hundreds of ways I could escape, but the eleven-year-old me had nothing that would make it easily available. I was useless, helpless, trapped and locked in.

The following day Ali Akbar knocked on my door and invited himself in. I lay on the bed, shrouding myself to the neck in the blanket.

"We are going to the bazaar. Do you want to come?" he asked.

"No, I don't," I said, throwing him a resentful look and turning the other way.

I could feel him standing there, silently, trying to work out the best response.

"Did I say something wrong?" he said hesitantly.

I didn't answer.

He waited a few minutes and then left without a word.

For days on end, I avoided him; his very presence made me want to hide. Ali Akbar tried to talk to me through my sister, on the boat crossing the river. He'd reach out his hand to help, and I would refuse. He would buy sweets and leave them on the bed so I could enjoy them when I woke. At night, when my brothers lay sleeping in the bed, he would linger on to talk to them, which irritated me. I would shout at my brothers because I wanted to sleep.

Much to my irritation, Mamajee and Babajee always had Ali Akbar chaperone us everywhere. One day he had taken us out to the bazaar when on our return the weather broke out into a storm. A heavy blanket of clouds curled into one another above us as the rain poured down, the mud thick and sloppy on the ground, and our sandals sliding ankle-deep as we walked back to the boat. We were soaking wet and tired. The boatman tirelessly battled through the storm as we kept shelter under the bamboo roof. Our eyes peered through wet eyelashes and soaking wet hair. The raindrops travelled down our foreheads and dripped from our faces. We were all shivering quietly in the boat. Ali Akbar offered me a jacket, which repulsed me even more.

"Who do you think you are?" I shouted at him in English, throwing his jacket back into his face. He looked at me, baffled and shaking his head, as he didn't understand English, and laughed.

It angered me even more; I felt revolted by him, the fact that he gave up his prize and loving cow and could still be sitting there smirking. I wanted to say something that would make him hurt for his actions.

"You are just as greedy and selfish as the rest of them," I shouted at him, again in English.

His expression was neutral now and confused.

"What are you saying to me? Did I do something wrong? I'm sorry your cousin is silly; he doesn't understand English."

"Oh, yeah? Well, maybe understand this." I grabbed some mud from down the side of the boat and was about to throw it at his face when Karim caught my hand.

"What are you doing? Stop shouting and calm down."

"Oh, you, be quiet!" I responded.

They all sat, silent. Ali Akbar stared down into the boat for the rest of the journey, and I looked out silently at the heavy storm.

*

That night we all fell ill; it was the worst form of sickness we had ever experienced. We had high temperatures and continual vomiting. Mamajee raced around from room to room, holding out buckets. Vomiting and diarrhoea went on for days. My legs swelled like tree trunks. We were besieged by mosquito bites all over our bodies and bedridden for a couple of weeks. Ali Akbar came to visit us in our room. I would turn the other way when he entered, and he would pretend that everything was fine, as though there was nothing wrong, and he remained silent during our encounters to avoid conflict.

One day, as we lay there half-dead from illness, he came into the room with a stereo. There were no TVs in the village, and even the radio was a rarity. He looked at my brothers in excitement as he presented them with this surprise. I turned the other way. I could hear them all excited.

"I got cassette tape," he said, pleased with his English. "It is Ma-eekal Jecksan."

The boys screamed with excitement, jumping up and down on the rug when he started playing "Bad". They clapped excitedly, mimicking the dance moves to the beat.

"Stop this!" I yelled out, but they continued on, ignoring my request, which infuriated me more.

I grabbed the stereo and threw it across the room. It landed on the mud floor with a thump that dented it. The boys and Ali Akbar stopped laughing. I felt disdain for what I had done, and at the same time, liberated. They looked down at the mangled stereo, the batteries and attachments sprawled out in our makeshift living space.

"Oh no! Sis, what have you done?" Masoud gasped. "It's broken!" He picked up the red plastic enclosure, trying to piece it together. Ali Akbar knelt down to pick up the batteries, silently displeased.

I hobbled out of the room with my swollen legs, wrapped in a blanket, and warmed myself by the kitchen stove, an earth mound with a hole in it. I watched the embers still burning, glowing as they crackled softly. I listened to the endless downpour of the monsoon rain hitting the tin roof. It had rained non-stop for weeks now. The days looked like night, owing to the heavy clouds above, and the only distinction of daylight was in the vivid greens of the palm leaves as they swayed and danced to the rhythm of the rain.

We were confined to our houses, and there was nowhere to go. The river was high, in some places almost touching the bridge. The rice fields were now vast seas sprawling out into the distance; it was difficult to grasp where the banks of the river once were. Even the village courtyard had become a pool of ankle-deep water. I longed more now for home than I had ever done before. I missed crispy buttered toast in the mornings, the aroma of it down the hallway. I missed the clean streets, the small garden that enclosed our house. I missed being with my friends from secondary school and our Western clothes. I had forgotten what it was like to be really cold, and I ached when I thought that one day, I would never see any of it again.

Just then I saw a face peer in through the kitchen window; she smiled at me.

"Shelley Afa." I smiled as she came into the kitchen.

"Hello, shundori. I have a basket," she said, smiling. I looked at her as she mocked the English she had picked up from us. *Basket* was her favourite of the words she'd heard us say. Shelley was Babajee's niece who lived in the village, Babajee's younger brother's daughter. Her father was no longer with them, as far as Mamajee's explanation went, and Shelley lived in a small mud hut no bigger than a bedroom with her brother and senile mother. She often helped Chachima in the kitchen with the cooking, and now, with our large extended brood that was cohabitating with them, the cooking had become an epic afternoon undertaking. Shelley had brought a large basket of broad beans that needed shelling.

"Here, shundori, help with these," she said, smiling and putting the basket on the ground in front of me. We both sat, squatting on short stools, shelling the broad beans onto a plate.

"Are you getting better?" she asked, busily shelling. "We have all been worried about you poor Londonis. You came all this way after so many years, and now you are so ill."

"I am getting better," I said vacantly. My Bengali was broken at times, or I didn't have the correct vocabulary at hand that translated well from my English-thinking mind. Shelley smiled. Her face beamed as though she had been sent from the sun, and there was an air about her as though she was content in herself, as though whatever the situation, she never needed to feel unhappy. She had a round face like a button, a flat nose and high cheekbones. Her skin had a sun-baked glow that permeated more when she smiled with every sentence. I loved how she laughed, and how it made her eyes almost close. Her hair was permanently tied up in a bun, and humidity made the ends curl into small waves around her ears.

"Do you know, since you have been here, you have never come over to our house for dinner? Not that I have much to offer, but it would be nice if you could come."

"Of course, Afa," I said. "I would love to." I delighted at the prospect of the change of scenery.

"Then tomorrow," she said. "You come, okay?"

I smiled. "With pleasure," I said.

*

It felt liberating to be away from my family and Ali Akbar for a change. Weeks had passed by being cooped up by the rain, and I was starting to feel better. Shelley's house was small. It was a mud house with a thatched roof made from bamboo and hay. It consisted of two small rooms, with a mud stove in one with some basic jars of spices propped up against a large bamboo cane that had been sliced in half to form a shelf. In the other room was a bed frame with a bamboo mat for bedding. There were no mattresses or padding on beds in Bangladesh, as it was too hot for that. Shelley and her mother slept on the bed, and Rahman, her seven-year-old brother, slept on the floor by the foot of the bed. By day, the bed converted into a seating area for guests.

Shelley welcomed me into her home and sat me down on the bed. I looked around in wonder as she boiled some water for tea. In the meantime, she had already soaked red lentils and rice together in a pan. The room was empty; there was no other furniture, no clothes drawers, no accessories, mirrors, clothing or picture frames. In the kitchen, only one instrument, a wooden slat used as a cooking spoon, lay in an empty powdered milk tin. I climbed off the bed and sat next to her on the floor in the kitchen.

"No, no, shundori," she said. "You don't belong here on the ground. You will get your beautiful clothes dirty," she said, trying to take me back to the bedroom.

"No, I want to," I said endearingly at her hospitality.

She smiled, not adding anything further. She poured the tea into two tin beakers. I must confess, it was pretty tasteless, but there was a sense of low importance to that. After all, her gesture, her kindness at even the offer of wanting to invite me, was humbling enough. How she had happily extended herself beyond her own means. The basic conditions she lived in, yet the way her heart was full of love and happiness. I could have almost asked her to swap places with me, given the reality I was facing.

"I am sorry that I don't have much to offer you," she said, reaching over to my cup with her pan to pour some more weak tea.

I smiled, sipping the tea. "Afa, you don't need to offer me anything; you have given me more than enough in time."

She smiled, placing the pan of water and lentils onto the stove for dinner. For a while we sat, watching the water boil in the pan as the frothy scum formed over and occasionally tormented the flame with a sizzle. She stirred the wooden stick around as I sipped the tea; she had flavoured it with bay leaves and sweetened it with cinnamon. Like most impoverished villagers, no milk or sugar accompanied it. She hummed an old folk song as she stirred the pot of rice porridge.

In the arms of the skies, there was a beautiful light.
To the hands of the wind, you were swept out of sight.
The nightingale sang, with such a beautiful sound.
Oh, how my world was lit when you were around.

When she finished, a smile broke out again on her beaming face.

"It's a beautiful song," I said as we watched the porridge thicken in the pot.

"Yes. My babajee taught me this song when I was a little girl. Babajee used to sing all kinds of songs, and we would both sit by the fire in the winter when the weather turned cold in the evenings. Babajee used to promise that after prayers he would teach me another song. I don't remember many songs now, though," she said dreamily. "It feels like a long time ago now, but I remember that one. I remember it because it was the last song Babajee ever taught me, before he left us. He told me how much he loved me and to remember him through this song. When I sing it, all the pain melts away, and it fills me with love, a love that can never be removed by anything or anyone." She sighed, taking a deep breath, filling her lungs with air.

"What happened to Chacha?" I asked inquisitively. "You said he left."

She stared down into the pot, calmly, her expression reduced to a half smile. "That's a long story." She sighed and continued. "Maybe you can ask your babajee one day. Now, let's eat before the rice porridge becomes too thick," she said, stirring the pot.

"Rahman, hey, Rahman, hurry up, the food is ready!" She clanged the wooden spoon against the pan, and from out of nowhere, Chachi, her mother, appeared.

"Ammujan, where have you been?" Shelley asked her mother as she looked up at her disappointed. "We have Londoni guests that have come to see you, and you are off gallivanting as usual."

The mad lady sat down on the bamboo mat, laughing, her voice deep and hollow. "Eat. Eat." She nodded insistently. She pushed the tin bowl nearer to me and beckoned profusely as she helped herself to her own bowl and ate noisily.

Rahman then appeared, skipping up to the high step, bare-chested with a lungi wrapped between his legs. Thick mud stuck to his toes. He sat cross-legged as he slurped the rice porridge from the bowl. There were no spoons, so we all did the same.

The porridge was unappetisingly plain, with a salted taste and quite watery, and I wondered how Shelley and her family continued without a complaint.

Shelley looked at me as she slurped it up. "Next time you come, I will make fish, I promise. This good-for-nothing didn't even try today when I asked him, so we had nothing to offer." She scowled at Rahman, who returned a scorned look as he gulped the rest of the watery rice porridge.

"It was wet and rainy, and the pond is overflowing. What do you want me to do?" he said, scowling with half a mouthful. "I told you."

She replied, "Why didn't you go over to the other side? The bank has steps there."

I smiled, as I could see it was all good spirited and she meant no harm when telling him off.

"How about we go fishing tomorrow?" she said, looking at me. I almost jumped with excitement at the thought that I didn't have to be near the torments of Mamajee and Babajee and the sickening re-minder of Ali Akbar. Soon Shelley and I were inseparable: she taught me how to fish, how to light a stove using flint and bamboo. We climbed trees in amongst the jungles along the perimeter of the vil-lage and picked out ripe mangoes and unripe ones for sour pickles. She knew all kinds of fruits and vegetables, where to find them, and in places where no one else bothered to look. She planted vegetables in these locations, which were quite cleverly protected in the jungle from the heavy rain. She took me out on trips to the pond as she washed clothes for Chachima and for her family.

Babajee and Mamajee were mostly too busy attending to house-hold affairs and didn't seem to question my whereabouts, until one day, when Shelley and I were playing in the rain, and I happened to scream as she splashed me. Babajee came dashing over to us. At first, I thought I was in trouble, but much to my surprise, he grabbed Shelley by a fistful of hair and proceeded to drag her into the muddy courtyard. He thumped her in the back, then, drawing up his lungi, kicked her into the ground.

"No!" I screamed, trying to pull him away. "What are you doing, Babajee? No!" I shouted, horrified. Mamajee and the rest of the household stood out on the veranda as he kicked and thumped continuously, watching how she cowered into a ball on the ground. I threw myself in front of her to protect her, which stopped him from laying another hand on her. Heaving, he stepped back, circling her slowly.

"I told your father, and now I am telling you, not to come near my family or me, do you understand?"

Shelley looked down, not a tear, with an air of unequivocal calmness.

"Ever since we came, I have seen your motives." Babajee pointed at her accusingly. "Your father was dishonest, and so is this shameless, cursed creature that is lurking around the village, making friends here and making friends there, going off giggling from house to house, spouting rumours. Shameless and honourless, that's what you are!"

Shelley sat crouched down. The rain poured down her forehead, her hair wet, tangled, in front of her face and disguising any tears. I could see she was shaking, not with fear but with rage.

"Let me tell you something," she said, raising herself slowly from the ground. "You might be a rich man, but you are as poor and as weak as any other man in this village. Maybe you want to tell her the shame you bring, the reason you had my poor father, not to mention your brother, your own flesh and blood, beaten up by two men and dragged from his own village."

Babajee turned his back to her, refusing to listen, shaking his head, his lungi wet, bundled up around his knees, as she continued.

"Maybe you want to tell everyone why Mamajee went senile, how you ripped us apart, penniless, over your wretched greed and pride."

Babajee turned with rage, his eyes wide with anger. "Don't you dare say another word, haramzadi. You have become a strong woman now, have you? You think you can beat me?"

He raised his hands, ready for the next strike.

"Go on, disgrace me. You can break my bones, you spineless man." Shelley beckoned him with a smile. "I have nothing more to lose."

Babajee stepped forward towards her for his next strike.

"But if you take one more move, you will have a lot more to lose," she said calmly, her breath heavy with control.

I pulled her away from him. I didn't want to find out how brave and gallant she could be.

But it was in that moment that I saw that look in Babajee again, one that I had seen before. It was the look of fear, of a frightened and weak man who was holding on to something.

Suddenly his hold weakened, his face pale and numb. He looked at me as I stood sodden and shaking. The once raging Babajee, just seconds before, who seemed capable of punching her face until she was disfigured, within seconds seemed powerless from Shelley's words, almost turning him flat, expressionless.

Everyone stood silently around the veranda as he turned away. Mamajee watched quietly, her saree scarf covering her mouth. Rain dripped from the tin roof along the veranda. I held Shelley's arm to protect her from any further attack and embraced her, the rain clinging to my clothes.

"Let's go, Shelley," I said calmly. "Let's go inside." I walked Shelley back to her house, leaving everyone standing in the court-yard.

*

That afternoon I sat with Shelley on her bed. I made her a cup of warm water. I rubbed tiger balm onto her bruises. She flinched as I peeled off the wet clothes, lifting them from her back, beneath which was a large and reddened welt. There were purple and green patches on her shoulder blade.

"Are you okay, Shelley?" I said, looking at her. "I was so worried. I am so sorry for the way Babajee treated you."

"Don't you be sorry, my dear." She sighed.

"No, I am," I said. "It's my fault."

Peering over her shoulder insistently, she shook her head. "This was the making of many things, Eleanor. When your babajee came back to the village, he was in a great rush to get married. He claimed he didn't want to leave his business in London. He said he was in a rush and had only two weeks. Boro Chacha (may his soul rest in peace) told me that the wedding that my babajee helped put together was arranged within a day or two. Is that my babajee's fault? Is that a reason for persecuting me? I was only ten when I saw my father, who had been chopping firewood outside by the barn, being kicked and punched until his limbs were loose, a trail of blood dragging along where his feet touched the ground. Mamajee was beside herself, of course. She tried to stop the men, but one threatened to axe her into pieces. After the men had left, I watched Mamajee struck with grief. She became ill, wouldn't eat, spent all the time in bed. We begged from door to door for days. All because of his greed, because he thought he was marrying into wealth, and that hadn't gone to plan."

"I am sorry," was all I could muster in my largely inexpressive Bengali vocabulary.

"Don't be sorry. I may have nothing in worldly terms, but what is there to fear, when you have nothing left to lose? That is when you are truly free." I have nothing to give you, but promise me you just remember that."

Later, when I came back to the house for dinner, I found Mamajee in the bedroom. She was packing away some of our belongings in readiness for our flight back home. I was worried she was going to shout at me for hanging about with Shelley. I sat waiting quietly, anticipating the lecture about hanging about with her, but she stayed relatively silent, folding up clothes and pressing them hard into the suitcase.

"Are you mad at me?" I asked.

She paused to turn to me and then continued placing a saree into the fold of another.

"You should know better than to hang about with Shelley. I warned you not to hang about with people too much."

I sat, silent; I knew there was a lot more coming.

"They are both as bad as each other, those brothers. Did she explain how her father threw all his books in the mud the week before his exams? How he sabotaged his chances of getting educated? He failed his exams because of it. Did she? Did she hear about that? No. She only sees it from her point of view."

"That doesn't justify Babajee's behaviour, does it, though, Mamajee?"

"Anger is like a disease that is passed on from person to person, and it hardens you over time."

I could see it had hardened her. She still justified it. She tucked some more clothes down the side zip of the luggage.

"Pain follows resentment; resentment follows pain," she said, pressing hard on the suitcase. "We all feel it because of this man. He just saw white, fair skin and fickle money; that's all he saw in me."

"White, fair skin?" I asked, confused.

I could tell she was trying not to cry, but I couldn't see her face. Her mouth sounded wet with tears as the pain filled up from inside. She paused, her back to me, looking up at the pictures. I sensed she was holding on to something.

"He is a bloodless, lifeless cripple in my eyes, that man. His greed and a selfish desire have left a trail of debris. I am just the slave he asked for that follows him around, picking up after him. I suppose she told you about that as well, did she?"

I shook my head blankly.

"The day of that dreaded letter five years ago, when your babajee found out that his marriage to me didn't stack up to any of the promises Suto Chacha had arranged. Did he ever think whether he played his end of the bargain fairly?"

She smiled, mysteriously gazing at the wall of pictures. "Well, we are all paying the price for that now, aren't we?"

Mamajee left the room silently, and as I turned to leave, I noticed the black-and-white picture she was looking at was of Babajee smiling in the field with the dark-haired lady. I could have almost mistaken her for Mamajee if it wasn't for the short hair and the Western-style dress.

I didn't see Shelley for days after the incident, and nor did I pursue her, in case it landed her in any difficulty with Babajee. She stopped coming to help Chachima in the kitchen, even when Chachima called out to her. Soon after this, Babajee had the whole family packed up and ready to leave for England.

The day we left the village, I looked back at the house where Shelley lived. I hoped that there might be a chance to say goodbye to her, but Shelley was nowhere. And as we sailed across the river, I kept one last watchful eye on the small mud hut, the forest and jungles we had hidden and played in together, and a smile came to my face at the tender song we had sung together. I thought about what she'd said: "What is there to fear when you have nothing left to lose? That is when you are truly free."

Years later, it would be these very words that would save me.

CHAPTER SEVENTEEN
– *School Is Not for Girls* –

We arrived back in London Heathrow at dawn, to pale concrete skies, pale people, monotonous grey houses, clean but lifeless streets and a piercing chill that made our skin prickle with goose pimples. It was December, and the torments of the winter winds had left the trees stripped of leaves.

Mamajee and Babajee looked glumly on at the motorway ahead, a long, straight highway dividing bare and barren landscapes on either side. "Why did we come back to this?" Mamajee sighed, shaking her head. Gone were the banks brimming with beaming faces; gone were the bright blue skies with wispy white clouds, the humid air that carried the floating sounds of cow bells and carefree giggles of children chasing chickens. It was all a distant land and now to become a distant memory that they would only look back on in years to come.

I was pleased to be coming home, though, to feel the cold and control my senses. The sweltering heat in Bangladesh was often debilitating and had exhausted me mentally and physically. The perks of having clean water and hot showers and washing my hair with shampoo rather than with soap felt like a luxury, and to shower in a bath rather than at the communal pump, where I had been met with luring glances from villagers at the sight of my Western-coloured flesh, was something far more than a blessing that I could be thankful for. I relished drinking water from a tap rather than the hard, metallic taste of warm water from pitchers, and more than anything else that I welcomed back, and trivial as it seemed, was the pleasure of crisp buttered toast with a big mug of tea at breakfast instead of dried rusks with black tea.

I also longed to be back at school, where there was order and normality. It had been a timeless four months in Bangladesh, with no clocks, no rush, and where the only rhythm that moved people was the sound of the azan five times a day, when there would be a rush to wash and get to prayer mats. I had missed the rhythm of my everyday life here, my school friends at the bus stop, who I shared my journey with, the walk to the bakery where we would order hot, freshly baked, crispy buttered baguettes that warmed and melted on our tongues on the way to school. I missed the cold air catching my throat and the comforting warmth of my scarf around my neck as my body resisted the chill down my spine, and most of all, I missed Mrs Abbots. Moving to high school had meant that we no longer had our encounters at the school gates, and now that I was back, I only pined to see her.

My sense of the ordinary had also been distorted in other ways: Mamajee and her continuous reminder of my coming of age, which in her eyes meant being shackled to a life of marriage. Yes, Mamajee had already begun priming me into the perpetual mould of herself, and anything that shifted outside this paradigm came under intense scrutiny.

*

The morning after we arrived, Mamajee waded into my room with a large pile of clothes from the suitcase. "Here," she said. "Pass me those old tracksuit bottoms and dresses over there," she said, pointing at the clothes on my cupboard shelf.

I did as she requested, handing them down to her. She placed them all into a large bin bag. "What are you going to do with them?" I said curiously, peering over.

"You won't need them anymore. Girls your age can't be seen around town in tracksuits. What will people think if they saw you? They'll say, 'Oh, look, do you see Hamid Rabbani's daughter over there, walking around in Western clothes? Not the sort of family I would want to associate with.'" She rooted around in my cupboard, clearing space.

"Well, it's never been a problem before," I said, confused. "I have always worn them."

"Well, you are getting too old for that. You are not a kid, you're a ..."

"I'm what?" I said, confused.

"When you get your you-know-what," she said, whispering, "it means things have to change, doesn't it? And don't you be talking about it in front of the boys, or any boys or men for that matter. It's a secret for only women. One inkling that they know, and it could have devastating consequences. You are going to have to stay pure from now on, cover up. Don't be going out without my say so. That's why I had these made for you. I don't want you going out in public without a headscarf. It's considered haram if you do from now on."

She tossed over a pile of tunics and pyjama trousers with matching dupattas or scarves in a variety of garish colours.

Mamajee had handpicked the brightest colours, such as pinks, blues and yellows, which were sometimes patterned in large flowers and vines.

"I am not wearing those," I said, picking up a cerise, over-patterned rag. "It looks hideous. They'll laugh at me."

"Brighter colours make you fairer. Look at the state of you, all dark from the blazing sun. I warned you about hanging out with loose girls like Shelley. She has her own mind, that one. Now look at you. You were much fairer before you went to Bangladesh. You look like a beggar. It would be impossible to pass you as anything else," she said sardonically as she folded up more of the shawls and suits onto my cupboard shelf.

I looked at myself in the mirror. It was undisputable, of course, that I had gone a shade darker. I had caught the sun on my forehead, arms and around my cheeks, and my long brown hair seemed to have turned paler, and indeed, there seemed to be some displeasing vagrancy about it.

"Well, there is nothing wrong with being darker. English people go on holidays, and they are always trying to get a tan and get darker."

At this comment, her face seemed to boil with rage.

"What did you say? Say that again! What did you just say?" Her hands were now on her hips, her jaw clenched together almost as if it were holding back words laced with venom.

I froze. "What? Er, I … I just meant that English people like dark skin," I stuttered nervously.

"Are you English? Is that what you are trying to say? Is that what you want to be? One of them? She edged nearer to me, and I tightened up with the inquisition. "Tell me, is that what you have been learning from that cousin of yours? Is it?"

"No?" I said, confused. I sat quietly, now shielding myself with a shawl from an attack with words or otherwise, praying that she might simmer down.

"Be warned," she said, pointing at me. "Just be warned you don't start thinking you are one of those English sorts, going out, getting boyfriends and having their frontage on show for everyone to see. You are no longer a little girl. Every wrong move you make will be at the cost of your parents' honour, and in the eyes of the Lord, there is no greater sin than a child who dishonours her parents' wishes. Allah sees everything, remember that."

I said nothing as I sat on the bed, my head low, my arms wrapped around my legs, guarded by the patterned shawl.

"Put those on and come downstairs," she said, leaving the room, her voice echoing down the hallway. "There's a lot of cooking to do, and we need to go out and get some groceries for it."

I breathed in, looking at myself in the mirror, relieved that I had not suffered any further injustices from overstepping the mark with Mamajee, which often, when challenged, would result in being subjected to all sorts of Bengali curses. I held up the cerise-coloured, oversized tunic against me and thought about ways I could style such an unsightly mess of colours such that it didn't hang on me unflatteringly, but it didn't help. The bright colours against me made me look even more rancid, and the pungent kerosene smell that lingered on the fabric was enough of a reminder of where I would be returning.

Later, as if it wasn't enough to abhor this new makeover, Mamajee had me parading down the markets in this sordid attire. I tried to mask the cerise tunic with my knee-length winter coat, but the thin cerise patterned pyjamas, together with my white socks and black plastic platforms, were enough to make a spectacle of myself. I felt people's stares behind me as we walked through the markets. The cold winter air waving through the thin silk made the material seem inappropriate for the cold winter months, and I shivered behind my scarf as I followed Mamajee from stall to stall, hiding behind her in her long bottle-green burka coat and black hijab.

I could see that she seemed oblivious to the stares as she rummaged through her handbag for her purse to pay for the goods. Mamajee had pinned the scarf tightly to my head so that there was no question of it falling off.

I only hoped that we didn't meet anyone who I knew from school or that the locals in the town didn't make any comments. Sometimes the looks they gave Mamajee and me walking through would almost warrant a comment on passing.

I longed to be back at school. At least there I could escape and wear trousers. It was the only exception with Mamajee, because the school didn't allow girls to wear shalwar kameez, and to my relief, it meant that I could fit in for at least most of the day. The school was a welcome retreat for freedom of thought, a place far from the fear of marriage and, most of all, the tight scrutiny of home life.

Mamajee kept a tight rein on the time it took to get home from the bus to the door. I could see her faint shadow behind the lace-edged curtains veiling the kitchen window, watching, counting and reminding me that my place was at home.

The door was tightly bolted when it came to my everyday life at home too. No sooner had I entered through the kitchen door than I could feel the timer of Mamajee's explosive device being reset.

"Bags down. Come and help when you have finished upstairs."

What I would have done for a moment to myself in my room was to stare at the ceiling and find pretty patterns in the wallpaper.

But this was an incredulous idea to Mamajee, one that spawned further insinuations as to what I might be thinking or what could be distracting me. "What are you doing up here on your own?" she would ask countlessly upon any mere moment I had alone.

"I'm tired, Mamajee. It's been a long day," I would say, trying to fend off any notion that I had ulterior motives.

But Mamajee had little empathy for the tiredness from school, the rush between classrooms, the toll taken from the walk home, and the isolation I often felt from the mental bullying I was subjected to at times from the girls there.

"Tired, hmm? Yes, well, this 'going to school' business was not meant for girls, was it? In this hell of a country, this is how they corrupt their women: send them to schools so that they can become wayward."

"How can you say that, Mamajee, when I go to a girls' school? Doesn't that suggest it was meant for girls?"

"Don't you talk back to me. You've become quite a madam now, haven't you? Hey? This is exactly why I didn't approve of coming back here: they are already corrupting you with ideas that you can disrespect your parents. Saying what you feel? Come downstairs at once. I need your help in the kitchen."

"But I have homework to do. I still have an essay that I need to finish."

She paused, turning around slowly to look at me, and I knew that I had once again pushed her over the edge. "From now on, you will do exactly what I say. You will come home, and you will help in the kitchen ... I don't care about homework. You should be reminding yourself of the name of Allah, and here you are, thinking you can behave like a man.

"She wants to be a man!" she said out loud, returning down the hallway to continue her rant as she directed the words at me. "She thinks going to school will help. Oh, she is a woman now, isn't she? She has her own mind. Hm? How many times have I heard the word of Allah mentioned in this house? That's the kind of creature I am up against; that is what Allah has bestowed upon me. People can teach animals quicker than I can teach her the word of Allah. That

creature, that is what I am up against, Allah. I said to that godfor-
saken man before, leave her there, bringing her back will corrupt her,
but he isn't going to listen. No, he wants me to suffer. Allah's will is
that I suffer, and he shall see that I burn in hell too at this rate."

I sat quietly, listening from the bedroom, the door ajar, sending
all her complaints echoing up the hallway from the kitchen. I refrained from retorting to argue my point any further.

I knew that challenging her on this would only lead to further
accusations and more twisted sentences, fuelling Mamajee's reasons
to have me removed from school altogether.

And so, I changed into my tunic, pyjamas and shawl, carried out
my prayers before joining Mamajee in the kitchen to assist with cooking, cleaning, preparing dinner and washing.

"Here, cut this tilapia for me," she said, placing the dha in front
of me on the floor, where I had busily started on the runner beans.
"I want you to descale it first," Mamajee continued. "Slit and gut it,
and then cut it into five pieces. Be careful of the head. I don't want
you poking the eyes or ruining it. Your babajee loves eating fish
heads."

I looked blank. "But I don't know how to use the dha,
Mamajee."

"You mean to say, all these years that you have been living here,
and you never bothered to pay attention? How do you think I
learned? Nobody taught me." She then busily rose to where the stove
was roaring away with four boiling pans of curry.

I sat crouched on a small stool in front of the crescent-shaped
blade, looking at the large tilapia waiting to be prepared. I could only
recall moments when I had seen Mamajee do this with ease, the way
she held it by the tip of its tail and head as the fish glided across the
blade of the dha and flecks of its silvery scales sprang out. Recalling
this became an ill-fated attempt at emulating Mamajee's skill and dex-
terity, and I could almost sense her watching, bemused.

"You see, they don't teach you that at school, do they? Twelve
years old, and you can't even hold the dha. My goodness, what would
they think of you if you lived in Bangladesh? Move over." She tutted,
pressing my hands firmly together on the fish's head and tail. "Hold

it tightly; it's slippery. Place the skin against the blade harder. Come on, a little harder." She pushed my hand down. I could feel its razor-thin blade grazing against the fish's scales. She let go, and I continued. "See. Now do the other side," she said. "And hurry up, the oil is burning on the stove."

I could feel she was already losing her patience as she waited.

"Oh, come on, you still have to cut it!"

Feeling the pressure building, I swiped the fish back and forth against the blade. The scales flicked out, and I could feel Mamajee's eyes watching me from behind.

"Right, now, cut its head first. Hold onto it tightly, as it will slip." She knelt near me, and her jaw tightened with gritted teeth.

"I said, hold onto the fish tighter. How on earth are you supposed to cut it if you are holding it like that?"

She brought my hands tightly onto each side of the fish, and I could feel her impatience at me intensifying. She raised my hands above the blade, and I could sense she was going to slam the fish down onto the blade with full force, her hands wrapped around mine as she did.

"No!" I said, feeling unprepared. I felt something hard hit my hand and let go of the fish. Blood dripped off the blade, and I sat shaking, staring at the mess of blood seeping from my palms and onto the fish.

"You stupid girl, why did you let go?"

Overridden by guilt, incompetence and fear, I was too alarmed to reply and sat cupping my hands together to prevent the blood dripping onto the floor. Mamajee rose up and turned back to the stove.

"Who's going to marry you? Ha? I am bringing up cats and dogs here; this is what I am up against, raising a whore-born from a whore." She slammed the frying pan, the hot oil sizzling with the thud as she turned off the stove.

It deeply saddened me that she didn't feel guilty or that she'd had any part to play in what had happened. I was accountable for it all, but what cut me up the most was not the wound itself but how she insulted herself, how calling me a whore-born had no bearing on the dishonour she gave herself. Could a person loathe themselves so much they could reduce themselves to that?

I washed the pool of blood from my hands at the sink as Mamajee continued her rant. I noticed the cut had severed the middle of my right palm, and as I washed my hands to see the gaping slit, it became clearer how fortunate I was that it had not cut right through.

"You never listen, and now look. Let me see," she said, pulling my hands towards her. "Go on, get a bandage, you silly girl. You should be thankful to Allah it wasn't worse." She continued as I walked through the hallway, clutching my patterned shawl to stop the blood. "One day you will thank me for teaching you all of this, when you serve your mother-in-law, and believe me, she will be much harsher than me."

I pulled out the first-aid kit that was stored on the living-room shelf, trying with all my might to wrench the tin open with my useless left hand. I eventually succeeded in prising it open with my left finger and thumb. And as I wrapped the gauze around my hand, I became immediately thankful that I knew how, owing to the few years that I had attended St John Ambulance. I had asked Syd to help me find somewhere to learn first aid, in the event that something happened to Mamajee. I wanted to make sure I could nurse her back to health after Babajee's heartless behaviour towards her. She didn't dismiss this idea of learning. It summarised to me only how basic one's need is to learn, and even when she relied on my knowledge, Mamajee could not see what a deficit it is to one's mind and body to be without it.

It was clear Mamajee reviled it. Any discussion about school or requests to study or finish homework was at my peril, and if I insisted, the clamour of pans angrily thrown about in the kitchen quelled any concentration or intention of putting pen to paper.

And without doubt, at school I was failing too. My absence for a whole term, owing to our visit to Bangladesh, had meant being reduced to the bottom set in all subjects and had been further compounded by the homework that my teachers had set to bring me up to speed with the syllabus. They had sent notes home, which I read and passed on to Mamajee and Babajee. "They said they will give me detention if I don't bring my homework in on time. And I'll get marked down," I explained.

"Well, they can come and speak to me if they want to do anything. We'll see what they do," Mamajee replied as she wiped down the kitchen.

I resorted then to the kitchen. I mastered the uses of the dha with extreme precision, attributed to the number of failed attempts that left cuts along my fingers and thumbs. Soon my hands were becoming more and more like Mamajee's, coarse to touch, rough as sandpaper and blistered where I had burned myself on the frying pan.

I succumbed to her ideas and embraced her teaching as much as possible, appeasing any conflict on tenterhooks by shelling prawns, sorting out broad beans, cutting onions as finely as possible and peeling potatoes in a swift motion. And once I became proficient in food preparation, she taught me how to cook lamb with potatoes in a way that made the lamb full of flavour and without overcooking the potatoes. Rolling out chapattis from rice flour. How to make delicious madras bhuna curries without the chicken becoming over dry, or frying fish without it crumbling in the pan.

But of all the things I loathed about Mamajee's incessant aspirations of moulding me into model-wife material, the worst was the coaching and priming she felt I needed in the presence of men. I detested being demure, modest and subservient in front of male guests. In the evenings, she would have me practise putting on sarees, the veil wrapped over my head, and sometimes have me pose in front of a camera, where she would take pictures of me. I later discovered these photographs were being sent to our extended family overseas.

One weekend we had guests who were the wives and family of Babajee's business associates. Mamajee ordered with her eyes that I cover my head with a dupatta and drape the veil over my non-existent breasts. "Make sure you cover up. I don't want you giving them any ideas," she said, handing me a tray of tea and sweetmeats. She watched from the doorway as I bent to place the tray down on the coffee table. "I'm sorry about my daughter," she said to Babajee's associate, who seemed too engrossed in conversation with Babajee to have given me any notice.

"Oh no, she is doing a wonderful job!" He chortled, then graciously accepted the cup of tea I had poured him.

"Did you give him your salaam?" Mamajee beckoned me from behind.

"Assalamualaikum," I said, lowering my eyes as Mamajee had taught me – one should not make eye contact with a man.

"Mashallah, with thanks to Allah. Your daughter is as fair as an Englishwoman," the man remarked to Babajee as a compliment.

"Well, you know, when you live in such cold climates and you don't see the sun, I suppose you always become a little fairer skinned. It's understandable, isn't it, don't you think?" Babajee laughed nasally, as he often did, and he seemed a little tentatively sheepish.

"Oh, but amongst many Bangladeshi women, you wouldn't see one that fair."

"That's true, Bhabhi [*sister*]," said the aunt to Mamajee.

Mamajee looked indignant. "Not sure if being fair is such a good thing. She wants to be like the English, this one, and as with many English people, she lacks any decency and decorum about her."

Babajee remained silent, picking up his tea and a biscuit as Mamajee continued.

"I have tried so hard to teach her, Bhabhi," Mamajee explained to the auntie perching on the lounge seat. "I can't even get her to understand. Even dogs could be trained quicker."

I handed Auntie tea, kneeling beside the coffee table, remaining mute to a conversation that, although I was the subject of it, I was not permitted to be privy to with my ears or with my voice.

"Oh, she's still young. She's got time, and I am sure she will learn."

"Young? Time? Girls this age are married already in Bangladesh. I am counting the days now, Bhabhi. The eleventh hour is upon us.

Do you see? How can I show my face to anyone? No respectable family would want to even look at her."

Often, they would refrain from commenting, and often that meant they departed with a lower opinion of me. And I wondered what she gained from humiliating me in front of friends and family this way. How could this be a wise choice, given she wanted me married? Or was this another way to demolish any hopes and self-belief I had within me?

"A glass of water for me, if you will," interjected Babajee, cutting through the ridicule-infested rant Mamajee was now having with the auntie at my expense.

"Go on then, go get your babajee a glass of water."

I vacated the living room silently and went into the kitchen, where Mamajee also returned.

"It sounds like you wanted that to happen. Why did you not cover up when I asked you?" she whispered.

"I did," I said, pouring a glass of water for Babajee from the tap.

"Well, it didn't seem like that to me. Look at your neckline; it's showing everything underneath," she seethed quietly.

I looked down and could see nothing that could cause such provocation. I covered my neckline, though, with the shawl, more to prevent any further scrutiny from Mamajee or discerning accusations that I may be trying to flirt or seduce somebody. The extremity of her insinuations nauseated me somewhat, especially when some of these men were regarded as uncles or brothers. Nevertheless, I remained mute, abstained from speaking the truth or defending myself as I served up guests with another round of tea and biscuits to the hum of humiliation and their roaring laughter, which often came with Mamajee's deprecation of me.

*

That evening, after the chores were completed and the guests had departed from an afternoon of jibes and heckles owing to Mamajee's ridicule, we sat by the flickering fire. Mamajee was cross-legged on the rug, wrapped in a scarf, her forehead covered, leaving a small triangle around her face. She hummed the words of the Quran, and I read the Quran in Arabic with her, the words bearing little meaning, as I sat mindlessly, distracted by the events of today.

"Mamajee," I said, "what is the purpose of reading the Quran if we don't know the meaning of the words?"

Then she stopped humming to look at me. "Because it is the word of Allah, it is what is written," she said. "Do you know Allah has written our lives? He is the knower of all things. Allah created this world from one grain, and you and I and everything in it; it's all part of his plan. We worship Allah, and as we read the words and pray for forgiveness, these words will bring you to become one with him. Everything that has happened or has yet to happen has been written, and when you trust in that, only then will you reach the next life, the eternal life in heaven. This is Allah's will that you pray, fast and surrender to him. Allah knows all, everything you do, every step you take; it's all been written."

I paused, looking at her, confused. "I still don't understand. Then why do some people end up in hell? Why do people suffer? Is this what Allah would have wanted?"

She looked up from the point that she was reading. "My dear, everything you do against your religion is what will lead you to hell, nothing else. Your actions, your thoughts, your temptations that are against our religion, these are things that will lead you to stray from the true path Allah has created for you, what Allah has intended. Everything I teach you is to keep you on that path, and when you learn to surrender and trust in Allah, then, and only then, will you find your true path, the path that leads to heaven."

"But then, how do you know what the true path is?"

"That is what I have finished explaining, and anyhow, why are you asking questions? Do you even know the meaning of Islam?"

"No?" I said.

"Islam itself means to surrender, to surrender to the will of Allah, and if you understand nothing else, then do that. Then you will find yourself on the right path."

That night, after my evening prayers, I sat on the mat with my prayer beads, rolling each one with a hum to the name of Allah. I thought about what Mamajee said. *It still makes no sense. How can everything be written already? So, what about every choice I make? Do I even have a choice? And what about this arranged marriage she is priming me for? Does this mean I have to accept and surrender to Allah's will?*

My heart raced at the thought that this was indeed Allah's intention.

You promised, came a voice, and I began to crumble inside at the sound of it. It was the seven-year-old me staring at me through the conscience of my mind's eye.

You promised, remember? I saw her little body shivering, her feet cold, her eyes teary.

Yes, I have promised Mamajee, and no, I can't betray her, not after everything that she had to go through. Yes, she is right, she has suffered. But then, if this is what Allah wills, then why does this feel so wrong? If this is what Allah wills, then why am I finding it hard to accept? If this is what Allah wills, then he would know that all of this feels like a lie right now.

But it's not a lie, what happened to Mamajee, is it? the seven-year-old me replied. *She nearly died for you. If it wasn't for her, you wouldn't be here. She gave you everything. This is the only thing she is asking from you.*

There was some truth to that. I sighed as I lay on the mat. I tried to accept the fate that Mamajee and Babajee were leading me to, opening my mind to that world and seeing what Allah had willed. Life in a foreign country, to a man twenty years older than me, a man who barely had enough means to support us. *It doesn't feel right*, I thought. Then I recalled a moment of conversation, sitting with Mrs Abbots under that tree by the school.

"You feel it; the truth is golden. It will appear and shine for a little while, but then your fears will shadow it. Keep that golden thought. Repeat it, whatever it is that feels true. Hold on to it, and you will find a way to it."

That golden truth was shining now; one word came to me, the one word that had been applied to everything that had happened so far. "Written," I said out loud.

If there is a god, then he didn't give me will and choice for nothing. He gave me a voice inside that felt true. He gave me powers in my control, that golden source of truth to me. And it was in my power to make sure that whatever was written I could choose to rewrite.

I wrote that night, and it was not a letter or a verse or an anecdote. I wrote what I wanted my life to be. I wrote the words "I choose to be free" and that I trusted in Allah to help me find the way to it. I went back downstairs to where Mamajee was sitting on the sofa, her mouth filled with paan, the red-blood stain from its juice seeping at the sides of her lip. Her empty, exhausted gaze at the TV set and her slouched body weighing into a cushion.

I sat and watched her, the slowness of it all, and I felt that golden moment of truth as I watched her sitting there in front of the TV. This was her definition of what was written, and not mine. I realised that as long as I could stay true to myself, then I could get through this, and I could achieve what I wanted.

"Go get me a drink," Mamajee commanded, still staring at the TV set.

I smiled and rose from my seat. It was a smile of inner revelation. I was no longer affected by her. She could cast me in chains, drag me down the same muddy path, but I indeed still knew there was something golden, something true that I couldn't easily be distracted from. That the future that lay before me was a journey of my own belief. This wasn't going to be the end of me, and I just needed to find a way out, and there was only one person who could help me with that. I went upstairs, crept into Mamajee and Babajee's room and dialled the number. The phone rang for a while, and I almost gave up. There must have not been anyone at home. My heart sank. Then suddenly I heard that voice.

"Hello?" came the answer.

"Hello, Mrs Abbots. It's me, Eleanor."

CHAPTER EIGHTEEN
– *Failing at School* –

I t was difficult to find an excuse to leave the confines of my house now that Mamajee had a strong hold over every move I made. There were only two places that I was permitted to be in, the kitchen and the school, and this made things very difficult. To meet Mrs Abbots would be out of the question, because there were no places where I could have such a meeting. I needed space; I needed time; I needed privacy; and none of these personal freedoms did I have liberties for.

I was being set up for failure, and I could feel it on each passing day at the school. I tried to keep up with the classes, racing through notes and books on my way to school on the bus, or jotting down homework before the class started. I tried to get answers from the other girls in my class and often begged them to help me through a homework question that was due for submission. I could tell I was becoming a burden on them. Often, they would turn away at the sight of me, or I was left to try to complete what I could during fifteen-minute breaks or at lunchtime, but it was impossible. Some of these exercises required at least thirty minutes, if not longer, and at school there was little time for that. I knew what failure would mean though. It would mean being removed from the school or performing so badly that there would be few or no prospects available to me other than fulfilling Mamajee's prophecy and proving that there were no unworthy reasons to send me back to Bangladesh.

I was failing each class I stepped into. My work was rushed and unclear. Sometimes my conclusions in essays were poor, or the arguments unsubstantiated. I failed the maths tests at the end of each week because I couldn't revise at home. I scraped through science labs by copying fellow pupils' work, and I could barely comment or answer any of the debates in literature. Each week, I brought my test papers back, and a little piece of me was set back with them. I was following a moving target; I was pedalling faster and yet still unable to get up to speed.

It didn't help that the teacher in the lower set had little patience for my lack of understanding on some of the theories, and even when he tried to explain, I was intimidated by him and found it harder to concentrate. One day, I was in this class and put on the spot.

"Eleanor, your turn. Sam bought three boxes of chocolates online. Postage was nine pounds, and the total cost was forty-five pounds. How much was each box?"

I blanked. "I don't know, sir."

"Well, that's obvious."

The rest of the class giggled.

"Let's break it down, shall we? What do we need to do first?"

I heard a whisper from behind me, giving me an answer, but I couldn't make sense of it.

"Come on, what do we need to do first?"

I blanked.

"Tell me, did you do the practice sheet I provided yesterday?"

I sat frozen.

"Well? Did you?" he insisted.

"No, sir," I said, shaking my head. It was enough to feel the silence, to feel the humiliation as the class stared on. I might as well have not existed. I was being mocked at home, and now I was standing in a place that often offered salvation from the ridicule of home in the same manner. I broke down in class, and I rushed out.

Mr Johnson followed me out into the hallway. "What seems to be the problem?" he said, bending down in front of me, his stony face and hardened wrinkles now looking less severe as he spoke. "What seems to be the problem?" he asked again.

I was too upset to speak. He paused for a few moments. "I need more help, and I don't have enough time to work through these maths problems, and I am already falling behind." My voice became squeaky, and I felt embarrassed by my teary state.

"Well, yes, it does seem that your marks are unusually low, and despite multiple warnings, I haven't seen your homework book being returned, so I presume you are facing some difficulties, and if that is the case, then we need to talk about it," he said softly. I had never thought he could have a soft, gentle side with the frontage he displayed in class. "How about you speak to Miss Walker this lunchtime and we can see what we can do? I will have a word with her. Now, do you want to go and clean yourself up and reconvene in a few minutes?"

I nodded. "Thank you, sir."

"You are very welcome, Eleanor." He headed back to the classroom and turned to face me again. "You know, if you get stuck on anything, you do know you can just ask." He nodded reassuringly. "That's what we are here for," he said.

*

I knocked on the door of Miss Walker's office at lunchtime. Miss Walker was the deputy head of the maths department. She was a tall lady of about six feet, with thick blonde hair that was cut to shoulder length.

"Come in," she said firmly.

I opened the door, holding my books nervously.

"Now, Eleanor," she said as she shuffled some papers away at her desk. "I hear from Mr Johnson that you are falling behind in class, and he has asked you to come and see me about it."

"Yes, miss," I said.

"Well?" She seemed puzzled. "So, tell me, what is causing you problems? According to your teachers' reports from year seven, it suggests you are highly capable and doing well in all your subjects," she said, looking down at my records. "Very impressive," she said, looking at my English report. "Good effort in maths. So, tell me something, Eleanor. I understand you have been away, and, granted, it will take some time to catch up, but if you are not willing to put in the time and effort required at home, I am afraid it will lead to some unfavourable consequences."

"I don't have enough time, miss, and—"

"Well, that's inexcusable, isn't it?" she said. "Why not? What do you mean, you don't have enough time?" I had many thoughts running through my head about how to explain myself. "Well?" she said, pressing for a response.

And then the words tumbled out. "My parents, they don't want me to study, so … I am finding it hard to study at home." I looked down at the floor, embarrassed that I had to confess my problems to a teacher and worried this was going to lead to more problems.

She paused, nodding slowly as she put her cup down in a new place on her desk. "And what do you want to do?" She spoke softly, almost a murmur.

"Well, I want to study; it's just that they don't want me to. They told me that there is no point in school and that when I finish school, they are going to send me back to Bangladesh to be married and …" I shook my head. "There is no way I would want that to happen." The words poured out like the monsoon rivers, and I realised there was no going back. Before I knew it, Miss Walker knew the intricacies of my situation at home.

"Very well, I will write to your parents and ask that they come and see me so that we can discuss—"

"No, miss! Please," I said, shaking my head nervously. "That won't work. I think … I think that will make things worse. No, I think that I will get into more trouble if they find out I told you."

She thought about it, nodding slowly.

"Perhaps I can come and see them instead. Would that work?" she suggested.

"No, I wouldn't suggest that's wise either, miss. I … I … I think my mother would be outraged."

"Well, we need a way forward, Eleanor. I don't see how we can continue this way. Your exams are approaching, and at this rate, I am not hopeful that you will be sufficiently prepared for them."

"Let me think about it, miss. I will work something out."

"Very well," she said in agreement.

I rose from the seat and headed to the door.

"Oh, and Eleanor …" I turned to face her. "If you need any help with your maths, you can also come and see me at lunchtimes. I am normally in my office."

"I am grateful for that, miss, and yes, I would very much like to be able to do that if possible."

She smiled. And I could have almost shaken her hand and hugged her before I left, but I returned instead a warm, teary smile.

I left the office for the cool air of the fields outside and clear blue skies above. I sat on the steps overlooking the fields with a cheese sandwich and apple that I had little appetite for. I had been skipping breakfast to get to school early and could barely muster lunch anymore. I pulled out the loose change in my pocket that was left over from the sandwich and apple I'd bought. Then I realised that there was something I could do. The school did have a pay-phone. I could call Mrs Abbots from there; I could speak to her, find a way forward.

I dialled the number carefully, making sure it was correct. The phone rang, and I sensed she wasn't at home. It went through to an answerphone, and I hesitated about leaving a message.

"Hello there," came Mrs Abbots recorded voice. "I am not at home at the moment, but do leave a message after the beep."

"Hi, Mrs Abbots. It's me, Eleanor. I just wanted to know if you can meet me. I could do with some help. If it's possible, could you … would you be able to meet me on the three-five-two bus home from school?"

I had run out of coins, and the phone call ended. That was stupid, I thought. How could she possibly do anything with that? I hadn't had time to tell her when I would be on the bus. What a complete waste.

The bell rang for the afternoon session, and I resumed position as the class dunce for another round of failures. The three sessions of geography, art and french were even more terrifying than the morning. I had essays to complete, portraits of a parent required back before the next lesson. I knew that it would be impossible for either of my parents to even participate in such an exercise. According to Babajee, drawing pictures of people was forbidden, and as for French, well, if Mamajee and Babajee were agreed on anything, it was that learning Bengali or Arabic should be given precedence before introducing any other language, and that therefore meant French would not be favoured at all.

I caught the bus along with the other girls who had pushed and heaved their way on and made my way to the back to seat myself. I looked through the assignments I had, and I knew that the twenty-minute bus ride would not be enough to get me through it. *There is no way I can get through all of this*, I thought. *Where is the time? I don't have time. And each time I fail to submit my homework, it's becoming increasingly difficult to justify it. I am pretty sure this is it. I am not going to make it through.*

"Are you okay if I sit here?" I heard a voice come from the aisle.

I turned and there she was.

"Mrs Abbots!" I said.

She sat down and squeezed me. "Hello, my dear! How are you?" She smiled that beautiful, beaming smile, and instantly I felt a warmth that I had not felt in a long time.

I looked at her as though it was the best moment of my life.

"I am sorry about my message earlier. I got cut off, and then—"

"No, no, don't be silly," she said. "I knew, I knew which bus to catch." She giggled as the bus rocked backwards and forwards.

"Thank you." I beamed. "I missed you," I said softly.

She took a deep breath with that, as if she had displaced her words. "Well," she said, "didn't I tell you? When you need me, just call." She nodded insistently. "So, tell me, is everything all right? I was a little worried when I didn't hear back from you."

"No, I'm sorry to say. Things are not good, Mrs Abbots. I need some help. You see, my mum and dad, well, they don't want me studying, and I am falling behind at school, and actually, what they really want is for me to be married."

"I'm sorry. I don't quite follow, dear. What do you mean, your parents want you married?"

"Yes, well, that's just it. You see, there is a cousin of mine in Bangladesh, and Mamajee has made plans that when I turn sixteen, I am to marry him. He is more than twice my age, Mrs Abbots. I don't see how that would even work."

"Well, we'll see to that, don't worry. And what's all this, then? You are not doing well at school?"

I could see the disappointment in her face, a look of confusion.

"Well, you know my mum, Mrs Abbots. She just doesn't like me studying. And when I go home, she's ready to bite my head off at the mere mention ... I mean, if I can't do my homework and I am expected to just do all the chores, then how am I supposed to do well at school? I suppose I know the answer to that one: they don't want me to do well. I am falling behind, Mrs Abbots. I think I am getting close to detention with the rate I am failing at, and I am really worried this will give Mamajee even more of a reason to send me back. I need a way out, Mrs Abbots. I need help."

"Oh, come here," she said, putting her arm around my shoulder and squeezing me. I felt a surge of warmth flood into my chest. "You poor thing, I know it must be very horrible for you right now, but you mustn't let this bring you down. You must listen to your inner voice of reason. Tell me something, do you remember when I explained about what feels right is golden?"

"Yes, I do," I said. "But I just can't see how I can put it in place. I can't, because they won't let me."

"Do you have the will in you to succeed?" she said firmly.

"Yes, yes, I do."

"Well, in that case, there is always a way. You must believe in that wholeheartedly. There is always a way, always, even if you can't believe it yet. And you must fight your mind to believe that it will happen the way you want. You have to start believing that you are going to do well at school, and you are going to make it through this. You are going to draw on all your power, every single ounce of strength, all your resources, all the help you can find, and then you are going to build your plan and action it. You have control, Eleanor, to change what you have the will to change."

I shook my head. "I can't see it. I just can't see it."

"Okay, look, how much time do you really need to do your studying and homework?"

"I don't know. Hours, it feels like."

"How much time do you estimate to finish the work you have been given today?"

"Not sure really. I think a couple of hours."

"Right, what I want you to do is start thinking about where you have pockets of time. You don't have to upset your parents; you can work around them. Have a think about the amount of time you have when they are not focused on you. You will find there is plenty of time before school, during lunch and early mornings, when they are busy sleeping, and then you will find a way." She smiled confidently. "Don't you worry, my dear; it's all there for you. You will make this work, because you have the will within you."

The bus drew nearer to my stop.

"Thank you, Mrs Abbots. I know it helps when I speak to you."

"Just call if you need anything, dear, and remember, where there is a will, there is a way."

I turned back to give her one last look.

She looked back at me, calmly, confidently, and I could almost see myself in her. How I aspired to be her. I recalled Mrs Abbots's advice on the walk home that afternoon, with the sun setting in the winter sky. "Draw on all your strength and resources, and you will find a way," she'd said.

*

That afternoon I used my time in the kitchen to devise my plan. I peeled the potatoes, stirred the pots and washed the dishes just as Mamajee wanted, but in my head I was somewhere else. I looked at the structure of my day for when I had pockets of free time, free from Mamajee's persistence. I knew that those were the times I could study: early in the morning before she woke, at lunchtime at school I could get through homework, and in the evening when she was downstairs watching TV. It equated to four hours of my time in a day that I could devote to studying without Mamajee even knowing. I could get the bus to school early, around 7 a.m., when Mamajee and the rest of the family were still sleeping. I could read my notes on bus journeys and get through maths with the help of Miss Walker. I started to see her regularly at lunchtime, and she let me stay at her desk to finish my maths homework. I was able to get back up to speed with my maths, and when I had, I concentrated on what I really loved: arts and English. This was a world of colour that lifted me away from the scorns and torments of my reality. Here I felt warmth and fearlessness and was vibrant with energy. I wished there was more time, and often I would spend my fifteen-minute breaks finishing the painting that I wanted to perfect.

This world had no physical boundaries. I was untouchable here, and I could roam freely. Mamajee knew nothing of what I created here at school, but my teachers did: the short stories about love, friendship and peace, the abstract artwork of flowers in close-up. My teachers guided me and became my closest allies in my fight for education; whether they knew the full story or not, they believed in me. Having listened to my issues, they were able to help me devise a homework plan that was more feasible and manageable with my home life. Soon things were becoming easier, and I was regaining confidence in myself.

One afternoon, during art class, as I sat painting a large abstract of flowers, my teacher Miss Roberts came over to my table.

"Eleanor, come and see me at the end of the class. There's something I need to discuss." Her tone seemed neutral and serious.

"Yes, Miss Roberts." It had sounded quite severe, I thought. Maybe I was not doing very well with my work. A surge of self-doubt arose, and I felt dispirited. *Well, you don't make enough time for it, and no, it's obviously not good enough, is it?* I heard myself say. This was an area I loved the most, and when I failed here, it seemed to reduce my confidence in everything else.

She perched patiently on the edge of her desk as the girls vacated the classroom. I observed the flatness of her expression, how it seemed to be pressing for the moment the class was empty. I stood waiting patiently with my art folder in hand.

"Eleanor," she said with a concerned looked that could have almost been mistaken as grief-stricken. "We had a visit today from the council."

Oh no, I thought. *This has got to be something regarding my level of work, and—*

"They came across some of your work that was displayed in the school lobby and were quite taken aback."

"Taken aback? You mean, they didn't like it?"

"No, no!" she gasped. "Quite the contrary, Eleanor." She smiled, laughing a little, then continued. "They have asked, with your permission, of course, whether they could display it in the opening of the new council gallery. Would that be something you would be okay with?"

My heart quickened, and I was slightly taken aback. The words *not good enough* still fading out in my mind's eye.

"Yes, sure, that would be, you know, more than fine." I could barely muster my words. "Could I be mistaken, dare I say it? I can take this as a compliment?" I said, crawling into myself.

"You needn't be so hesitant to receive it as such, Eleanor. You've worked hard this year, and this can only be a testament to your efforts. So, well done, Eleanor, and if we do have your permission, then your work will go on display at the town hall gallery over the summer."

I couldn't help but beam speechlessly.

"Of course, it would only be an honour to be worthy of such praise!" I laughed, shaking my head with disbelief.

"So, I will let them know, and of course, we will be sharing this news at the next school assembly. I am sure your parents will be pleased." She smiled.

I looked at her like a wilting and fading flower. "Well ..." I hesitated. "Like you once explained, art is subjective, and that in essence is what makes art both liberating and beautiful in itself, isn't it?"

"That is right, Eleanor, and I am certain that your work will be seen as desirable by many. I will see you in the next class." She smiled pleasantly.

When I walked away, I had mixed feelings of excitement and sadness. I was certain in myself that there would be no interest from my parents to encourage me into art, nor would they have any interest in visiting an art gallery where others would be appreciating my work. So I made no mention of it.

I did, though, share my news after the school assembly with Mrs Abbots on the bus home that day, and she beamed with pride at my achievements.

"So, are you going to be visiting the opening of the gallery?" she asked. "It's quite an achievement. You must be very proud of yourself."

"Well, I don't think I can go. Well, they won't let me, and I don't think there is any point in stirring up another argument with them."

"Hmm, yes, that's true," she said, looking a little subdued and in thought. "Well, I will most definitely be there," she said in earnest.

"You will?" I said, surprised.

"Of course. I wouldn't miss it for the world, Eleanor."

To that, we both smiled.

I missed the opening of the gallery, despite much persuasion by Miss Roberts and Mrs Abbots to visit. I couldn't find a way to persuade Babajee, given his time for family matters was minimal, and I knew this was a forgone conclusion with Mamajee. My absence was made up in other ways, though, by their support, by their attendance and, most resonant of all, by their belief in me.

"Eleanor," Miss Roberts said in class, after the visit to the opening of the gallery, "you were missed. I would have liked to have introduced you to some of the members of the Arts Council. Really, they loved your work, and you were praised generously. You have made the school very proud, and of course, the Arts Council could see a very promising future for you."

"Thank you, Miss Roberts." I felt deeply saddened at the same time. "I am not sure that I could make a career out of it. My parents wouldn't agree to that." I smiled meekly, the incongruity of what should have been a positive exchange.

"I do understand the difficulties you face at home, Eleanor, but do remember that your true colours shine the brightest in your artwork. You have a true gift. Promise me you will keep that creative flair in you as a hobby at least. There are no limits to what you can do with it, I can assure you of that."

I was deeply touched. "Yes, I will. I promise you that."

Years later, I treasured those words when Mamajee had thrown all my artwork away. There are no physical limits to imagination and creativity, and of course, where there is the courage, you will succeed.

CHAPTER NINETEEN
– *The Final Year* –

With my schoolwork now manageable and order restored to home life, I was beginning to see progress, credit to supportive teachers and much-cherished guidance from Mrs Abbots, who was only a phone call and a fifteen-minute bus ride when I needed her.

I enjoyed writing and poetry more so because it was an outlet, a way of consoling myself.

The issues and restrictions at home continued, with the reminder from Mamajee with every false move of what was predestined for me when I finished my fifth year at school. "Be warned," she would say. "You know your obligations." I often felt it then, that sensation of isolation and despair arising within me. I felt it in those lonely walks home, or as I wandered the halls and corridors, or on the bus rides to school, and it was in those moments that writing became my voice and the pen became my friend.

One day in literature class in my final year, we were tasked with writing a poem, and nothing could have come more easily to me.

"Now," said Mrs Holloway, our English teacher. "Who would like to go first?"

There was an air of reluctance from the class and much hushed silence. I was hesitant to stand: I wasn't sure whether what I expressed in writing could be seen as appropriate or relevant. My hand flinched a little with a desire to reach it up, but my mind quietened it.

Mrs Holloway scoured the room for one volunteer and, upon seeing the slight twitch from me, urged me to come forward. "Eleanor, I would suggest you come up first and share." She smiled.

A rush of nerves tingled in my body, and I jittered my way to the front of the class with my journal in hand.

"It's called 'The Wedding,'" I said, and began reciting.

The Wedding

There I stood, weighed down in gold.
Bowing with grace as I was told.
At the centre stage, I take the bow.
In my red ordained dress to make the vow.

Like a coffin carried down the parade.
The undertaker's arms at my aid.
I felt the walk of the Green Mile.
Descend upon me without a smile.

The parents gloated, looking so pleased.
And all the family pushed and teased.
He was the prince to make me his wife.
To close my future and my life.

And as the garlands pressed their thorns.
It grazed my heart, ripped and torn.
Tears of pain beneath my veil.
Those happy people to tell my tale.

Scattered petals at my feet.
Like ashes flaring from the heat.
I burned my soul into the fire.

Of all that life could ever desire.

The truth is known to be denied.
For the face of fathers and their pride.
We are here to voice what's in our heart.
And only that till death do us part.

The class fell silent, and Mrs Holloway's expression seemed a little speechless, and I thought it was likely I had shared something no one else in the room could relate to.

"Well, Eleanor, thank you for sharing your poem. Can you perhaps explain a little more about your poem?"

"It's about arranged marriages, miss, and about a girl whose life has already been written by her parents. The poem expresses the bride's experience of the wedding day, and through similes and metaphors, we learn that her experience is more of a religious hell."

She again paused as if to take in my explanation.

"Thank you, Eleanor, for that explanation, and I can see that you have grasped the concepts of metaphors and used them well in your poem. Go and take a seat."

After class Mrs Holloway asked whether I could remain seated, as there was something she would like to discuss with me. "Yes, Eleanor, I very much liked your poem and am impressed with your ability to compose such interesting and poignant verses. We do have a poetry competition this summer that our school can submit poems to. Would you like to maybe submit this one? I would say it is a good piece of work, and you delivered the story very well."

Much to my amazement, it won the UK national prize and was published in a collection of short poems that further led to an award at school. That afternoon, I came home brimming with pride at my achievements.

"Babajee," I said at dinnertime, "I got the UK national prize for my poem, and it is published in a book, look!" I passed it over to where he sat in his prime position on the rug as he ate his meal of tender lamb and potato curry with rice. I saw, for a moment, a smile and his eyes light up.

"Very good, Beti. Show me after dinner," he said, placing it at his side.

I thought it was something worthy of sharing with Babajee, given his interest in literature, and after dinner I hurried to sit with him. I began reciting. Mamajee sat vacantly watching the news on TV. Neither of them understood English very well, and I explained each line in detail, but as I read, I could see that Babajee's expression looked less than enthused.

"You are equating marriage to death. How could you speak so ill of our culture?"

I remained silent. "No, I am only talking about how it feels, that's all. I don't mean to speak ill of anyone."

"What do you think our community would say if they ever read it?" Babajee said through furrowed brows and pursed lips.

To that Mamajee's ears pricked up, and as she learned of Babajee's outrage, it became more inviting for her to chime in.

"Hmm, she is a poetry writer, is she now? I told you all about that, didn't I? Look at the disgrace and mockery she makes of our culture. I've told you before it's not in her blood, and now she is letting the world know of it!"

I shook my head, bitterly regretting that I had mentioned it, and immediately felt the walls around me closing in on me.

What was I thinking? Of course it's not going to be well received.

I vacated the room to the kitchen, where I cleared up the remainder of the dishes and listened to the rant Mamajee was serving Babajee as she folded up some laundry.

"I've told you before, send her back, time is running out, and as the days go by, this will only lead to more complications, more issues. The more time you delay and procrastinate, the more you will regret it. She won't elevate your honour, this one. You can't teach someone to believe if they weren't born a believer."

"That's enough!" Babajee finally remarked after ten minutes of uninterrupted verbalisations from Mamajee.

By the summer that year, I was entering into my final exams. It meant longer hours studying and revising. I needed more time to concentrate. The early evenings were a write-off. There was no question of revising; any mere mention of it to Mamajee would lead to the banging of the pans in the kitchen and complaining under her breath, and after dinner she found it insulting that I wouldn't want to sit and watch TV and make conversation with her. I worked tirelessly through the night, sometimes until 3 or 4 a.m. under the covers with a torch when I knew she was asleep. There were times I would fall asleep on the bus and forget to get off at my stop. I crammed my way through my exams, dipping high and low through the anxiety. The sickening thought that if I didn't pull myself together, then I would fail, and that would lead to further failure.

"I can't do this," I said, rocking backwards and forwards on the bus anxiously with Mrs Abbots.

"Why, of course you can, Eleanor. I can't see anyone more prepared than you."

"They are going to send me off to Bangladesh, and that will be the end of it. Mamajee's already persuading Babajee."

"They won't send you to Bangladesh, not unless you let them, of course, and anyhow, you have weeks to go. You've still got time. And you know as well as I do, the first question you have to concentrate on is what is in your control. And that, my dear, is to do your utmost, to persevere with studying relentlessly."

I sat despondently low in my seat as I watched the other girls going about their day home. I could only imagine that they weren't struggling to find the time like I was.

"You can't be a victim of circumstances, Eleanor; you can choose how to respond to it. You have a choice, Eleanor."

"But how? How do I have a choice? I feel so paralysed," I cried, feeling deflated and helpless.

She brought herself closer to me, holding onto my hand. "Listen, even if you were paralysed, had no arms or legs, couldn't see, I know that you would find a way. Why? Because you have the will and courage to do this. You are not going to give up, Eleanor, my dear, because the consequences are far greater if you did just give up. Just do what's in your control right now. Don't think about the future; just think about the best you can do right now and have faith that it will lead you to the right outcome. Stay true to that word; you know that word is golden."

I looked unconvinced.

"Oh, I've got you a present," she said excitedly.

She pulled out a box from her large shopping bag.

"Oh? What is it?"

"Go on open it; it might cheer you up a little."

I smiled. "Thank you, Mrs Abbots. How thoughtful." I delighted at the floral wrapping paper and the bow. I unwrapped the paper, and inside was a box.

"A Walkman?" I said.

"Yes, well, I thought it would be handy to record your notes in class, and you'd be able to play back your revision notes when you are cooking. Nobody can say no to that now, can they?"

I beamed. "That's a great idea! Thank you, Mrs Abbots." And I hugged her. "I am so grateful that you are here in my life."

And, for once, I saw how touched she seemed by my words.

"I am just as grateful that you would allow me into it." Her face dropped the smile, and her lips trembled as she resisted the tears.

"Now, will you remember to be true to your word? The golden truth. You are going to do very well in your exams, and no fear or obstacle will get in the way of that, will it? Promise me that!"

I nodded. "I am going to do well in my exams."

"Have a go at recording your notes and playing them back to yourself; it's a good way to remember facts, and listening stops your brain from worrying. And also, you are less likely to upset anyone at home."

It was difficult to avoid agonising over my future, but of all the things I learned in that final year, perhaps the most important was that I didn't need the time I thought I needed to devote to my exams. Yes, there were challenges, but I was setting my mind to failure mode rather than using my time to focus on preparation.

When I recorded my notes on tape, I realised I could condense my revision notes into an hour each side and play them as often as I liked throughout the evening. Mamajee wasn't even aware of what I was listening to when I cooked or helped her in the kitchen, and with my scarf tightly around my head, she couldn't even see the headphones. It felt empowering and liberating. I could play the tapes on my way to school, on the bus home, in the evenings when I was helping Mamajee in the kitchen, and at night when everyone else was sleeping.

I disengaged from Mamajee's incessant phone calls to friends and family, conversations that often antagonised and disrupted my concentration.

"No, she isn't very bright, not very good at studying, always panicking and crying. I say to her, 'What is the point in all this stress when you are getting married anyhow?'"

The words conjured in me a sour, bitter taste, like that of lemons, only harder to swallow.

"Oh dear, what are your plans for her?" I could hear them ask.

"Well, marriage, of course. Oh, I am panicking: all the girls her age are getting married. How can I face Allah if I don't do what is in my responsibility as a mother to do?"

I spent the summer in constant emotional turmoil; I fought through the lows to get to the highs. I ignored the comments whispering in my mind: "failure", "you are not good at this", "you'll never get through it." Or Mamajee's knock-backs in the kitchen. I shunned any self-doubt with "I will" or "I can" statements. And often, when I broke down in tears because I couldn't see any hope in passing, I remembered Mrs Abbots's words of advice that she gave me over and over again: "Golden, be true to your word, and you will succeed." The encouragement that all of my energy was needed to focus on the desired outcome. I often didn't know what would happen if I did pass, whether it would have any consequence to Mamajee's intentions for me. I knew, though, that if I tried, there was a fighting chance, a far-fetched idea albeit, that I could go on to advanced level, or at least I could find a way forward. Without these exams though, my options potentially would be limited.

Mrs Abbots met me at the school gates on the day of my final exam. It was a stunning summer morning. The clear, bright skies above were untouched by clouds, and I could hear the calm sounds of the breeze through the trees.

"How are you feeling?" she said. "It's your last exam now?" She smiled.

I nodded calmly. "I feel okay actually. I guess this is it, Mrs Abbots." I moved to the shade of the tree, where the light was less piercing on my eyes, and Mrs Abbots joined me to perch on the school wall.

"You must remember, whatever happens today is just the beginning; you've worked hard, and you will do your best. That's all you need to think about right now."

"Yes." I nodded reassuringly to myself. I could have only wished I could swap places with her. We watched the girls walking past as they made their way through the main entrance of the building. Some nodded or smiled or waved as they passed us.

"How long is your exam today?" Mrs Abbots asked.

"It's two hours, and there are three essay questions," I said.

"There's enough time; don't rush. Remember, you have your notes in your head, and you can jot them down before you start the exam."

"Thank you, Mrs Abbots."

"Good luck, my dear, and if you need anything, you will call, won't you?"

"I will."

I walked towards the entrance, giving Mrs Abbots one last glance before I found myself amongst a crowd of girls signing into the exam hall. I realised that this may also be the last time I would see these girls, the last time I would set foot in the school and walk the halls, and I wondered whether this would be the last time I'd ever feel free.

By the time I arrived home, Mamajee had already been in discussion with Babajee about the marriage arrangements and the trip to Bangladesh. "So, when are you booking the flights?" she asked him as she wiped the dining table for dinner.

I skirted around the table, placing down the pan mats one by one, listening tentatively but pretending not to hear. Babajee looked disengaged, his usual disposition around Mamajee. It angered her when he never responded.

"If you don't book the tickets, the flights will only get more expensive."

Babajee looked on at the TV. He lit another cigarette and took an irritated drag that caused him to cough and sputter. He cleared his throat. Mamajee stood, paused, waiting for an answer.

"This man will never be worried about his future, even when he is ready to be pushed into the grave." She marched off into the kitchen. Babajee continued to flick the channel with the TV remote, despondent and expressionless.

How invisible I felt. I seemed as transparent as a ghost to them. They were deciding my future in front of me as though I was nothing more than an object being passed through the luggage carousel.

I watched the drama unfold as Babajee continued on vacantly at the TV, the jibes at his lack of interest. I watched Mamajee's tantrums being taken out on doors being slammed and as overboiled pots of curry were placed on the dining table with a huff and a thud, and Babajee all the while, silent, bearing only the sound of a deep sigh of resignation. It was as though I was sitting on death row, not knowing the verdict and when my time was up.

That night, after prayers, I lay on my bed, looking out at the stars, relieved that the stress of exams was now over, but intense about what fate the day of my results would lead to and whether Mamajee and Babajee had decided that a trip to Bangladesh was on the cards before or after result day.

I could hear the usual commotion downstairs, Mamajee talking to someone at the door, but I couldn't bear to be around her. I knew she would be in a bad mood with me, given her outburst earlier on at Babajee.

Mamajee was desperate to fit a trip in during the school holidays so as not to disrupt my brother's education. Of course, for Mamajee, there were no objections here: it was essential for boys to be educated.

If I could just get to results day, I thought, *it would be ideal, but that's a month away.* At least then there would be a chance of proving that I had potential, that I was capable of being more than a housewife. And the more I thought about this, the more I loathed the idea of being a woman and myself being a housewife. The woman they wanted me to be, the woman Mamajee was shaped from and the woman Mamajee was preparing me to be. A perpetual mould of herself. *Damn you, Eleanor, that is not your life. Your life is here; you are worthy of more, and you will succeed. You will find a way. You won't be going to Bangladesh. I'm going to find a way.* I needed a plan.

I heard Mamajee calling from downstairs. "Eleanor, oh, Eleanor."

"Jee, Mamajee," I said with a raised voice.

"Why are you upstairs? Come down here."

I stormed down, already in a mood. *She doesn't even give me time to think or breathe. How am I supposed to do anything?*

When I came into the living room, Mamajee had a smile that I hadn't seen in a long time.

"Look," she said, holding up a wedding invitation.

"Your aunt Nashira is getting married." She beamed.

"Oh, when?" I said as she handed me a heavily embossed white wedding card.

"This month," she said, busily opening up another envelope.

"Look, this is the picture of the groom. Isn't he handsome?"

I was too busy scouring the address. *Oh no*, I thought. *What if the wedding is in Bangladesh and we all have to go back this summer?*

"Where is the wedding going to be?" I asked calmly.

"The groom is coming to London, so they have hired the mosque hall in London."

"Oh," I said, relieved.

"Yes, they sent your cousin to come by and hand out the card personally."

"What? You mean he just came all the way from London?"

"Yes, of course! I am one of the eldest in the family. In Bangladeshi culture you are meant to invite people personally and give the invitation by hand. Otherwise, people often won't attend."

"Oh, I see," I said, scouring the card.

"And of course, we'll feel obliged to go. Nanni wouldn't be impressed if we didn't, so she made sure that the invite was sent to us by hand."

I could feel myself bursting with joy inside, but of course, I kept neutral in case it triggered a negative reaction in Mamajee's outward appearance.

"So, when are we going?"

"Well, we are going to have to go down there and help with the wedding. There's a lot to do, so probably next week."

"Okay," I said calmly. "Does Babajee know?"

"I don't care what your babajee says; we are going, end of story," she said, turning her back to put the wedding invite up on the fireplace, and began immediately fussing.

"Oh, I best give your nanni a quick call and let her know we received the card!" Mamajee immediately dashed to the phone, gathering the tray of betel nuts as she sat down to make her call.

I left the room and made my way up the dark stairway, where the silvery light of the moon shone on the steps leading up to my room. I could only see it as magic that Mamajee's plans had been stalled for a while at least. I reached up to the heavens, stared at the infinite skies. I smiled at what seemed a miracle. "Thank you," I said, smiling at them. "Thank you."

CHAPTER TWENTY
– *The Arranged Marriage* –

We arrived at Nanni's house in Luton to the commotion and excitement of hugs from my khala (*maternal aunt*), Naheeda, and Nanni (*maternal grandmother*), who were overjoyed with tears at our arrival. The remainder of Mamajee's family lined the hallway, greeting us and all talking at once.

The fragrance of bay leaves filtered through the hallway and into the kitchen, where Mamajee's sister-in-law, my uncle's wife, Mami, sat by the dha, slicing onions, her face barely recognisable from the tears streaming down her cheeks, induced by the large basin bowl of onions she had evidently prepared.

"Say your salaam, then," Nanni instructed Mami.

She immediately rose from her stool to grace Mamajee's feet with a cordial bow, a sign of respect that an in-law should make when greeting elders. Mamajee looked at me as if it to say, "See, take heed. Your time will come, and you will be doing the same."

"Are you well?" Mamajee asked her sister-in-law. "Looks like there is a lot of cooking to be done."

"Jee." She answered with a one-word reply. That was all that was required of her before she continued on quietly covering her hair with the end of her saree.

"Let's go upstairs," said Naheeda Khala, excited.

"Where is Nashira Khala?" I asked.

"She's upstairs in her room, you know," she added. "It's not allowed for the bride-to-be to be out before her wedding day now, but come, she's upstairs; let's go and see her."

I left Mamajee and Nanni downstairs in the kitchen with Mami.

"You should see the outfits we have for her!" Naheeda Khala explained as we made our way up the stairs.

I could only be semi-excited about this, given the toll the idea of weddings had on me, and the way marriage had been exerted on me over the past couple of years. What was more unsettling was that both my aunts were the same age as me. Nashira Khala was sixteen, and Naheeda Khala, only a year younger. Both were being primed for marriage and had taken to this idea as being quite normal. Upon our arrival into the room, Nashira Khala looked demurely down at the bed, where she had been sitting with her arms wrapped around her knees. Her face seemed pale and withdrawn.

"Assalamualaikum, Khala!" I said as we hugged.

"She's not been eating. I have tried all sorts, but she just doesn't have any appetite," Naheeda Khala said, looking at her.

"I can only imagine what you must be going through," I said, concerned. "Have you met him yet? Have you seen the picture?"

"Well, I spoke to him on the phone, but that's all. I haven't met him yet," Nashira Khala said quietly.

"What? You mean you haven't even met him …?" I was baffled. "But the wedding is in a week!"

She nodded vacantly and added with a sigh, "That's what Allah wants, right?"

"Are you excited?"

"I don't know. Mum chose him, and she thinks he is from a good, respectable family. I don't know. It's what they want for me, and I have to do right by them."

"Well, do you not want to find out?" I asked.

"There's nothing I can do, even if I did. That's what was planned for me, and only Allah knows what he has in store for me, they say."

Naheeda Khala prodded my arm, diverting my attention. "Look, Eleanor, look, look at all the gifts." She turned to open a large chest that had been presented to Nashira from the groom's family.

"Ooh, look at this red wedding saree!" she said, wide-eyed. "Afa is going to look stunning in this."

"It is beautiful, I must say." But I was more interested in how this had all come about.

She then proceeded to pull out more gifts from the groom's family. Sequined sarees with matching blouses and petticoats in an array of colours. There were handbags for every occasion, along with jewellery sets and vanity boxes with a dozen eyeshadows, eyeliners, nail varnishes and lipsticks, and there were hair grips, accessories and shoes to go with every outfit.

But all of this made me feel less than enthused now about the wedding, hearing that Nashira Khala hadn't even met her husband-to-be, and her blind faith in the decision that was made for her was only more disconcerting. She seemed resigned and accepting of this plan, and yet I could sense a real emptiness in her, a hollow existence of a bride that had only materialised through worldly possessions. I could see that my questioning had already disrupted the atmosphere in the room. Nashira Khala looked vacantly on upon Naheeda Khala's excitement over the bridesmaid's outfits that Nanni had ordered for us.

"Look, Eleanor, isn't it nice? Mum had them made to order, and they arrived from Delhi yesterday."

"Yes, they are beautiful," I said rather nebulously. Somehow, I could not get past how accepting Naheeda Khala was about her sister's imminent wedding. How could she allow her sister to be married to a man who she had never met?

"Have you met him, Naheeda Khala? Does he seem nice?" I asked inquisitively.

"He's really nice, Khala. Well, I know from Mum. She told me she thought he was very kind and softly spoken." My aunts often called me Khala endearingly, as I was older than them, and in Bengali culture, it is often seen as disrespectful to call someone older than you by their name. Hence why they often referred to me as Khala.

"So you haven't met him either?" I said, looking utterly bewildered.

"No, not yet." Naheeda Khala responded rather matter-of-factly.

"Then how do you know?"

"Well, we will soon. He's coming from Bangladesh tomorrow."

"What do you mean, coming from Bangladesh?"

"He's actually only arriving here as a visitor; he lives in Bangladesh."

This all seemed too much. I smiled but all the while was becoming more and more discontented.

"Don't worry, Khala, inshallah; you will get to meet your new uncle." She laughed, softly pressing her hand on my shoulder reassuringly.

The week before the wedding seemed to overflow with the chaos and commotion of people, children and goods that had all congregated in a small house fit for four. We spent our days preparing decorations that Naheeda Khala and I cut from tissue paper and threaded tightly with cotton string to make garlands. The rooms in the house were decorated with these white-and-orange garlands, and Mama (*uncle*) helped make a stage where the bride would be seated for the Mehndi – a traditional occasion of festivities and dance to celebrate the bride's impending wedding day. We dressed the stage in pleated red and orange sarees and draped them elegantly over the canopy. We cut patterns from crêpe paper, dressed trays for placing food and paan, and the older women spent the day cooking curries, fragrant rice, sweet dishes, samosas and snacks to serve the continual arrival of guests and neighbours. Naheeda Khala and I made rose garlands to give to the bride and groom on their wedding.

"I want to make a really beautiful one with red and white roses," she said, smiling and threading them the day before the Mehndi.

"They are very thorny, aren't they? I hope they don't prick her when she is wearing it."

"There is always pain with being vain. No pain, no gain," she said, threading through another rose.

"What do you mean?" I retorted angrily.

"Well, this is vanity, isn't it? We gain some physical pleasure from wearing it, but it all comes with a price." Naheeda smiled plainly while threading another plump red rose.

"Don't you think this is going too far though? Going blindly into something that may not have the outcome you desired for your life?"

"Well, maybe this is right. We can't judge what is right or wrong. We can only be guided by our faith. Nobody knows. Only Allah knows what is right or wrong," she continued pleasantly.

"I don't think that Nashira Khala upstairs looks happy. I don't think she is making the right choice."

"Well, you might think that, but I think she knows exactly what she has agreed to. I think you have to let life take its course and have faith that it will work out the way Allah has planned for you."

"Maybe," I said, holding up the rose garland that I had just made. "But here, try this on. See how it feels." I placed it around Naheeda Khala's bare neck.

"Ouch," she said. "It hurts!"

"It's Allah's will, isn't it?" I said, turning to see her frowning face before exiting the room.

*

The day of the Mehndi saw even more commotion than the previous days leading up to it. After breakfast, I was tasked with fixing the bride's hair and make-up. I discovered a newly acquired skill of creating barrels and buns, and fashioning hair into styles fit for queens and princesses. Nashira Khala seemed less subdued, owing much to the distractions of hair grips I placed into her hair and hours of perfecting her make-up. I had barely even worn that much make-up myself before and was learning as I went. Nashira Khala had not thought about the style she wanted for the Mehndi or the wedding day, and we flicked through the pages of Asian wedding magazines for inspiration until finally she came across a picture of a bride in a red-and-gold saree that was heavily ornate.

"That's the style I like; that's what I want to look like."

"And that's all that matters," I said, looking at her eye to eye as I applied her eyeliner. "That you can see it, you can see that is what you want." I think she could sense that I was pressing her indirectly.

"I don't think my life was meant for anything more," she said. "You know, I am not like you. I didn't have the chance to get educated. Mum spent most of the time waltzing back and forth between Bangladesh and here. I have missed my final exams, the past three years of school, and how long am I supposed to depend on her? When Dad died, we were in a lot of financial stress. I know Mum is still paying the price for all the issues that were left from the will."

I could see what she was telling me. "But, Khala ... still ..."

"No," she refused. "There are responsibilities we all hold ... This is my responsibility."

I nodded, quietly. "I do understand, Khala, and I just want you to be happy."

She looked down as I continued fixing her hair.

"Just promise me you will not talk about this anymore."

"Sure," I said. "As long as you promise to let me know if you need anything."

"I will," she said.

I finished dressing her in a green saree that had been chosen for the Mehndi party. The pleats were pinned into place, and the saree veil crowned her face with shimmers and sparkles.

"You look beautiful," I said.

Naheeda Khala then entered the room.

"Are you ready? Everyone is waiting downstairs to start the Mehndi ceremony," she said excitedly.

We both linked arms with the bride, steadying her down the stairs to the fascination of onlookers and the video cameraman, who had been patiently waiting to start recording. The hallway was filled with people, and we shuffled through to the living room to seat the bride at a brightly dressed stage and canopy. The spotlights shone lustrously, and the August heat became wearing, with the crowds of guests that had descended into the room.

It is customary at the Mehndi party for guests to apply turmeric on the arms and face of the bride and feed her sweetmeats. The tradition goes that turmeric is a wonderful beauty treatment for the skin and will radiate the bride's beauty and fairness for the upcoming marriage. Giving her sweets is also a customary way of sweetening her mood the night before the wedding.

I watched Nashira Khala, sat demurely on the stage, as one by one each guest placed the turmeric on her palms and teased her while feeding her Indian sweets such as gulab jamun, ras malai and laddu. Later, after the sweet-giving ceremony and the departure of the more senior guests, I decorated the bride's hands with mehndi while Naheeda Khala and the other young girls danced and sang to wedding songs set to their favourite Bollywood hits. Mamajee and Nanni came in every so often with trays of drinks and snacks. I had managed to steer clear of Mamajee for a while, owing to the amount of cooking Mamajee had been assigned in the kitchen. It took hours to decorate the bride's hands with mehndi, painting each side of her hands and feet with delicate vines and intricate Arabic patterns.

Nanni came in to have a look at the designs. "It looks beautiful" she said, sitting next to her daughter and looking at her hands. "And this is only your first time at doing this? My, you are a bright girl. Make sure you do her feet too. You know the bride's hands and feet are often the only things a man can see on the wedding day, and hence why they are adorned like this. You must leave it on all night. The colour is a sign of longevity: the stronger the colour, the stronger the marriage."

By nine o'clock most of the guests had left, and I took the weary bride upstairs to rest. It is tradition to leave the mehndi to set overnight, and as old wives like Nanni would say, the longer you leave the henna on your hands, the stronger the henna stain, further signifying longevity in the marriage. I wrapped her hands with a cloth dowsed in water and olive oil before wrapping them in another cloth to protect anything from staining while she slept.

"Are you all right?" I asked Nashira Khala.

"I'm okay, yes," she said vacantly.

I didn't feel so convinced.

"I'm just tired," she added.

"Well, you have a big day ahead of you tomorrow." I helped her into her nighty and unbuckled her sandals.

"I know."

"I'll have to wake you up early, as it will take some time to do your make-up and hair," I said.

"It's a big day, isn't it?" she said.

"Well, Khala, of course. It's your wedding day tomorrow," I teased.

*

I woke early the next morning. Nashira Khala and Naheeda were aroused by my stirring when moving to the bathroom, as we were all sharing the same double bed.

"Come on, girls, it's seven in the morning, and we need to get the bride ready for her big day."

Nashira's eyes opened instantly as she lay in bed. I pulled the curtains open to let the sun hit her face. She looked gaunt, her face pale, her eyes less vibrant, giving her a fatigued appearance. She stared at her hands, which were still wrapped in cloth from the mehndi I'd placed on them the night before.

"Come, let's get those hands washed so we can see how it turned out."

Naheeda Khala rose from the bed. "Oh, I can't wait to see how it turned out," she said in the middle of a wide-mouthed yawn. Nashira Khala rose silently, and I helped her to the bathroom. I washed the caked henna from her hands, scraping and loosening it, the orange tones peeking through on her wrinkled palms.

"Well, what do you think?" I asked as Naheeda Khala and I peered at her hands.

"It didn't come out red, did it?" she said.

"That's okay. It's the colour of henna; sometimes it's not always that strong."

"But don't you see?" Nashira Khala replied, horrified at the state of her palms.

"See what?" I said, peering at them.

"This is a bad sign," she cried.

"Don't be silly. You won't be defined by such nonsense, will you? Come, I need to get your hair and make-up done," I said, passing her a tissue.

"Come on, sis, it's beautiful. The decorations are so intricate," Naheeda Khala chimed. "I will go get you both some tea and toast."

Nashira Khala held out her palms, subdued and bemused by the colour.

"Now, where's that magazine picture you said you wanted your hair to be made up like?" I said, walking her back to the bathroom. I rummaged around the room as she sat at the dressing table, looking at her hands.

"Oh, yes, found it; it must have slipped off the bed." I turned to see Nashira's reflection in the mirror, where she had sat at the dressing table.

"Are you okay?" I said, looking at her.

She clasped her hands around her face. "I guess so," she said, staring down. I could tell she was crying.

I put my arm around her. "Tell me, what is upsetting you?"

"I don't know. I am not sure if I am doing the right thing. What if this doesn't work out? Then what?" she wept into a tissue.

"You don't have to do this. You don't have to go through with it." I could have almost begged her.

"Oh, that's easy for you to say," she said with a frown.

"Well, you don't have to," I pleaded.

"Oh, is that right?" Mamajee stepped into the room with a breakfast tray. "You don't have to, is that what you are telling her?"

"No, she doesn't. She's not even met this guy. Why does she have to agree to this?" I rose defiantly.

"Don't you dare say another word, haramzadi. Everyone is downstairs waiting. The mullah will be here in an hour, and she's still not dressed. You won't go against our religion and her parents' wishes. Get dressed and come down with her as soon as possible."

I remained silent. She was right. I wasn't in that position to say what was right for Nashira Khala, and I couldn't predict the future for anyone. Maybe we are all blind, and the only truth is what feels right, what feels golden, as Mrs Abbots once said.

I brushed her hair silently, combing each strand and rolling them into barrels around her bun. I set her make-up and adorned her forehead with bindis. I placed the gold jewellery around her hands, neck, forehead and, finally, crowned the bride with the most precious item, her red veil.

She stared back at herself, and there was that look of uncertainty in her again.

"Look," I said. "I can't tell you what's right for you or wrong for you. I just want you to hold on to your own truth. You'll know what that is. Everything else will work itself out."

She nodded.

"Golden, just remember that."

"I will."

The mullah arrived, and I could hear more people had joined in the living room, where the vows would take place.

"We need to go downstairs," I said.

Mamajee stood by the door, ushering us. "Come on, people will be arriving at the wedding hall soon, and we need to get the vows done."

The mullah sat on the floor, where a cotton sheet had been placed for the prayers to be held, and where Nashira Khala, bejewelled in her bridal gown, sat quietly while the mullah muttered the prayers. Soon after, the vows were exchanged, and the bride agreed to the marriage.

*

There was little time for anything else after the prayers. Naheeda Khala and I fussed over our make-up. We tried to dress quickly in our emerald-green silk lehngas that Nanni had ordered as brides-maids' outfits, and tried to hastily put on our jewellery, although the time we took was to the consternation of the bridal car and chauffeur waiting outside.

I brushed my hair quickly and left it down. We escorted Nashira Khala through the wedding hall. A large, plain hall with long banquet tables was dressed with paper tableware and plastic cups, and down the centre of the aisle, hundreds of onlookers, guests, cousins and cameramen flashed their cameras at the bride's entrance.

This was the first time that I had experienced a family wedding and seen so many of my close relatives come together in one place. Mamajee followed us to the wedding table, where the bridesmaids and close family members were to be seated.

It was the first time that I had worn such heavy make-up, such a heavily sequined outfit, and the first time that I had felt people's eyes on me as I sat next to the bride. My relatives didn't recognise me. Family members who had only seen me once or twice when I was a child marvelled at me, awestruck.

"Is this your daughter?" they asked Mamajee.

"Yes, this is my eldest daughter," she said as if she was embar-rassed by that acknowledgement.

"Oh my! Where have you been hiding her? We must talk later," they would say, peeling their eyes away from me as they walked away through the banquet hall.

Mamajee looked down for a moment. I looked away from her awkwardly. "Cover up," she said disapprovingly at me. I put my scarf over my head.

She heard the cameraman call out, "Beautiful girl, look this way at me."

I watched her stare at me again, her face stern and disapproving. I covered my face more, trying to hide from the glare and the spot-light of the camera. I knew what was coming, and it wasn't going to be good for me.

CHAPTER TWENTY-ONE
- *Surround Yourself with What You Believe In* -

I t was becoming increasingly difficult to find ways to see Mrs Abbots now that exams were over, and I desperately needed her more than ever now. I would often borrow books that had short lending periods just so that I had an excuse to return them frequently, buying me an hour to meet up with Mrs Abbots.

We would meet on the upstairs mezzanine floor of the library, where we'd stare into the creepers and vines of the seventies' flowered wallpaper and make patterns and objects appear. Sometimes we'd point out the continuous patterns of larger shapes, pretty birds, hand shapes and people.

"Mrs Abbots," I said, staring into the wall one afternoon, "do you think this is it? That this it for me?"

She rose up from the chair, looking up at me reproachfully. "Oh, Eleanor, is this what you think? What you have worked so hard for, to just resign? You can't give up now; you've come too far."

"Well, how can I stop this? How can I stop them from doing this to me?"

"You need to make them believe in you, and the only way you can do that is if you surround yourself and everyone around you with people who believe in you, in what you believe."

"You have to be kidding me. Wouldn't that make them want to send me back more than before? Everyone around them has daughters going back to Bangladesh to get married."

Mrs Abbots smiled with certainty, as if to say I was an idiot for not seeing this.

"Not everyone. Are you telling me that everyone who your dad and mother know is uneducated or believes it is not right for girls? Think about the girls you know, about the many associates and daughters out there. Surely, Eleanor, broaden your thinking now; there must be people you know who can influence your father," she said calmly.

"Well, I can't think of anyone." My mind wandered into my internal directory of people and faces, scouring for the source of her certainty, and then it came to me, Babajee's accountant and old friend.

Babajee met with his accountant and long-time friend every month to go over the bookkeeping or to find ways in which he could reduce his tax. It was a daunting and jittery task for Babajee. The restaurant often didn't break even once he had paid the staff. And often he would spend hours with his accountant, at his house, drawing in cigarettes one after another until clouds of smoke lingered above their living room. Uncle Surji was Hindu Bengali and originally from Calcutta. Mamajee used to disapprove of Babajee's time there, because of the difference in religion; his house was filled with pictures of elephants and idols. It didn't matter what Mamajee thought; in Babajee's opinion, it wasn't her business how he did his accounting.

In my early years, when I was seven or eight years old, Babajee used to take me with him. Uncle Surji had a little girl called Karla, who was a year older than me, and while the men busied themselves with financial matters, Karla and I would play in her room. It was about the only opportunity when I saw life from another perspective.

Karla was an only child and spent most of her time reading and writing in her room.

Karla wanted to be a doctor when she grew up, something that Babajee admired about her, and Uncle Surji had already set up plans to get her into grammar school. Babajee used to rave about Karla in the car, how she was so clever and smart, and only smart people got into a grammar school, implying that I wasn't and disregarding my potential completely. The truth of the matter was that Babajee had no desire or time to encourage me. My seven-year-old cries for education fell on deaf ears.

One afternoon that summer, when Babajee was getting ready to head to his accountant's house, I asked whether I could join him. "Would it be okay if I came along, Babajee? I haven't seen Karla in such a long time."

"Sure, if you want," Babajee said, lighting up his cigarette.

Babajee didn't think too much about it as he jingled his large set of keys into his suit pocket. Babajee drove all the way in silence, plugging in a cassette tape of his old folk songs as if to drown out any unwanted noise from me.

Karla had changed a lot since I had last seen her. She stood at the top of the stairs as we entered through the hallway, enviably taller than me, her neat frame bundled into fitted jeans and a long-sleeved green top. Babajee greeted her, honouring her poise, elegance and intellect with a big agreeing grin, as if he had never met anyone so worthy of praise. It made me wonder why it was always someone else's child and not his own that he could feel so passionately about.

Small and inferior, I stood humbly next to her, smiling like a child who had nowhere to crawl under. I glanced at myself through the hallway mirror and saw a raggedy image, an oversized orange, black and white Aztec-patterned shalwar kameez, flared out and hanging over me like a large white marquee. I wrestled it to one side, to make it lean against my skinny frame as Uncle Surji greeted Babajee and ushered us both to the living room.

Karla smiled calmly. "So pleased to see you again, Eleanor. Wow, you look so beautiful in your suit," she said, stepping back to admire it while both fathers settled into the living-room armchairs.

"My mum's choice," I said, embarrassed. "Let's just say it's not the fashion statement I would have made!" I said, sheepishly looking down.

She laughed warmly at my self-deprecating humour. "You're so funny. Come, let's go into the kitchen."

In the kitchen, Karla's mum was busy stirring a huge bubbling pot of red lentils for dinner. She wiped her hands dry and came over to give me a big hug. "Eleanor, you have grown, haven't you? It's been a long time since you have been here, hasn't it?" She made a large pot of brewed masala tea, as if by default this was what she had learned the men enjoyed. She brought it into the room, where the fathers were in full laughter over a topic from yesteryear.

Karla took me into her room. It was as though nothing had really changed in eight years, except the expanse of her knowledge. A full library of biology, chemistry, maths and physics books lined the shelves. A white, barely visible desk piled high with papers and pens stood in one corner. It was a large room that at home my two brothers would have occupied between them in bunk beds, but here in Karla's world, it was a world of knowledge, study and education that I craved for, that I had to fight for, and that was becoming increasingly inaccessible to me. Karla would be commencing her final year at advanced level and had already received her first-year advanced level results.

"I passed," she said modestly, but on pressing her on her grades, she had achieved As in all subjects: biology, chemistry, maths and physics. What's more, Karla had provisional offers from Cambridge, Nottingham and Manchester Universities, where she could pursue medicine. I could only feel gutted for myself but held up my self-esteem with the deepest regard for her hard work and achievements.

"What about you?" she said excitedly.

"My exam results are out soon, so I will find out if I passed my GCSEs." I nodded at my response, assuring myself of the response yet holding back my real thoughts of my parents' intentions, that I was going to be getting married soon.

"So, what do you want to do after that?" she asked inquisitively.

The seven-year-old me backed up a full list of responses. "You are getting married," she would say, looking at me bemusedly in my mind's eye. Then I remembered Mrs Abbots's advice: "Surround yourself and everyone around you with people who believe in you."

Karla was still looking at me patiently for a response. I sighed, staring at her wall of certificates and achievements. "My parents are looking to take me back to Bangladesh, Karla, so I am not sure what my future will be right now." The seven-year-old me smiled triumphantly inside. *Mamajee would be happy at least*, I thought, and I forced a thin smile outwardly.

"Oh?" she said, looking at me, her back leaning into her study chair, where she had sat. I didn't have to say much more; she knew it wasn't what I wanted. She looked endlessly into the wall towards the door. I sat on her bed, hands pressed down on the bed deeply. She let out a deep sigh as though she regretted my situation, and I could almost sense her world had been disturbed by the negativity of mine. "Well," she said, trying to draw a satisfactory response. "Should we go downstairs and see what our parents are doing?"

Downstairs Uncle Surji and Babajee were immersed in conversation over tea, with papers neatly piled on a coffee table as they worked through some documents.

Karla's mum insisted on dinner, and we all sat in the kitchen as she served out dal, curried potatoes and homemade wheat chapattis. I watched the pleasantries displayed by Babajee to Auntie (Karla's mum) and Karla, something that Mamajee would never have heard him say if she had made dal. Babajee would have had an outburst of rage at being presented with such plain "peasant" food. His face brimmed with enthusiasm.

"This is delicious cooking, Bhabhi. Karla, well done on your exam results, and your dad says you want to study medicine?"

Karla looked over with a modest smile as she broke off a small piece of chapatti to mix into her dal. "Yes, I have been accepted at Cambridge University."

"Well done, well done, shabash, Beti, shabash, Beti." Her parents smiled as Babajee raised his excitement with his hand gestures, applauding her.

Uncle Surji turned to me. "And what about your plans, Eleanor? What do you want to do?"

I paused, hesitated, breaking the chapatti into small pieces as I mustered the will to eloquently put my parents' plans positively. "Well," I said, clearing my throat, "my exam results come out soon, but—"

Karla interjected. "Eleanor mentioned she would like to also study medicine and continue her advanced levels."

I was surprised at Karla's response, and no sooner had she mentioned it than Uncle Surji bellowed out with surprised joy. "Ahh," he said, "what wonderful news. Then we can have two doctors in our circle. We will never be ill in our old age again, Hamid Rabbani," he chuckled, clapping his hands and smiling at Babajee.

Everybody smiled, except Babajee, who at the time had a mouthful of chapatti that he was consuming slowly as he collated his response. Babajee looked on at me as he chewed into his last morsel. "You know, Eleanor is okay with her studies, but I don't think she will do well enough for medicine. You know you would have to study and work very hard and do very well to succeed in that."

Uncle Surji smiled, patting me on the back. "Don't worry, Bhai [*brother*], you have a good one here. She will do well, she will do well," he said, grinning at Babajee, then turning to me. "So, your exams are finished now, aren't they? The hard work is done. So, when are your results due, dear?"

"In a couple of weeks," I said. A fresh concoction of fear and anxiety surged to my face as I realised the imminence of that all-important day and all of the effort towards it. The late nights, the worry, sneaking under covers to study, listening to tapes, studying on the buses, days spent in tears from worrying about failing these precious exams could all have been in vain.

*

I decided to try to convince Babajee about pursuing my studies on our drive home.

I watched him press the car lighter down to start a fresh cigarette. "Karla is doing well, isn't she?" I said. "She must be pleased with her results."

He said nothing at first and continued to stare at the road, breathing in the smoke from his cigarette. "That's because she works hard, and she is a clever girl."

"Babajee, I really want to study and do my advanced levels too," I said, trying to make eye contact with him as he stared on at the road ahead.

"No," came his reply; it was cold, empty and devoid of any explanation. My whole life was off balance. They were happy to set me up for failure, and all I received from Babajee were two letters, N-O – no reason, no explanation, no apology. It was evident I was nothing more than a hindrance to their grand master plan for what they had destined for me.

"Why?" I said, challenging him. "I work hard," I said. "I am clever; my teachers praise me; everyone who knows me believes in me, except you and Mamajee. All you want is—"

Babbage interjected. "Why? Do you want to know why? Because honour is the most important thing you can hold, and what is destined for a woman in our culture is to hold up the honour for her family. So far, I can't show my face around here without people talking behind my back about you."

I argued back. "Why? What on earth did I do to deserve that? I'm bringing you shame? How? Tell me how?"

Babajee turned to look at me at the traffic lights, his eyes full of rage, it seemed, but then it faded as I looked at him for an answer, and I realised it wasn't a look of rage at all; it was that look of guilt, of fear, of holding back. His hands trembled on the steering wheel as he changed gears, and when reaching out for the cigarette, he seemed jittery.

"I just want to understand, Babajee. Whatever I did wrong, I didn't mean it, and I am sorry if it has led to this."

He remained silent all the way home. I decided not to take it any further. I realised that if I did, it could endanger my plan.

*

The next day, I worked on my list of possible family and friends who could persuade Babajee and Mamajee's perspective. Babajee had lots of business partners, friends and associates, each one of them with a son or a daughter who was either going through school or had completed their education. I went through his address book. I invited some of them over casually for tea. Mamajee seemed very surprised that we should have so many visitors, although at the same time very pleased to have people over. I would shuffle Mamajee out of the kitchen so that she could spend time with the guests, and while Mamajee and Babajee talked and laughed, I served them cardamom tea and wispy milk-white vermicelli with almonds and tea rusks, and won over their praises at my ability to serve guests elegantly.

I tried to do everything right by Mamajee's priming and teaching that she had tirelessly taught over the few years since my proposal. I wore a scarf around my head in front of guests, pinning it across my bosom. I wore loosely fitted but nicely pressed suits, trying to avoid the garish ones that I couldn't bring myself to wear. I made sure I didn't bend too far forward and kept my back upright when putting the tea tray on the coffee table. I never turned my back on guests when leaving the room, and spoke in a low and calm voice when responding to guests.

Mamajee used to say that Nana (Mamajee's father) once went to a friend's house for tea and left after ten minutes because the women in the kitchen were making too much noise. "It is bad etiquette to let your guests hear all the commotion when you are entertaining," she'd told me were his words. I made it my mission to prepare food quietly, elegantly and without a clatter of a plate or a tinkle of a spoon. The guests were always delighted by my ability to entertain as I served them tea, kneeling at the coffee table with straight shoulders and neck, and gently and courteously offering them tea in china teacups, my arms elegantly outstretched in their direction with the teacup and saucer.

When serving tea to a senior guest, it is customary that the guest is served the tea with both hands, one hand (the right typically) used to hold the teacup and saucer, the other hand (the left) placed under the wrist of the right hand, to support the weight of the teacup. Mamajee had taught me that when you serve this way, it does two things: it allows you to have a steady hand when serving the teacup, so that it doesn't clatter on the saucer, and secondly, when your guests receive it, you are not crossing the undisclosed boundary between you and your guests. Staying at arm's length is polite etiquette and prevents you from infringing on their space.

I learned that when guests were impressed by my hosting, they were always more inclined to talk and ask me questions about my plans. I served tea calmly, quietly, never giving them eye contact, as this was also a sign of bad manners to seniors. Your gaze should always be lowered, especially when the senior was male. Doing things slowly and impressing them meant there was some airtime and opportunity for guests to politely make conversation.

"So, what are your plans?" they would ask, and this was my golden opportunity, the moment I marketed myself, when I would calmly and politely tell them, "Oh, Chacha and Chachi [*Auntie and Uncle*], I have been working hard all year on my finals and have just finished my exams." I would smile politely and endearingly at them with my lowered gaze and only sometimes softly look up at them to gauge their response.

"Ah, very good, very good," they would say. "And what are your plans next?" And this was the golden question, the one that all my energies had been working towards. My moment of exposure to their thoughts and opinions that would hopefully remove the stones and rubble from Mamajee and Babajee's closed and lightless cave.

"Oh, Chacha and Chachi," I would say demurely, "only Mamajee and Babajee will know." I would then leave the room slowly with the tea tray, walking backwards with a smile, looking courteously down at the floor.

The guest would continue the conversation with Mamajee and Babajee, exchanging their plans for their own daughters and sons. Soon enough Mamajee and Babajee were exposed to successful associates and their daughter's or son's future, how they were getting them educated, the exam results, excellent achievements and what it meant for their parents' pride and status. In Babajee's eyes, I saw the longing from his own years of wanting to be educated, the years he'd spent by the oil lamp, reading Tagore, Chandra Bose and Nazrul Islam, that were later sabotaged by his brother's jealousy.

Each and every guest left an imprint; they were helping to take away the stones of fear that culture had buried them alive in. I had awakened their senses more and more, and slowly the cave door was opening, and they could feel the light. Mamajee was forced to drop the subject of a trip to Bangladesh in front of esteemed guests, as this no longer elevated Babajee's status: guests fell silent and didn't see pride in this accomplishment. Such ideas amongst his associates would have come across as backwards and unappealing. Babajee was learning that if name and honour were to ever become a topic for discussion amongst this circle, then the success of his children was the badge of honour he would need to be showcasing.

"Look at so-and-so's son and daughter. Look at their grades. Aren't they doing well?" he would say once the guests had left. These were comments that often silenced Mamajee or became a moot point if she saw differently. I started wondering who was moulding who here. Was there really a grand plan? Or were Babajee's decisions based purely on honour?

CHAPTER TWENTY-TWO

– *Judgement Day* –

The day of the exam results came with much intensity. I woke early, a bundle of nerves, my belly soured with anxiety. In light of all recent academic success from children in Babajee's circle, Mamajee could no longer bring up the subject of going back to Bangladesh, and this offered some promise that I could prove to them (Babajee at least) that I was worthy of continuing my education. The danger was that I may not have done well. After all, my exam preparation had been crammed, rushed, filled with fear and unease for the prospects of marriage, and accompanied by the constant banging of pans and disapproval of Mamajee.

I wanted to cry as I walked through the entrance of my school hall, the thought this might be my final moments of schooling. My footsteps echoed through the hallway as I heard the murmurs of teachers and pupils congratulating each other. I wanted to take two steps back to delay the moment. When I got to the desk, a queue of girls were hugging each other. Some looked happy and cheery, and others seemed a little lost or shocked. I gulped in some air, the pulse in my head throbbing, a slight burn down my neck at the thought of failure. *I couldn't have done well*, I thought. *How I could expect such a thing when I am not that smart?* Babajee would be right, of course, about that: I wouldn't be good enough to continue on with my education. I shrank into my clothes like a turtle into the confines of its shell. Then

I thought about Mrs Abbots, her face, a calm smile. *Don't worry, whatever happens, you will find a way out of here.*

I was one girl away in the queue now. My mind chattered in endless debate with itself. *If I fail, it will be okay. You will find a way, Eleanor. I have failed; I know I have failed.* My heart quickened as I approached the desk.

The teacher at the counter smiled at me. "Can you confirm your name, dear?"

"Eleanor Rabbani," I responded nervously.

She flicked through a deep box of envelopes as I tried breathing through a tightened chest and tense belly. "Eleanor Rabbani," she muttered as she continued to work through the list.

I thought about Babajee's name now, how his associates and friends all knew, how it would shame him now if he had to explain that I had failed. I started to regret my campaign, inviting them over for tea, and dreaded the follow-up calls that my parents would now receive, explaining my poor performance, while they expressed their son or daughter's excellent achievements. I wanted to leave – if I didn't have to open the envelope, then I could walk away and pretend that I couldn't collect them, that the results were unavailable. I backed away from the queue, hurtling into another girl as I turned.

"Oh, hold on." The teacher's voice echoed through the lobby. "Your results!" the lady at the counter shouted.

"It's okay. I won't need them," I said, turning my head quickly to respond. Just as I headed to the door, I heard another voice.

"You won't need them?" The voice echoed through the corridor as I stopped. My mind became still. I turned to see the disappointed face staring back at me.

"Mrs Abbots," I said, calmly approaching her. In an instant, I felt as though I was betraying her more than I was betraying myself. She held the envelope in her hand and looked at me firmly.

"Truth is the real path to freedom. Give yourself this opportunity to choose it. It doesn't matter what the results are, the real truth is in knowing and honouring who you are now. Opening this envelope won't measure your ability, it will only serve one thing: the opportunity to discover where you want to go next. Here," she said, passing the envelope to me.

A surge of electricity bolted through me as the envelope touched my hand. I tore open the wafer-thin envelope that revealed inside the perforated trace paper, where lines like programming code dotted out the results. I couldn't believe what I was reading.

"Oh my!" I gasped out loud. "English literature, A; English language, A; art, A star; French, A; religious education, B; science, B; physics, B; history, B; maths, D." I wasn't sure what to believe at first. I jumped and squealed, and Mrs Abbots had a look of triumph and elation. She hugged me, and I laughed at the hilarity of it all, and as she embraced me, I wept in her arms a concoction of tears conjured from sadness and felt liberated from weeks of fear and despair.

"Well done, my dear," Mrs Abbots cried, her cheek against mine. "You did it. That's all that matters. You made it here." She squeezed me.

I turned to face her. "It was all thanks to you. Your encouragement and support, Mrs Abbots."

"My dear, the real effort is in putting it into practice and having the will to succeed. You, and only you, can credit yourself with that." She smiled, her eyes gleaming with tears.

We walked slowly together through the lobby, reading the results over and over until I was able to count my grades.

"I have four As, of which one is an A star, and four Bs, Mrs Abbots. Can you believe it?"

"I can. Of course, I can. You did well, dear."

"I can do the subjects I want to. I have enough to go to college, although, not sure if Mamajee and Babajee will let me." I fretted, the reality kicking in as Mrs Abbots strolled and listened to my concerns.

"What happens from here? Do you think they will let me go?"

"Eleanor," she said, resting both hands on my shoulders, "the only thing that will stop you from going is you. There are no limits to what you can achieve; you have just proven that. You are strong, courageous and have all the will to succeed. Harness that truth; that is what separates gold from dust. Stay true to that, and you will always work a way out."

"Thank you, Mrs Abbots."

"Come, I think we should celebrate before you head home, don't you?"

*

It was only after Babajee had spoken to his associates that he realised what my results meant, whether it was seen as good or bad. It was never in his nature to show any excitement towards any of what the children brought home or did. What really mattered to him was whether other people saw it as something credible; that was only when it would ever be considered a success or failure.

Babajee silently looked through the results, the faint inkjet print making his English even less proficient. I patiently waited for a reaction, a response, an emotion or excitement of some sort, but any promise of this was sent away with his hacking smoker's cough. Continuing to cough, he put the paper down and reached for the cup of brewed tea, skimming the layer of milk foam that floated on the top. The news flickered on mute in the background. He stared emptily at the TV set, slurping the tea with gulps, gasps and a gurgling of his throat.

After a few minutes of waiting, I decided it wasn't going anywhere. I rose from the large flower rug and headed to the doors that led to the hallway and into the kitchen. Mamajee stood in the kitchen, stirring a pan of bubbling curry. After Babajee's response to my grades, I decided it might be better to not discuss this further with Mamajee. I could tell she wasn't happy by her cold silence upon my entering the kitchen. The way she looked at me slowly, silently and wordlessly, returning to the stove to continue stirring the pot. Where I'd first felt triumphant in winning over Babajee, I now felt tamed by that reminder, the excitement fizzling out slowly from the silence from Mamajee's wall of disapproval. I could sense how it would fracture our relationship. I suddenly felt small, and my seven-year-old self came back to remind me. *You promised her that you would do every-thing to honour those wishes. Now look at you. Selfish, can't you see it? The years she has dedicated to you!*

I slowly made my way upstairs and sat in my room for the rest of the day. I recollected how, during my exams, I'd thought this day would feel if I managed to see results day, how I'd envisioned it would open doors, and the excitement, but that now felt far from reality. How deeply unsatisfying it felt now as I sat staring at the wall. Experiencing their responses only made me feel that I should do right by them, honour their wishes if it made them proud of me, so that they could continue to keep their word to the people they owed it to. I thought about Mamajee's promise to Chachima all those years ago, to take her son. I pictured Ali Akbar waiting in the fields, the years he had spent in the hope that marrying me would change his life for the better, and then I thought about how marrying him would change mine for the worse.

Just then there was a knock on the front door. I heard faint laughter as people entered through the hallway and into the living room. Babajee's upbeat voice meant that it was someone who he enjoyed socialising with. I looked out of the window but couldn't make out the car that was parked in front of the driveway. I continued to sit miserably in my room: I wasn't in the mood anymore to entertain. The most important day of my life had zero effect on impressing Mamajee and Babajee.

What do I do now? I cried out in my head. *I mean, they don't even care? It had no significance to them whatsoever.*

I pictured Mrs Abbots's smile. *Be patient. It will all work itself out.* I imagined her saying it as I lay on the bed, staring at the ceiling.

Then there came a knock on my door. "Eleanor, come downstairs and help," Mamajee said, peering through the door. I sighed and tutted disappointedly as I made my way down to the kitchen. The sounds of roaring laughter became louder from the living room as I walked past through the hallway. I found Mamajee rushing around the kitchen, brewing tea as she placed cakes and biscuits onto small plates.

"Go on, go and take this in for them," Mamajee ushered.

I walked in with the tray of tea and cake, the tray rattling a little and my headscarf slipping off as I did. I nudged the door open, and the laughter spilled out through the doorway in higher volumes.

"Ahh, here is your clever girl!" bellowed a joyous voice from the lounge. It was Uncle Surji, Babajee's accountant.

"We thought we'd come to congratulate you," came a calm and female voice. Karla looked at me with a contented smile.

"Sit, sit," ushered Uncle Surji smilingly.

I looked at Babajee to see the response. His temperament had changed since a few hours ago, like a cold and frosty meadow melting on a spring day.

"I hear you did amazingly well in your exams, dear." Uncle Surji beamed at me.

I gave a faint smile, silently. *What good are any results if you can't do anything with them?* I thought.

"Can I have a look at your results paper?" he asked, shuffling the glasses on his face. Babajee leaned over from near the fireplace and handed the wafer of thin paper to Uncle Surji. He inspected the paper. "Ah, four A grades and four Bs, and one is an A star! Well done, well done." He chuckled with a beaming smile and patted me gently on the back.

Karla smiled too. "What are you going to do? What subjects are you going to study?" she asked.

"I don't know." I shrugged. I could no longer be excited about it. I looked over at Babajee, who had an expressionless face.

"What is an A star?" Babajee asked Uncle Surji after a short pause.

"A star means she has done exceptionally well in one subject. It is normally very difficult, very difficult to achieve an A star, isn't it, Karla? I remember you would have had to work very hard. They wouldn't normally give them out so generously unless they thought your work was exceptional."

"Oh, yes, you must have been exceptional in that subject; it's quite an attainment," Karla added agreeably to Uncle Surji and Babajee, and then drew her attention back to me.

"Well," said Karla, "the choice of subjects is yours. You have done well in all of them." She gave me a wide-eyed, excited look, encouraging me to speak, to express my opinion and to share my thoughts. For that I could only be grateful, their support, encouragement and belief. I owed them that, I thought, regardless of the outcome. There was almost a sense of duty in sharing my wants, even if there was no hope left in achieving anything further. I could be no less a person for speaking out what I humanly desired. They sat in anticipation as I contemplated, as I fought a mental war of resignation to Mamajee's wants and valour to speak out my own truth.

"I think I want to do a mix," I said, subdued and with inconsequential candour. "English, biology, chemistry and psychology," I chimed vacantly, my mood inflated with positivity at the thought but deflating slowly with apathy upon seeing Babajee's perplexed expression.

"What are you going to do with those subjects?" Babajee asked disapprovingly.

"Oh, Rabbani Saheb, at this stage, let the girl continue and do well in the subjects she is good at. The rest will be worked out in due course. Don't be afraid of her ability: she will do well."

Babajee looked to the ground silently. I knew I had Babajee's blessing, albeit with an air of unwilling reluctance. I could now move on. I could silence the voices, the guilt, the obligations and promises I had made. At least with small steps, I could wrestle through it.

*

Later that night Mamajee sat squatting in front of the TV, shelling peas in preparation for cooking tomorrow. I could sense the distance as she sat quietly. I knew she wasn't happy: I had got my way, and it was evident there were no plans to go back to Bangladesh. She continued shelling silently. I didn't want to strike up a conversation in case I got a knock-back.

She stretched her back, rising from the squatted position with her eyes still glued to the TV as she spoke. "Your Naheeda Khala is coming over in a couple of weeks. Your Babajee and I have agreed she can stay with us so that she can learn English."

"Oh, that will be nice. Where will she stay?" I said, relieved that Mamajee was in a good mood and she wasn't going to have a go at me.

"Well, she will go to college with you, and you and Naheeda can share the same room."

"I am so glad she can stay with us," I said, smiling.

"I'm pleased too," she said. But Mamajee didn't smile back, and I knew that meant her intentions weren't as clear as her words.

CHAPTER TWENTY-THREE

– *Suicide*–

Although my parents had silently and passively allowed me to continue with my education, I became more bound by terms and conditions than I had ever been. There were restrictions for the subjects I could study, the classes I would be allowed to take, the amount of time I could devote to study, and conditions that household chores could never be compromised. Much to the displeasure of Mrs Abbots and my newly acquainted art teacher, who had been impressed by my portfolio, Babajee refused to allow me to study arts and English. Despite their wide use vocationally, he could not be made agreeable to it.

"No, you are not studying art or English. Why arts and English? You know how to do both, anyway, and where is that going to get you? What will people think of me if they hear all you are doing is drawing and learning English? There's no future in that. You can study sciences. That at least has more status than the arts!"

Reluctantly I resigned from both subjects and enrolled in the sciences, but Mamajee was in uproar when I explained the timetable. "You have classes in the evening? Well, you won't be able to go to those. Absolutely not! Don't they know girls aren't allowed out at night? Can you imagine what people would say if they heard? They'll say, 'Just look, there she goes, Rabbani Saheb's daughter, gallivanting around at night, cavorting at college like the English girls.' There won't be any evening classes. I don't care if your tutor has given you seminars. Tell them that you are not allowed out in the evenings."

"But if I don't go, I will miss half the lessons!"

"I don't care; you will have to."

In the end, I negotiated with them and continued with English literature and psychology, unfortunately having to miss some of the evening seminars.

My time at college aroused much suspicion in Mamajee. It begged her to question everything: the way I dressed, why I spent so much time brushing my hair, why it was left down, why my make-up had been applied. All of which were laced with the insinuation that I was developing a dangerous mind, one that only had intentions to seduce and further dishonour and endanger their reputation. Of course, none of these would have been a danger had she known that my sense of curiosity and passion was for only one thing, the freedom to learn, and I was treading a thin line in having that privilege. I was buying time from my parents for this privilege, with obligation and honour to my parents' causes. I also knew I was still in debt to them. The fact that I dishonoured Mamajee's wishes of seeing me married meant that my pursuit of education could all be taken away with any wrong move. I couldn't let that happen, and anything that could help strengthen Mamajee's belief in me was sure to prevent this downward spiral of destruction.

And so, in my eyes, when Naheeda Khala first arrived to stay with us, I could only see it as a welcome relief, that it might offer some respite from the brewing tensions that came with balancing college and home life. I could have almost hoped that Mamajee would be in better company with her sister staying, that there would be extra help around the kitchen and she may have company in the evenings, somebody she could enjoy watching her favourite Bollywood films with and exchange idle conversations about the past with.

Mamajee had suggested the idea that Naheeda Khala come and stay following a huge argument between Naheeda Khala and Mami (Naheeda Khala's sister-in-law), although neither of them ever explained the cause of the argument. Something had happened at home to lead Mami to lock Naheeda Khala out of the house overnight, and that had the whole family in an uproar. Whatever had happened had warranted the need to relocate Naheeda Khala and had led to Mamajee's compassionate suggestion to come and stay with us. I should have only empathised with Naheeda Khala's situation when she spilled out the story, a girl of sixteen being left on the street overnight, the disgrace and indignity that Mami had subjected her to.

"Oh, she is so horrible, Khala!" she cried and sobbed. "She started shouting at me, and then the woman went crazy! She started throwing things at me. I was so afraid, Khala, I wasn't even sure if I would come out alive, and then she pushed me out onto the street, and I had nowhere to go!" But when asked what had started the argument, she remained quiet and reluctant to explain. "I don't know. She is just a horrible woman. I can't even explain it! She is like a jalebi. You know, it's sweet and brightly coloured, but it's twisted and sickly if you consume too much of it, and often, if it gets too hot, it can burn you. You can never trust a jalebi woman. You might think they are nice and sweet, but all things nice can also be bad for you. That's what I was dealing with there!" she cried.

"Surely, though, such anger would have erupted from something," I said, looking doubtful.

She looked up at me from behind her scarf. "Khala," she said, "it sounds like you don't believe me."

"No, I couldn't doubt you or anyone. How could I possibly be sure or doubt anything when I simply cannot understand it yet?"

"Your mama is married to a hideous, mean and selfish woman who doesn't know how to even cook and look after him, or anyone else for that matter, and I am glad to be out of there. All the cruelty I have had to put up with because of her." She wept more into her dupatta.

Mamajee added fuel to the fire with a full psychoanalysis of the entire district, town, village and tribe that Mami's family were descendants of. "Oh, it's in their blood. They were all peasants; they lived on grass. She should feel lucky to have made it this far in life."

When I refused to participate in the slander and disparaging gossip that Mamajee and Naheeda Khala occupied their evenings with about Mami, it became increasingly clear that remaining impartial had also led to distrust and increased revulsion towards me. I had become more of a traitor by not subscribing to their beliefs on the injustices she had suffered. What I hadn't realised was just how dangerous it was to remain impartial, to not go along with the crowd, and more than this, how detrimental and compromising it would be for my future.

*

At first Naheeda Khala and I were in a way more like sisters than an aunt and niece. We were the same age, but although we had both finished our GCSEs, unsurprisingly, through no fault of her own, Naheeda Khala had failed all of them. Nanni had had the youngest of Mamajee's siblings towed back and forth between Bangladesh and England over the years of their schooling, leaving their education severely disrupted. And of course, just as Mamajee would see it, Nanni saw no need to educate girls when in due course they would be married off.

I couldn't have been happier, though, with the arrangements Mamajee had proposed at first, that she lived with us, attended college with me and shared the same bedroom. In my eyes, I had someone to talk to now, someone my age, someone I could be close to who I could walk home from college with, someone who could help prove to Mamajee that I was trustworthy and all these suspicions she held about me could be eradicated. As far as I could observe, it could only have been positive. If Mamajee could support her own sister's aspiration for furthering her education, then it would give rite of passage to mine. What I hadn't realised yet was just how contrary to my beliefs this would be, how my interactions with Naheeda Khala would adversely affect me.

If you were to have ever met my aunt, you wouldn't have met a fairer, more elegantly dressed and more beautiful Bengali girl. Her silky dark hair was always neatly combed and tied in a loose bun on her head that showed off her elegant neck and striking eyes and cheekbones, and you couldn't ever have mentioned her beauty without her returning the same compliments.

"Oh, Khala." she would say in the kitchen with Mamajee, "You are so beautiful, with your long, silky hair, your fair skin and your hazel eyes. I wish I had your nose. All the boys at college are crazy about you. Some of them would mistake you for an English girl or something," she would say. And at first, I could only be flattered by her admiration. But I knew this was going to cost me in front of Mamajee. I noticed there was always a price to all of these compliments.

"Oh, Khala!" she would say. "You are so good at sewing and making things, and I am rubbish, as you know. You wouldn't be so kind and help me with making one?" Knowing full well I had an essay due in the next day. And even when I had kindly refused, it was difficult to object. "Oh, but I have seen how quickly you sew them," she would say. "You will see. I don't think you are aware of how swift you are. I saw your speedy hands the other day with Mamajee." This made it even more difficult to refuse.

"Oh, Khala, you are so clever and bright. I wish I had your brain. Could you help me? I am stuck on this coursework," she would explain, knowing full well I had an exam the following morning. And of course, she lacked understanding and depth for any assignments, attributed to her lack of background on certain subjects. This took up most of my evenings, dispensing advice and explaining to the point where I had written her essay and finished her work for her. It would then mean another endless night of study until three in the morning to finish my own work.

At college she was able to see my goings on, who I hung out with, and any slight attention from boys gave her a reason to compliment me in such a way in front of Mamajee that it only reinforced Mamajee's suspicions about me.

"Oh, Khala, all the boys look at you. I wish I could dress like you. You have such a slim figure and especially when you leave your hair down. It never ceases to amaze me how many heads turn when they see you coming into the canteen or getting a coffee."

"Oh, Khala, that's not true," I would say back laughingly, to appease any suspicion Mamajee might be having. "Everyone says the same about you."

"No, no, not me. I can't speak English very well. Not as smart as you. I don't even have any nice clothes." All the while, Mamajee listened quietly, without a word.

But this was just the beginning of something far worse, something that I could have never imagined they could do, or would want to do. A beginning they had in mind, that would lead to a terrible end. Never in my wildest dreams could I have imagined how one person's charm could lead to such harm.

*

One afternoon a couple of weeks before my final exams, Khala and I met in the canteen. She was sat idly drinking coffee, while I jotted revision notes, when she spotted one of the college students looking at me.

"Hey, Eleanor, do you see him over there?"

I turned to see who she was referring to. It was someone I had known for a long time. "Oh, Adil," I said, going back to my notes.

"He's looking at you," she said cheekily, nudging me.

"Yeah, he is one of the local boys," I said, unfazed. "His father and Babajee have known each other since the sixties, when Babajee started his business. At least, that's what I've heard from Babajee's brief comments." I continued busily jotting my notes.

I thought it would be enough of an explanation for her, that it may quell any notion of a potential success at matchmaking. Babajee didn't respect his father much. He worked in the kitchen, but in Babajee's opinion, Adil's father lacked any conviction in his work. Babajee also didn't like socialising with people who worked for him.

"So, what about him?" I said, turning back from Adil's large eyebrows and puffed-up hairstyle, which seemed to be the fashion at the time.

"Well, he has been nagging me for days now to ask you if you would like to meet him," Khala whispered secretively.

"No way!" I said. "I'm not interested, and besides, he is a real player. He has a bad reputation for womanising and playing off with lots of girls. There is no way I would even think of going near him."

"Oh, come on," she said, "that's a bit harsh. He really likes you, and he is so good-looking."

"Well, if that's what you think, why don't you go out with him?"

Naheeda Khala sighed, smiling. "He doesn't fancy me, does he? He fancies you! Anyway, how could you say such a thing to your khala?"

"No way, Naheeda Khala, I just wouldn't. Look, I have to go. I have a seminar to attend in five minutes."

"Please, Khala, just meet him. You don't have to like him. He just wants to talk to you."

"No, Khala, I don't want to, okay?" I said bluntly before walking off.

*

That night, when we were both sleeping in our shared double bed, Khala woke me in the middle of the night.

"Eleanor, Eleanor," she said, shaking me.

I turned to face her. "What is it?" I said with bleary eyes.

"He's here," she said, gasping.

"What are you talking about?"

"Khala, it is Adil! I'm really sorry; he just wants to talk to you."

"Oh my gosh! What? Who? At two in the morning?"

"You know he just wants to speak with you because he really likes you."

"What? Khala, you are going to get me in trouble."

"Look, this guy is really in love with you. He kept begging me, and I told him that you would be okay to speak to him. Please, just see what he wants and then leave it."

I didn't understand the urgency and why she just couldn't say no to him. What was the big deal about him? *Why is she doing this? What is this leading to?* I thought.

"Khala, open the window. Go on, just talk to him; see what he wants," she begged, prompting me to open the window.

I looked out of the window. A strong outline of Adil glimmered under the lamplight, his face, turned upward towards me, now glowed a yellow bronze under the beam.

I opened the window wider. "What do you want?" I whispered out to him. Disappointed by the whole fiasco, I wanted to rudely tell him to get lost, but I just didn't have it in me.

"Eleanor, I can't stop thinking about you. I just want to see you. I find it hard to sleep at night, because I am going crazy dreaming about you."

"Hmm, that doesn't even make sense," I said to Khala. "He can't sleep and yet he is dreaming of me?"

Khala giggled from behind the curtains. "You see, he really loves you. Come on, just say yes. How can you say no?"

"Look at this, the summer roses are in full bloom, and even they remind me of you." He gazed into one of Mamajee's roses and then tried to throw one up to me. It hit the window, causing petals to scatter everywhere.

It made me cringe, and a part of me wanted to rudely close the window without saying another word, but again I couldn't bring myself to do it.

"My dad will be coming back from work any minute now, so please can you go?" I urged.

"Eleanor, Eleanor, please, please, I am crazy about you! What do you say? How about we meet tomorrow and get a coffee somewhere?"

"No!" I said, now whispering loudly. "Just go before you get me in trouble!"

Just then a set of car lights flashed against the window of the house opposite. To my horror, it was Babajee on his way home from the restaurant.

"Oh, shit, my dad's coming home. Get out of here!" I said in an urgent hushed tone.

He crouched behind the wall as he moved to his car.

Babajee got out of his car as Adil raced into his.

I closed my bedroom window as I saw Babajee look up.

Naheeda Khala and I hid underneath the covers.

"Shit, Khala, you are going to get me into trouble." I felt like swearing at her stupidity.

"Shh," she said. "He's coming up the stairs."

I heard the car keys jingle in Babajee's pocket as he came in and closed the front door. This frightened me even more, as he would have normally come through from the back door.

He paused, and then his footsteps creaked up the stairs.

"Oh no, he's coming upstairs. Pretend you are asleep," I said to Khala. While I was panicking, she seemed to find the whole thing hysterically exciting and giggled even more.

"Eleanor," came a stern voice from my bedroom door. "Are you awake?"

I breathed as quietly as I could.

"Eleanor, I know you are awake."

Oh, shit, I thought. *What do I say?*

"Can you get up when I am calling you?" Babajee's voice became louder and stronger.

"What are you doing up at this time of night, and who was that boy sneaking outside the house?"

I pulled down the sheet as calmly as possibly.

I thought he would understand if I just told him plainly and simply that I had no interest in that guy and that he had just come to persuade me.

"It was Adil," I said, about to add more words, but before I could muster another word, I felt a sudden blow of darkness fall against my face and my head slam sideways against the bedroom wall. I didn't have time to sense the pain along the brow of my left side, or the way the jagged texture of the wallpaper scraped my face, because the knock sent me into survival mode.

Several blows came against my head, sometimes a hand, sometimes his shoe. I felt sick from the pain and couldn't breathe out.

I managed to move enough to roll from the bed, where I caught sight of Khala's feet. She was standing shell-shocked. He pulled me by the hair, dragging me across the floor, out to the staircase landing area. My body shook incessantly.

"No, Babajee, let go of me! Tell him, Khala! Tell him!" I trembled.

"You stupid, harami, child of a swine!" He glared as he kicked each side of my thigh.

"You good for nothing girl, how many fucking times have I told you about tarring my good name, dragging me down with the dogs? Today you are going to have your throat slit open." Babajee stamped his foot into my side, sending me down the first set of stairs.

I felt the words "I'm sorry" tumble from my mouth as my grazed body scraped the floor to the landing area.

I caught a glimpse of Mamajee coming out of her room and standing over the balcony.

The bedroom light turned on, and Karim came out, staring at me from the top of the stairs. Behind Mamajee stood Khala. I could tell she wasn't going to say anything. She wasn't going to help me.

"Babajee, please," I begged, crying. "I didn't do anything. I don't even know why …" I trembled with shock.

"Shut up! You know everything, you deceiving little whore. You went out of your way to make midnight meetups while I am away."

"What? At this hour?" Mamajee chimed in, looking at Babajee, horrified. "She is going to ruin us! That's what you sent her to college for. That's what you call it, college girls cavorting and fooling around at college! Hmm, do you see?" she raged, pointing at Babajee. "You don't listen to me, do you? How many times have I warned you, warned of this day? Hmm? Well, today has come now, hasn't it? Your angel is a good-for-nothing, shameless girl."

Babajee was livid, and he charged down the stairs, grabbing me by the scruff of my neck, slapping me in the face. "You fucking know what this means, don't you? No more college or school, you fucking shameless whore. You won't be going anywhere."

I choked on my tears. "Khala, tell him. I don't want any of this. I don't want to even know about that person." I begged her as she looked down from the top of the stairs, down at my pitiful state on the floor. She looked calm and as though she knew nothing about it. She shook her head as if to agree with Babajee.

Mamajee looked at me. "Hmm, do you see? Do you see what you have done? You need to send her to Bangladesh," she told Babajee. "I told you that before," she said, pointing her finger at him. "You need to keep girls under control, on the straight and narrow, but you are just as irresponsible."

I felt utter disbelief at my situation. How could I have got so far? How could it be the end of my education? So overwhelmed and upset, with all my might, using my jittery hands, I pulled the tie string from my pyjama waist.

I tied it in a tight knot around my neck and felt the world blacken around me. If I wasn't going to study and they were going to send me to Bangladesh, then I didn't want to be alive.

CHAPTER TWENTY-FOUR
– *The Awakening* –

I heard a cough, then the smell of cigarette smoke. My eyes were sore, and as my senses came alive, I felt my head and face burn.

I could barely open my eyes; they felt puffy and swollen. I resolved that I was in my room, and it felt like morning. I recognised the ceiling and the embossed wallpaper.

I slowly looked over to my left. Babajee was sat there. He hadn't noticed me awake, and I watched him for a moment as he stared out of the window, puffing on a cigarette.

I tried to move my neck, but it felt harsh and sore. With my body aching and stiff, my thoughts finally compiled what had happened last night.

Even with his back to me, I could see he was deep in thought as he looked straight out at the hills. That place that had become his obsession for many years seemed to be of concern again.

I felt relieved he hadn't noticed. It bought me some time to recollect what had happened and how I was here in my bed. I couldn't work out the day or the time now. I remembered what had happened last night. Babajee's face filled with fury and disappointment.

I recalled the kicks, the way he'd dragged me by the hair down the stairs, his eyes filled with scorn when he picked me up by the scruff of my neck. Mamajee pointing her finger at him. There were shouts, but the thing that had hurt me most was seeing those people look down on me and watch as I pulled that cord around my neck until I fell into darkness.

I let out a cry from the culmination of thoughts that had been recalled.

"Eleanor." Babajee turned.

I closed my eyes. I didn't want to see him anymore. I didn't want to be there. I had made my decision, and once again they somehow had stolen another choice from me.

"Eleanor," Babajee called again. "Are you awake? Can you hear me?"

I didn't answer. I prayed I could return to the blackness, that someone could remove me from this place.

He came closer to me.

I felt him sit beside me on the bed.

He cleared his voice, his breathing heavy, hesitant.

"What am I supposed to do, huh? Tell me. What am I supposed to do?"

I stared emptily at the ceiling.

This is all Babajee has to say right now? I thought.

I could have filled in a few sentences for him. *How about throw me in a grave somewhere? How about beating me a little more, Babajee, so that you can use me as a door wedge? Or maybe the choices are even simpler for you, Babajee. How about you fucking continue to stare out of that window?*

But I didn't say anything. I looked on at that ceiling. I wanted him to open up, tell me what his plans were for me now. When my flight to Bangladesh was booked, and the infamous wedding that had been planned my entire life.

The thought of it made my breathing irregular. My stomach tightened into a knot, which made me want to vomit. It sickened me, the way they wanted to engulf my existence for their vain attempts of showing face to society, their community.

"Say something, ah? What do you want me to do?" Babajee stared on out the window again. I could have killed him for wanting to ask rhetorically, as if he was making a point of my failure, not his. He was asking someone he was giving little choice to.

"Izzat. Do you know what that is? Honour, your name, your respect. If you lose that, you have nothing."

There was no room for these justifications, I thought. I was lying here battered. He had won the battle, and he still couldn't dismount from his horse.

"I could have made that decision easy for you," I finally mustered, my voice coarse and raspy as I stared blankly on at the ceiling. "You were halfway towards making that decision for me, anyway."

Babajee's face pointed downward as he breathed in heavily. The air was thick with silence. I thought about what it must have been like for Mamajee. All the years of abuse. Those blows from him last night had taken the wind out of me. How had Mamajee tolerated that from Babajee all those years? Then I thought about why they had stood there apathetically instead of coming to my aid. How could they condone such violence? Was it possible to have caused so much anger that they didn't want me in their lives? There were no comforting words, no sympathy, no one to defend me in the way I would have them. I scoured my thoughts for a reason, and I couldn't fathom it, their reason, their intentions. "Why?"

"What do you want to do?" he asked.

His questions infuriated me. He already knew my dreams, my ambitions. He knew it all.

"Tell me, what do you want to do?"

I looked up emptily.

"Listen," he said. "I don't want a repeat of what happened last night."

Sometimes silence is the best medicine. I looked at him, speechless. The truth stares you in the face in those moments. I scoured it. Was he talking about his actions or referring to what he assumed were mine?

His expression was not anger but one of fear.

I realised that Babajee was only thinking of himself again.

I could tell that what he meant was not about the situation he thought I was in. His conscience had kicked into play.

"What happened here goes nowhere. You do not go out for a while, do you hear me?" he said quietly.

I thought about my exams, the endless hours of revising at night to make up for the time I was losing to help Mamajee and, most of all, Khala. It had all been in vain.

I was now compromising the final weeks of my exams again. For what? The consequences of his mistakes.

"I have my exams," I said, horrified.

"You are not going to attend them. Tell them you are ill."

I swallowed down the tears; my swollen eyes filled up, concealing my view of his face. I could feel him leaving me as he moved from the bed and closed the door behind him.

I thought about Babajee's words as I lay there. I missed Mrs Abbots. I thought about what she would have said in a time like this: "In times of crisis, you need to pull on all your resources and do the best you can with them. You can still achieve everything."

I thought about all I had been through, the studying, the long nights. Pulling through with all the resources I had.

"You have to use all the resources you have. You can achieve everything," Mrs Abbots would say.

I longed for that belief, but I couldn't feel it. I couldn't believe it anymore.

I hobbled over to the mirror in my bedroom. I saw the cord marks along my neck, the bruising across my face. My eyes were swollen. I pulled up my vest to see the bruising on my back and down my thigh. My body looked like a map of the world in blue and green.

"Why are you still here? You shouldn't be here?" I screamed at the reflection in the mirror, giving it a shake. I hated her. The victim. The girl crying, the helpless one, the self-pitying, lost and abandoned piece of shit she had been turned into.

I didn't deserve this. I wasn't going to be her. I should have been dead, but I was not. I was still here. If they were not going to let me die, then I was not going to live this way, and if I was going to survive, then I needed to pull on all my resources. I could find a way to be who I wanted to be.

I needed to find a way to see her. She was the only support I had that would propel me further. It was Mrs Abbots who had inspired me, and it was this advice that had saved me before.

"Pull on all your resources," she would say. Then I imagined what she would say in this situation if I told her. "Keep revising and studying; stay in the room; use it to propel yourself further. Don't give in to the darkness. This isn't over."

She would have been right. I didn't have to stop studying; my books were all in my room. Being locked in here gave me even more reason to study. I didn't have the torments of Mamajee nor the distractions of Khala.

I denied her access to my room, and she didn't push it either. I closed myself off from the world, occasionally leaving to clean or wash but otherwise steering clear of the family downstairs. I refused food when Mamajee brought something up.

"Come on, eat," she would bark. I couldn't see her in the same light. I could not care how she reluctantly and obligingly brought a plate of curry with rice.

It was my youngest brother, Masoud, who won me over on the food front. He would make sandwiches and crisps and coffee. He knew things were not good, and these small gestures paid off. But it wasn't enough. The night before my exam, I came down with a fever; the lack of sleep and food and the stress had brought on ulcers in my throat, and my temperature was soaring.

"Where are you going?" Mamajee asked that morning. "You know you are not well. Why are you doing this?"

I barged my way past her as she barricaded the door.

"Just wait till you hear from your father about this," she said angrily.

"Yes, why don't you do that? How about you beat me up until I kill myself?" I retorted.

I had nothing to lose anymore, and it was liberating to stand up to her.

I pushed my way forward, setting her to my side. The morning light blinding as it shone in the east, the weight loss, lack of sleep and sore throat, no longer shackles.

I didn't feel confident in the exam. I knew there were gaps in my understanding. There was room for improvement, but given the barrage of mental and physical abuse, I pardoned my ability. I hadn't put in enough groundwork or concentration to make it through, but I wasn't going to let this fail me. I had escaped death, and failure seemed insignificant now. Everything now was an opportunity to explore. The college foyer swarmed with students signing in for the exam. Sarah, a classmate, gasped when she saw the state of me.

"What happened to you?"

I tugged at my scarf around my neck to hide the scars.

"Are you okay?"

"I am not feeling too well. I have a temperature and ulcers in my throat."

"Oh dear," she sympathised.

"Here, have you taken anything? I have some paracetamol, if it helps."

I was fortunate she gave me those. How obsessed I had become with my inner mental state that I had not thought to take any medication for my physical state. My exam was in an hour.

Sarah looked at me as I scoured the floor. I felt dazed and weak.

"Shall we go get a coffee?" she said, looking at the time. "We still have an hour."

"Sure." I felt safe and comforted by her, somehow sane again with her words.

"How do you feel about the exam?" she asked as I popped the paracetamol with a slug of coffee. It made its way down my throat painfully.

I shook my head. "I don't think I am going to pass."

"You look in a bad way, Eleanor. I have never seen you like this. Is everything okay?"

I breathed in, dismally trying to find the right words, pinching my eyes to hold back tears.

"Hopefully, I will feel better after the paracetamol."

It brought my temperature down, and as the sweat gathered on my forehead, I felt immediately better before the exam. But my mental state was failing me. I was worried about failing.

I told myself, *You have nothing to lose, Eleanor. Do your best, and just let yourself relax.*

I turned the page of my exam paper. Amazingly, it was a question on the poem "Still I Rise" by Maya Angelou. I smiled because I knew the poem well. It was clearly talking to me. It was as though it was about me and the words flowed on the paper when I read the first verse.

You may write me down in history
With your bitter, twisted lies,
You may trod me in the very dirt
But still, like dust, I'll rise.

*

My friends were surprised when I joined them outside the exam hall. I was more alive that day than I had ever been after reading that poem. It resonated with me, and the answers to the questions about the poem came out as though in a flood of words on the exam answer sheet. I felt as though I had been fighting demons all the way through my life, and the poem reflected all that I was fighting for. It only substantiated what Mrs Abbots had been saying all along: "Don't give in to darkness. Nothing is over until you have lost the will to seek it." Well, this much was true; I felt vibrant with life now. I could really feel the light. I saw things differently after that exam.

"You look a lot better than before, Eleanor. How did it go?" Sarah asked outside the exam hall.

I smiled. "I am not sure what the outcome will be, but I am just sure I will rise above it all. I have to."

*

That year I failed one of my subjects because I couldn't physically attend the exam. Another I scraped with a pass, but I received an A in English literature. That poem saved me. It was as though it was speaking to me. I had planned to go to law school and become a solicitor or a barrister, but the grades were not good enough, as I didn't have enough points.

I was devastated: Mamajee would have her way as usual. Now, this would definitely mean I would have to be married. I had failed; I was useless; and there was no way I could do anything with my grades.

I met Mrs Abbots one afternoon at a cafe in the town centre.

I had told Mamajee that I would be at work. I had, over the summer period, started working part-time at a shop so I could have some money to buy things like books, clothes and other items that I couldn't ask Mamajee or Babajee for easily.

However, today I had bunked my half-day salary just to see Mrs Abbots.

"I don't know what I am going to do with these grades. I barely have enough points."

She sipped her tea while flicking through the paper with a look of despondency at my self-grieving comments.

"Babajee and Mamajee will definitely send me back. There is absolutely no doubt about it. I could have done something. I should have done more." I started to weep.

"You can't think like that, Eleanor! There is always a path out. Always."

"How? Tell me how? I can't see it?" I said.

"Well, what are your options?" she asked.

"I could resit, but I don't want to. I couldn't bear being there with Mamajee hurtling fireballs at me for another year."

She continued to flick through the newspaper.

I stared dismally out of the window.

"She's probably so smug," I said. "She's probably arranging plane tickets already."

"Could you look at anything else?" she asked.

I looked blankly. "What can I look at? I am rubbish. Babajee wanted me to go into medicine or law, but I don't have a chance. And there is no chance of them letting me try the arts subjects. I am just doomed to failure."

"Come on, Eleanor, remember what I said. Pull on all your resources. What options do you have right now? Think about your strengths, and I am not talking about the subjects you are good at here, I am talking about you, as a person."

I shook my head, cradled my forehead with my palms. I had no energy to think. I had low self-esteem, low self-belief, no nothing, and my reserves were running on empty. I couldn't see any resources that I could turn to; the one wild card was Mrs Abbots herself, her belief in me. I had no real money, no real experience of anything. Yes, my school exams were okay, but nobody was going to look at those now. I looked at her, exasperated.

"I am a failure, Mrs Abbots. I have failed my exams. I don't have anything to offer. I am rubbish at everything, and I can't see how I could get into university, or anywhere for that matter."

Mrs Abbots looked on, bemused by my melodrama. "Eleanor, do you not see? It's not your successes that will make you. It's your failures that will make you. That is the point of failure. Do you remember what I told you? It isn't designed to keep you there, it is designed to propel you further. If you put your hand in burning oil, would you keep it there? No, you would pull it out. You have a choice: suffer the consequences, become a silent victim, or choose something. Choose to change your circumstances, your situations, to a life that you want."

I looked emptily on out of the window as she continued.

"You have to embrace failure. It's part of the process of growing and learning. It's there to help guide you. You know where you don't want to go, don't you? So, choose where you want to go. Choose it. Choose it, Eleanor. I can't choose it for you. I think you made that decision a long time ago. You've already made choices. You have been scared of making them, because you fear something. It's easy to sink into darkness, into fear, into those negative places where you feel trapped, but it's the courage to choose the person you want to be that is often harder. Now, tell me, Eleanor. Tell me. Did you not choose a desire to learn? Did you not choose education above all else for your path to freedom?"

I sat silently, staring at the waitress wiping down a table before Mrs Abbots drew my attention back to her.

"I can't see it. I just can't."

"Listen, Eleanor, listen. Once upon a time, a little girl said to me that one day she wanted to go beyond these hills. Well, now you know that you can."

She was right. I just wanted freedom. I wanted to be allowed to choose my destiny and not be told what to do with life. Education would free me from the shackles of fear, of a closed mind and my parents' beliefs, which were not really mine.

She slapped the paper down on the table in front of me.

"Look," she said, pointing to the newspaper. "You always have choices." She flicked through page after page of adverts for jobs. "Can you see how many jobs there are here, Eleanor? Just see."

I peered down to glance at the first job, which listed qualifications and experience.

"Well, I don't have the qualifications," I said, perplexed and unconvinced.

"Just look here," she said. "Look closer."

"Well? All these jobs are in IT, and I don't know the first thing about computers. I can barely type in a Word document, and—"

"And this is the future, and this is the beginning." Mrs Abbots spoke insistently and interrupted my urge to spiral into negativity. "You just have to think out of the box and look at what you can do with the best right now, with the best you have got. Look, with the points that you have, you can still go to university. You can still be educated; you can still fulfil any ambition you desire. You can still choose education; you can choose to learn and grow and find a way to your goals. Your goal, to choose, to be free? Go on, open your mind; expand your horizons; don't let your fears lead you to the outcome you didn't want, what you don't deserve. Have a look at the universities and what you can do with the points you have. You are never limited. I would imagine you have a good chance of getting on one of these computer science degrees. It's the way the world is going, and it will open opportunities for you."

*

Later that afternoon, I contacted many universities. I spoke to their admissions departments and found many would accept my scores. I wasn't limited. I had blocked myself off from opportunities because of darkness and fear, when all I needed was to search for the switch to turn on the light bulb. If you give up looking for the light, then, yes, you will surrender to darkness. I could see it now. Pull on all your powers, resources, strength; turn on the light. The real you was always there. There are options, and this was the beginning of an endless road full them.

*

Mamajee watched as I packed my bags the day I left for university. She had been silent when I'd mentioned I had an offer at Sheffield and when I had found rental accommodation by myself. I could see it burn through her rationale. I tried to avoid quiet moments alone with her, the guilt that pierced through me when our eyes made contact. I knew it would not be her choice, and I was no longer allowing her a choice.

"You will be taking this with you, won't you?" She pointed at a scarf and a prayer mat. "You make sure that you pray and you keep yourself covered in front of men."

It was as if it were her last attempt at salvaging some control.

"Remember the word of Allah and what has been written. It's all been written; Allah sees everything, knows everything. I can only do what is in my control, but you must remember that you made a promise to me."

"A promise?"

"Why, have you forgotten? The day I was beaten up by your father, how you begged me to stay. I kept true to my word; I stayed.

I sacrificed, and you must stay true to your word; you are still under oath, remember. I have kept my end of the bargain, so you must keep yours, that you will marry as we wish for you, that you will keep our honour and dignity. I don't want to hear our name in the mud. Do you hear me?"

I could have almost retaliated with "Well, look at what you have put me through." But I didn't. I just nodded at her. There is no point in making a point that leads to no positive outcome. *Anything*, I thought. *Anything that gives me the right to an education.* I hadn't thought about the next chapter of my life or the consequences of that promise, but right now, this was the truth. It was golden. I remembered those golden words I'd said once: "One day I will go beyond these hills." I remembered saying it, and now I would. *And nothing is going to get in the way of pursuing that..*

CHAPTER TWENTY-FIVE
– *The University of Life* –

Four years had passed since persuading Mamajee and Babajee had allowed me to continue with my education. That accomplishment alone had opened a jar full of dreams that I could now look forward to. I graduated two points shy of a first-class degree. I excelled in my dissertation and scored a first. It was no surprise that neither Mamajee nor Babajee were able to attend my graduation.

It was Mrs Abbots who sat as my honorary guest and clapped when it was time to collect my certificate on stage at my graduation ceremony. Her smile filled me with happiness as she applauded. I could almost sense this was as much her moment as it was mine. She was filled with tears and hugs after the ceremony.

"I am so happy that you got this far; well done, my dear."

This was the first time I had seen her teary with joy. We had always had a teacher–student relationship, so I was touched by her excitement at my achievement.

She looked at me proudly, holding onto my shoulders. "I told you, didn't I? You can achieve it if you choose it."

I smiled, nodding. "You did. Thank you for all your support through my life, Mrs Abbots."

Sometimes I struggled to believe her and often knocked back her ideas or suggestions. I often felt they were overinflated with hot air, sending me somewhere far out of reach. Often, they sounded whimsical, advice that anyone could prescribe for a good or bad day, but it was only her words that made me rethink or re-edit what I thought was written for me.

It was a miracle that I had been able to break through my parents' grand plan to have me married off after high school, and I had Mrs Abbots to thank for that.

She looked back at me now with smiles, but it soon faded, as if something was troubling her. And as her face loosened, she seemed withered, tired, older, and I felt deeply concerned. It saddened me to see her smile disappearing.

"Is everything all right, Mrs Abbots?" I asked.

She said nothing, as if considering her words. We walked through the white glass atrium of the university building, where a reception of drinks and canapés awaited parents and new graduates.

"Well, this is a rather splendid way to celebrate, isn't it?" she said, observing the congregation. She stood uncomfortably, as though she felt out of place or she didn't fit in, but I would have refuted anything of the kind if she had made such a claim.

"Mrs Abbots, you look beautifully dressed for the occasion."

"Thank you, my dear. I must say, I don't get out that often to wear anything fancy these days."

The way she dressed seemed only smart to me whenever we met. There was always a hat, which matched the coat and mid-length skirt or dress.

One of my university friends came over. "Oh, hello, Eleanor! Congratulations! Is this your mum? Let me get a picture of you both."

"Oh no, this is not my mum!" I laughed awkwardly, turning to face Mrs Abbots.

I linked arms with her as my friend took the picture.

Her smile seemed a little neutral when I glanced at her, and she seemed a little quietly overwhelmed as she observed the young graduate return to his group. I asked Mrs Abbots again, "Is everything okay?"

"I thought I best let you know that ..." She seemed to be hesitating. "Well, I may not be able to see you for a while, that's all," she said rather sadly.

"Oh, Mrs Abbots, that will be a shame, but why?"

"I am going away, so I might not see you for a year or so."

Some more friends came over with champagne glasses clinking and started talking.

"Well, that is sad to hear. I ... I will miss you," I said, intently looking at her, rather puzzled and yet trying not to pry. "Will you keep in touch?"

"Yes, of course, dear, nothing to worry about. I have been offered a teaching post in Shanghai, so I will keep in touch, of course." It seemed rather vague, but over the years, being away from home and going to university had become all-consuming, and I could almost count the number of times we had met. The chatter from the graduates became increasingly loud, and I felt her slowly moving away.

"You take care of yourself now, won't you, my dear?" she said with one final hug.

"Of course, I will. For you, always, Mrs Abbots."

Mrs Abbots hugged me with a tight squeeze, and it felt blissful, and I cherished it almost as if it were the last.

*

Although I didn't see Mrs Abbots for a while following my graduation, I could still remember the year of 2000 as one of the best years of my life. Her words of encouragement had empowered me to choose the course of my life, and I learned that Mamajee and Babajee's wants and desires were only signposts for where I didn't want to be or what journey I didn't want to go on.

I discovered that my childhood dreams could easily become a reality. I didn't just go beyond those hills, the Pennines and Peak District, to a university in Sheffield, but further, and there were even

more opportunities for discovery when I got there. I no longer hesitated over taking action or doing things that I wanted. Choosing life
was the equivalent of walking into a supermarket and deciding what
I'd like to scan through the conveyor belt. I no longer hesitated over
choosing what I wanted to experience, and the more I became comfortable with making fearless choices, the more I became ravenous
for it. I learned different languages, learned to dance. I went to the
gym. I joined many societies and learned about many cultures. I relished every opportunity to learn and grow, because I knew that I
couldn't take it for granted. The current of fear was that life may end,
that the freedom I had now could be taken away. Every opportunity
became an instant acknowledgement for a free life, and I wasn't going to waste any time squandering it. It was borrowed, after all, from
my parents, who still kept a watchful eye on what might not meet
their approval. The question was, how far could I go?

*

One day, following my graduation, I was walking past a travel shop
when I came across an offer for a round-the-world trip. Without
hesitation, I bought the flight, much to the shock and hesitation of
the sales agent. The following day I was to fly to Australia and
planned to travel by bus two thousand five hundred kilometres along
Australia's east coast. After this, I was to travel to New Zealand, Los
Angeles, Hawaii, San Francisco, before returning home.

Mamajee was horrified and confused when I landed in Australia,
thinking that my flight was to Austria, not to Australia. "Where are
you? It's been two days, and you haven't called," she scolded.

"Mamajee, it's a twenty-four-hour flight."

"What?" she barked. "To Austria?"

When I explained it was Australia, she was horrified and puzzled,
and her silence spoke volumes about her thoughts on the matter. She
had turned a blind eye to most of my whereabouts, as it was often
too difficult for her to embrace my ideas. Ignorance also meant that
she didn't have to justify it to anyone.

"I don't know what has got into you," she would say. "But I hope you are not putting our good name on the line." She no longer pressed it any further though; me being away seemed to protect her from all the unsavoury looks from our extended family. I could feel my self-determination being met with disapproval on my visits home. It wasn't acceptable in my culture, wandering the world by myself, going to university, working alone and living in mixed-gender houseshares. It was unbearable for Mamajee, and I chose to ignore it. The guilt would flow in phone calls, not in words but in the undercurrent of energy between us, in her tone when asking how I was, or in the white noise that vibrated down the receiver. Still, I turned a blind eye to it. I couldn't let these things hold me back now. I was living my dream, and by 2000 I had fulfilled most of what I had wanted on my road map. I had travelled most of Europe, Australia, New Zealand, and America overland. I had completed my degree in computer science and had started working for one of the largest technology companies in the world.

Over time I became taboo in my parents' eyes, unspoken of, back in their small, sleepy town where nothing ever changed. The rolling hills, the rickety petrol stations with one working pump, the shops with the sun-blazed faded sales signs, the people who only called you "love" and "duck" and never by your real name. Upon my visits home, my stories would often shake them with awe and horrified gasps. My stories were parts of my life they would rather I didn't make mention of, their reputation hanging on every sentence I uttered. Success for a woman was not defined by the number of countries she had travelled to, the countless job offers or working and socialising with some of the most established people in her field. Success for my parents was defined by how well a woman stayed within the boundaries of culture, the modesty in veiled life, the fuss and commotion in preparation of everyone else's life that you did without complaint backstage. It was defined by how well she looked after her brothers, uncles and fathers, who were the real celebrities of everyday existence. I learned to become unmentionable in their world. I learned it from their silences, the change of subject, like the muted news Babajee watched. I learned that these achievements were not theirs, that this jar full of dreams was toxic and not really for consumption, and so I stopped talking to them about what I did.

Going home to my parents' house was nothing more than a physical sign-off that I existed for them, and a chance to reconnect with my siblings, who were still getting through high school or college. I saw how they wished they could travel like I did with my job, but also how impossible they thought it was for them to do so. When I came home to visit, I saw that nothing had changed other than the passing of time reflected in everything. Babajee still sat by the fire, reading a book or watching the news, his hair greyer than ever, his body limp and thinner, and with a rounder belly that at least gave me some satisfaction that he was eating well. His jaw was propped up by a set of false teeth; his face wilted when he wasn't using them. The frown lines between his brow were more resonant of his time with Mamajee, the tired nights of slow business at the restaurant and the monotony of troubles in Bangladesh or with the issues with my siblings that had repeatedly remained unresolved. Mamajee spent time in the kitchen, bending and kneeling as she cooked and heaving as she rose her merciless back from the pain.

Time had only changed with the imprint of age that showed in everyone's faces or in the worn-out edges of the table, chairs and sofa. I saw it in the carpet and in the faded plastic flowers that once upon a time Mamajee had stolen pocket change from Babajee to buy. I saw it in the rust on the plate rack or in the now oranged kitchen tiles singed by the heat and grease from the hours of cooking Mamajee was devoted to daily. Mamajee's hair was still long; the tresses fell down to her waist when it unravelled on the odd occasion, the ends now wiry and coarse. I saw that age had started to show on her face, the fine lines that cut into the smile lines, the deep hollows in her eyes. Sleep now was stolen not by children waking her up at night but by back pains and head pains, and slight rheumatism in her wrist.

The boys, my two brothers, were now bordering adulthood and were hardly seen. They had the freedom of being out with their friends in the evenings. Mamajee would only get upset if they hadn't come home, and it was often the only times I would see them. They had all the typical traits of Muslim boys, filling their plates with a mountain of food at dinnertime, eating noisily, shovelling handfuls of rice and mixing them with curry. They swaggered to the dining table with entitlement and expectation, and acted as if Mamajee's cooking was an inconvenience to their lifestyles. They would rather have takeaway, as they wouldn't have to hang around patiently for it. They had adopted Babajee's fistful of complaints that it didn't taste right, which in most cases Mamajee barely responded to now. Their hair would be gelled fashionably upward like shards of glass, with clothing to match the latest trend in sports or casual attire. I would sometimes get the odd yell of excitement when they first saw me, but in most cases, it barely made a difference whether I was there or not.

I would drive the two-hundred-mile journey back to my parents' every month from London to Manchester and often wondered what purpose it served for them. Sometimes we barely talked. Mamajee would have dinner ready for me, a silent checklist, a hug at the door, followed by, "Do you want to eat your rice now or later?" There were long-drawn-out silences in those hours at home. I no longer talked about the places I went to or the people I met or what I had achieved at work. It was too painful for her to hear it. She had once again in her life bitten her tongue, closed her hopes that may have made her life worthwhile. Her long suffering was still not over. I watched her stave off funny glances at invites and dinners where family and friends asked about my whereabouts, wrestling the backchat and small talk that fed idle tongues at socials. I became unmentionable, the unspoken truth, the evident flaws in Mamajee's parenting that showed she hadn't raised me well enough at community socials. Mentioning my name in her world was like striking a chord on an untuned violin. It didn't play well, and it sounded awful.

It was only my sister who delighted at my stories, her sixteen-year-old, naive eyes lighting up when she saw me. It was Suraya who always called to find out where I was or ask me when I was visiting again. She marvelled at photographs of the places I had been to, like seeing Sydney Harbour Bridge or dropping four hundred and forty feet on a bungee in New Zealand, or when I had climbed the Three Peaks in twenty-four hours for charity. While I would watch my sister's eyes light up, I often saw Mamajee's eyes fade out. I could see that she wouldn't want this repeated again, that my sister's ambitions would be limited.

I had changed though. I was no longer in fear of Mamajee's and Babajee's opinions. And while they muted me out of their life, the distance between us was not just physical, it was a mental one. I had come to accept the flaws they found in me and tuned in to face the music of my own heartbeat, where I danced to the rhythm of my life, my reality. I would change the channel of my own television box if they tried to bring up marriage, or what my plans were for coming back to Manchester to live. I left their questions unanswered about when I was going to settle down. I had found the hidden treasures of life, freedom to live and be as I wanted to be, without the fear of opinion or the wondering opinions of gossiping uncles and aunts.

To Mamajee, I was the pest on the oak tree, one that she had masterfully patched a gall around to prevent infestation to the rest of the family tree, but no matter how much she contained me, all she was really doing was allowing me to flourish. I hadn't fallen victim to her boundary, but was silently incubating, growing, changing in my own little world. The only fear I had now was how far I could go with it. It was only a question of time as to how long she would entertain it, how long before honour and reputation would form on her lips again. The words that I secretly dreaded. The words associated with one word. Marriage.

PART 2

CHAPTER TWENTY-SIX

– *Love War* –

The year of 2000 was one of the best years of my life. I had graduated with the degree I wanted, travelled around the world to countries that were once beyond my imagination to ever dream of roaming, and I had secured a role in one of the largest IT companies in the world.

I had far exceeded Babajee's expectations with bewilderment. He was speechless when I told them a staggering fourteen thousand applicants had applied for the same job, and I had been selected. To achieve this, I had passed eleven rounds of interviews, three aptitude tests and two technical presentations. To my parents, I was unstoppable now, and I could hear it resonate in their muted expressions. I was floating on a freedom cloud, one that I was mindful I was drifting too far away on, because back on earth, I was about to experience something heavenly, something that would cross more than hills, mountains and material things, and yet something I would fear crossing the borders of. Something that is naturally infinite and yet bounded by family, history, heritage and culture. Love.

*

Much to my bemusement, my first day in the office was unexpectedly quiet. There appeared to be no one in the office. I scoured the floor, looking for signs of life, only to find myself deserted amongst an array of empty cubicles and padded dividers. I sat through an hour or surfing the world's dullest intranet pages and wondered whether I had stepped into the wrong office. Then, to my relief, I heard noises from beyond the cubicles.

"Come, let's go for breakfast," someone said.

I peered over the wall of my cubicle, and a jolly-looking Sikh man had strolled into the open space.

"Oh! Er, hello!" he said, looking a little surprised to see me.

"Hi. My name's Eleanor," I said, leaning over the cubicle to shake his hand.

"Oh, hi! It's Jay. Nice to meet ya," he said, winking. "Are you, er, one of the new grads on the team reporting to Stef?" he asked.

"That's right, I am," I said. I was starting to feel a little at home with the introduction; he seemed like a friendly character. "I had wondered where everyone in the office was. I thought maybe I had stepped into the wrong place," I chimed.

"Oh, yeah, well, we sometimes work from home too." He laughed as he let go of the pressing grip on my hand. Then I heard a voice coming from behind him.

"Are you coming, then, Jay? What's the hold up?" And there he was, standing there. The kind face, the eyes that gleamed back, the black jeans, fitted long-sleeved white top. He stood handsomely with a smile that seemed to move through my body, causing my heart to pound through my chest. I still recall the intensity that came when those deep, smiling eyes looked back at me; it was as if I had known him from a time before. That split second was filled with something I could not fathom. I felt a rush of joy sweeten my lungs as I breathed in the moment, and I was overcome with an overwhelming sensation of love. I could not compare it to any other pleasures I had experienced before, and the only approximation was that of the encounter with Mrs Abbots that very first time in the car park all those years ago. And yet in that moment I also became fearful of the feelings I was presented with.

I tried to look away, to control my senses.

"Hi," he said calmly. He paused for a moment before approaching me. "I'm Rohit." His eyes smiled again as he said his name. "You must be the new grad." His voice softened like melting candy floss on the tongue. I could have listened to that voice silently all day.

He leaned over to shake my hand.

"Ah, yes. Hello, Rohit. My name is Eleanor," I said, looking down at his hand as he shook mine. I couldn't bear to look into those penetrable eyes in case he saw right through me. His palm felt warm and silky; the sensation of his touch lingered on my hand even after he let go of it.

A warm scent of his aftershave circled around me, and trickled through me as I breathed in.

"Nice to meet you, Eleanor." His warmth and tender smile captivated me.

"Did you want to come down for breakfast, and we can catch up there?" he said coolly, looking over at Jay. Jay had a smirk on his face, and I dreaded him saying something to embarrass me, even though I didn't really know him well enough to suggest that he would.

"Well, now that we have all been acquainted," he said, looking at us both, "let's do that. They will be closing up the breakfast bar shortly, so we better move quickly."

The three of us strolled into the office canteen, and Jay passed out a few trays to place our food on.

Rohit towered over me as we moved our trays down the hot-food counter.

"What are you having?" he asked. "It's my shout." He smiled.

"Oh, thank you. Er, I think I will have some eggs and toast."

He reached over to get a plate. His elbow grazed my shoulder, sending another rush through me as my inner voice gave way to a relentless chant. *Stop thinking of him. Don't run away with yourself. He's a colleague, remember, and your parents will never approve.*

Now you are really running away with yourself, I heard myself arguing. *You have barely met this guy, and you are already calculating to the nth degree!*

Oh, shut up, Eleanor, I argued with myself. *We are colleagues and nothing more.*

We moved over to a table by the window that overlooked the technology park and where trees lined the driveway leading up to the building.

"It's really unusual to see any women in IT," Rohit said as both men sat down at the table.

"Yes, it's, er, quite male-dominated, isn't it?" I said, looking around the cafeteria filled with men. There weren't any women anywhere. I pressed my fork against the cold eggs now sitting on my plate. I was finding it hard to eat in front of Rohit, in case I flinched or did something stupidly embarrassing.

"Wow, you really eat a lot, don't you?" Jay said, raising his eyebrows at my cold plate of food.

I laughed. "I know. I must admit I have gone past that stage of hunger." I somehow needed him to break up the tension.

"Hmm, yes, I can't see why. You've barely touched anything," he said. I smiled. "Shall we head back?"

"Yes, let's do that. I can take you through another route, so you know," Rohit suggested helpfully.

"Okay, will see you guys later. I have a conference call now," Jay explained as he raised himself from his seat.

We headed back to the office floor. It was a new building with glass panels all the way round, allowing us to see out across the business park. Being there made me feel as though all my efforts were finally being realised, that I had achieved something, that I had finally made it, that the years spent fighting through education were finally here, but I could no longer take pleasure in it. It was all being drowned out by my subconscious. All the achievements, success and glory were being absorbed out by one sweet and bitter truth. *You love him, and you can't be with him.*

I knew that falling for Rohit was like tempting myself with the forbidden fruit, that under my parents' eyes, I would be placed in the fires of hell. It was forbidden to marry for love. In fact, my parents' culture despised love marriages. Mamajee once said that she would rather kill us if we were caught dating or being with anyone. Love, infatuation and sexual attraction were all sins, a distraction from the word of Allah, and a parent's honour was at stake when anyone was caught in a relationship outside marriage. I had heard of enough honour killings of girls in our family circle, parents sent to prison for killing their daughter for the shame and dishonour they had brought them, or parents killing themselves or ending up in hospital with heart attacks because of the dishonour or shame that their daughter had brought them. I had already come close to death once just from mentioning a boy's name.

Would I be prepared to sacrifice my right to freedom? After all of the hurdles I had come up against with my family for the right to education for freedom? Wouldn't this be compromising it? What I had been granted was a privilege in their eyes, and I owed them something for that. It was all in one word that I had been given such a privilege, *honour*. It was by their decree that I would save them from any disgrace and spare them any dishonour. Falling in love was one of those disgraces, and moreover, with someone who was not the same race and religion was culturally equated to playing with hellfire. I knew I was entering dangerous territory, one that would lead to being cast out, beaten up and chastised by the whole community.

And most important, beyond the disgrace and dishonour, was my word. That promise to Mamajee that I had made all those years ago, when I had vowed to honour her wishes if she would stay with us. I could only think how much of a betrayal it would be, how all the years she had sacrificed to raise me would all have been in vain.

I couldn't do this to her. *No*, I said to myself. I resisted my feelings, pushed them down somewhere.

But the denial only fortified those feelings more for Rohit, and when they surfaced, it became harder and harder to resist them.

Seeing Rohit every day unravelled an unspoken divine trinket of feelings that my mind, body and soul could not deny. He had a tender and overwhelmingly joyous effect on my entire being. I craved his presence when he wasn't present, and immediately blocked those sensations when he was present. I also denied and refused to acknowledge any interest he had towards me, although we both knew that our work together was more of an excuse to be around each other. Our days were spent in the engineering labs, analysing and testing new solutions that secretly gave way to new meanings. *At least if I can't be with him*, I thought, *we can work together. I could get by if he's just present.*

Soon enough though, we became inseparable. The long coffee breaks, discussing theories seemed almost cryptic code for "I can't get enough of you." The discussions at the whiteboard became a moment to mutually admire each other, and the endless time in the labs were the closest encounters of tenderness I had experienced.

We were without words, silently and in an unspeakable language connected in some timeless, boundless ecstasy.

One afternoon I came to realise how timeless it felt with Rohit. I looked at the clock and discovered it was almost 9 p.m.

"Oh no!" I said, surprised and baffled. "I really have to go; it's getting really late, and I didn't realise we have been here that long."

"Yikes!" he said, jumping from his seat. "My goodness! It is late."

We both laughed, and it faded into a long smile that felt intense and awkward at the same time.

"Are you going to be okay getting back?" he asked.

"Oh, yes, absolutely … I am driving home, anyhow."

He looked at me intently. I could have spent the rest of the night gazing back at him, but my mind resisted as I unlocked from the heavenly trance.

"Let's pack up, then, and get out of here," he said, putting his things together in a pile. We walked towards the car park together. It was dark and quiet, and there were no cars around.

"Let me walk you to your car," he said. As we walked back, I could have almost wished that our time wasn't ending. I didn't want to leave; I didn't want to escape the warm, fuzzy and addictive state I felt around him.

"Thanks for showing me all of the new features with that solution," I said. "It is pretty amazing stuff," I said coolly, hoping I didn't stumble over my words.

He paused, stopping to take a breath as he turned to face me eye to eye. "I am really glad you are here, Eleanor, to help with it."

Help me break free, I said to the seven-year-old me inside.

Come on, just go. This will hurt, I pictured her saying, and tugging at my arm.

A cold wind swept my long hair across my face, shrouding my view of his face, and I could almost feel relieved that he could no longer read me. I know it would have only taken one slight move and I would have been in his arms.

"I best go," I said calmly from beneath the veil of windswept hair. "I will see you in the morning?"

He smiled calmly. "Of course. See you tomorrow."

I turned to open the car door.

"How about you call me when you get back?" he said abruptly. "Just to make sure you got home safely."

"Oh, sure, yes, let me do that. I will call you." I felt the words melt in my mind like warm butter as I tried to keep my cool. I was secretly bursting inside.

He smiled tenderly back. "Okay, Eleanor. I will speak to you later."

*

When I arrived home, I found my housemates, Andrea and Sean, in the living room, watching TV.

"You are back late," she said.

"Yes," I said. "It's been a long day. I have been in the lab with Rohit, going through things."

She looked at me with raised eyebrows. *Please don't ask any questions*, I thought, but knowing Andrea, she had her way of seeing right through me, and I sensed that she knew something was up.

"Oh, I am so hungry. I think I will get changed and grab a bite," I said, trying to move from the subject.

"Oka-a-ay," she said with a smirk. That normally meant more questions later.

I went back to my room, where I collapsed on the bed to melt into the moments with Rohit. My heart filled with butterflies as I went over my day with him, every conversation. The way he looked at me, the small token gesture of him walking me back. His beautiful, calming voice that made every vein in my body pulsate. I kept an imprint of his smiling face in my mind's eye. He was to me everything beautiful and all things magical in one place. I sank into my pillow, closing my eyes to indulge in this feeling.

Then suddenly my phone beeped. I had a text message. It was Rohit. I excitedly read it. "Hi, Eleanor, great to have got through all of that work today, thank you for your help, did you get back home safely?"

Oh my! I thought. My fingers trembled as I read his text.

"Hi Rohit, thank you for all the items you went through. I did get back safely, thank you for asking, how about you?"

We continued to exchange texts the whole night in this way.

"Oh wow, this is crazy!" he said in one text. "I have never texted anyone this late."

I started to worry that I was taking up his time. "Oh, I am sorry, I will let you get on!" I replied, texting frantically.

"No, I just mean that it is really nice to have met someone like you, Eleanor."

I smiled, and I felt a sublime warmth from his words. "You too, Rohit, goodnight, will speak tomorrow?"

"Yes, goodnight Eleanor."

It was 11 p.m., and I still hadn't had dinner and had no desire for food or water. All I could feel was love, a love that brought joy and sorrow all at the same time. It was a path I was told I couldn't take but felt consumed in my desire to take it. *I can't allow this to happen,* I thought. *I mustn't.*

The following morning, I woke to a panging hunger. I was late for work and skipped breakfast. Slipping into some jeans and a T-shirt, I headed straight to the office.

I felt my heart skip a beat as Rohit walked in.

"Morning, Eleanor," he whispered softly as he passed my desk. His warm, velvety voice hummed through my ears. I looked up coolly from the desk divider.

"Morning." I smiled. Oh, how I loved the sound of his voice. I recounted it in my mind. *No, Eleanor. No*, I told myself. *No, it must stop. You can't do this; you can't indulge anymore.*

The seven-year-old me came out again. She was standing in white tights, a blue dress and with bob-cut hair this time. *You promised, remember?* she scolded.

I tried to snap out of it and busied myself with reading some emails, but I could feel his presence as he leaned over the desk divider.

"What are you doing?" he whispered.

I looked up, trying to ignore the thoughts in my head. "Oh, I was just checking my email," I said, blushing, as if it was a stupid thing to be doing.

"Have you had breakfast?" he asked.

"No, I must admit I haven't."

"I'm starving. I didn't eat last night," he said, shaking his head.

"No, er ... neither did I," I said, absurdly vanquishing relief and revelry at his mention of it.

"Shall we ...?"

"Yes, let's do that," I said, trying to stay within the realms of professionalism. I closed my laptop and followed him down the stairway. Just then we passed Jay.

"Morning, Jay," we both said, jumping at the sight of him as he made his way up the stairs. I am sure it looked a little odd. He paused to look at us suspiciously.

"What are you guys up to?" he said, addressing us with a wide smile.

"We were just going to breakfast," Rohit added quickly. "Did you want to join us?"

In my head I wanted Rohit all to myself, but I calmly chimed in. "Yes, Jay, how about you join us?"

"No, no, you two lovebirds go ahead without me." He winked.

I looked at him, incredulously, and tried convincing him that his comment had no credibility, and as Rohit and I tried laughing it off, I could see in Jay's face it was plainer than words, what we were trying to hide.

We both sat and ate our breakfast silently, our eyes never making contact as we sipped our coffee. It was almost unnecessary to speak as we both stared out of the window, our backs resting on the chairs, our hands wrapped around our mugs of coffee.

"Listen, Eleanor, I am sorry for being so intense last night," he said, looking down at his plate in thought.

"No, you weren't intense," I said, shaking my head and sipping coffee. I didn't want him to apologise. I wanted him to take back his words. There was something subtle yet meaningful in our silent breakfast that I couldn't let words spoil.

"Shall we go back?" I said, looking at him eye to eye. I sensed he knew it. He knew it was okay, what he felt.

"Yes." He nodded, his eyes penetrating mine. "Let's go back up and finish off that lab."

We spent the rest of the day in the lab, refocusing our minds to our work, through testing applications and trialling new technologies, almost as if there was a silent agreement between us on staying professional.

After our labs, we wandered back to our desks, where we found Jay smiling at us with a grin as wide as a Cheshire cat. We both responded back with a straight face.

His grin faded out. "So, what are you guys up to on Thursday?" he asked, straightening himself in his chair. I looked at Rohit as if it wasn't a question for me.

"No ... no plans really. What about you, Jay?" Rohit asked casually.

"Just thinking maybe we should all go out for drinks, get the grads out for a bit, especially when you have been working them so hard in that lab," he said, grinning at me for an answer.

I remained silent, not wanting to acknowledge his tone or insinuation.

"Yes, sounds good, Jay. Where are you thinking?" I said calmly.

"Well, Dom had some ideas; there's that place in north London that has music until quite late. We could go there."

"Okay." I nodded.

Rohit looked at Jay and nodded in agreement. "Okay, you'll be getting the beers, then, Jay?" he replied cheekily.

Jay smiled. "Well, you know, that depends if I can count by the third beer!" he said with an inside giggle at his own witty remarks.

I didn't want to let myself go: I worried about what would happen if I got drunk, what would happen if we opened up. I brought myself back to reality. *There isn't anything to worry about: we don't know each other; we don't love each other; and there is nothing,* nothing, *that can happen here. And besides, we work together; we have to stay professional.*

CHAPTER TWENTY-SEVEN
– *Love Conquers All* –

The office drinks were held at a large pub in north London that smelled of cider and had sticky floors. There were low-lit chandeliers that added to the seedy atmosphere. I was convinced I was the only girl in the entire pub, let alone the only girl in our group, as an army of brutes winked when passing me. The flow of beers queued up on my side of the table, and I could no longer keep up with the pace.

"Drink up!" urged Jay. "What is it with you? You don't drink or eat?"

I looked at the three rounds that had been bought by the other team members. "I am such a lightweight, I know! I won't get through three of these, Jay. Anyone want one?"

"Eleanor," Jay said, resting a meaty arm on my shoulder, "if someone buys you a drink, you have to drink it."

I laughed at him, completely knowing there was no such rule. Obligingly, I still managed to drink all three pints over the course of a few hours, and as the music became louder and the noise from the base buzzed in my head, I could no longer hear Jay's long-drawn-out conversation about work. I could see Rohit from where I sat, laughing and talking to the team. I could sense the deliberate distance between us, avoiding each other's eye contact in case it aroused any suspicions.

The drinks kept flowing, and before I knew it, another round of shots was laid out on the table. Soon I was forgetting conversations and losing track of time. Some of the group left, and the rest of us made our way to hear the band playing upstairs. Jay had already fixed us all with another round of tequila shots as we made our way up. The guys went on ahead as Rohit and I followed them up the stairs. The lights were low, and the wooden stairs were hard to trace with my fuzzy head. I hobbled on my heels, trying to balance on the next step. The upstairs led to a dark hall with dim lighting that made it difficult to see ahead of us. Music echoed from each corner, and as the base got louder, my ears felt deafened by the noise.

Rohit slowly followed me up the stairs. I felt him subtly holding my hand to steady me, but in the darkness of that hallway, I felt the profoundness of this gesture. His fingers locked into mine came with tiny morsels of unspoken words, intense, irresistible and no longer deniable. I squeezed his hand gently back, signalling a mutual desire. We approached the floor and headed into the light, where we silently faced each other. The spotlights beamed on our faces in different colours, our hands left with an imprint of each other as we let go. There was nothing that needed to be said; the truth stood between us. We could barely look at each other without it staring back at us. We knew. We knew what we felt; we knew what it meant; and we knew we couldn't be together.

*

For the next few weeks, we continued on silently, as if there was nothing other than work to be focused on. We were in full motion with the testing and switched to professional mode. Rohit occupied himself on other projects. We exchanged messages now and again about work.

"How are you getting on with that report?" we would ask each other. Messages that seemed more cryptic code for "Hello", "I miss you", "I love you, and I don't care", but we kept our distance and avoided working together as much as possible.

It didn't seem to matter what we exchanged in practice; we both knew we were locked in something far more than work or friendship, something that seemed only guarded by the physical, outer world. We could see there could be no future in those desires and mutually sensed that denial between us. But there was no mistaking our bond for our colleagues in the office. We weren't easily getting away from the rumours; everybody who saw us together immediately thought we were a couple, and even during our business trips, the travel attendants assumed we were an item. We were quick to deny and laugh off any assumptions. After all, there was nothing physically being exemplified in our behaviour towards each other. It didn't matter though: what we didn't say in words or actions was unmistakable to those around us.

"Come on, guys," one colleague commented after a meeting. "There is definitely chemistry there." I could almost feel his insistence on the matter, as if it were of prime importance to him.

We joked and laughed at these moments, but in our hearts, we knew we denied ourselves something the world around us already knew. It became debilitating as we proved to the world there was nothing between us. We siloed ourselves further, avoided lab work or being in the same meeting room. In our minds this truth was unbearable, unthinkable and tasted of severe consequences and divide between our families. Rohit being Hindu and I being a Muslim would leave our parents devastated. It felt selfish to fulfil our own needs when our families would suffer. Their reputations ruined? No. We couldn't. We wouldn't want that. We didn't want to create such a huge dent in our family lives.

I only entertained those thoughts of Rohit alone in my room. There, I was free to indulge in the kind of life we would have if we could be free to love each other. I thought about what it would be like to spend time with him openly, without a care about what anyone thought at work, the places we could be seen at together and the conversations we would have, but all of this was overshadowed by the dark reality and disruption it would bring to our families' lives. I would bring shame to my family and would leave a permanent scar on his. And so, we continued to bury those feelings by focusing on work and pretending that every precious glance at each other was not felt lovingly.

*

A couple of months went by, and our professional relationship became somewhat closed to the idea. Rohit had organised a meetup in London with our work colleagues. It was a new bar called Heaven. With our minds now closed to any such feelings, we resumed in a professional manner with our friends from work. That night, a large contingent had joined us from the Paris office, and most of the party had dispersed to the club upstairs by the end of the night. Rohit had spent most of the evening in deep discussions about work with some colleagues and occasionally had glanced over to see who I was talking to. The conversation that I was having with the pair of Parisian architects had long been exhausted, and I excused myself to the bathroom.

When I came back, Rohit had gone; his bag and coat were no longer at the table. I went looking for the rest of the group in the club, making my way through a sea of hands and bodies on the dance floor, some lingering on my behind as I waded past. The music pumping loud drew in a lucid-dreamlike scene. I found one of the girls who we had met earlier on and asked her whether she had seen Rohit. She replied blankly that she hadn't seen him, and she thought he might have left.

I felt devastated. I didn't think he would leave like that without me. *Perhaps he has just had enough*, I thought. I carried on aimlessly walking through the sea of people in the club. It could easily have been the alcohol, but why did this hurt so much? *It would have hurt less if he had stabbed me with a blunt object*, I thought. *How could he just walk out on me like that? Or could I be getting worked up over nothing? After all, we were just colleagues.*

I roamed the terrace, filled with partygoers drinking, subdued and disheartened, before deciding to collect my bags and leave for the night. Then I saw the girl from the dance floor approaching me.

"Hey, wait!" she called out. "Rohit, he's here! I found him! He has been looking for you!" she said, smiling delightedly. Behind her stood Rohit. He looked at me with a smile of intense relief, and I looked back at him, feeling the same. Then the girl looked at both of us.

"Are you guys together?" she asked. We both laughed at this as if it were an undeniably funny statement.

Then something quite extraordinary happened. The girl, who we had only met that night and who had no prior knowledge of our relationship, took us by the hand, joined us together and said before departing, "It doesn't matter what anyone else thinks. You guys were meant for each other."

I was left in stunned silence by her words, and as we both locked in that warm embrace, we relented and could no longer deny it. I still remember the smile as we looked at each other, that warm acceptance of the truth and that we should just give up pretending. I felt this amazing rush, his warm body against mine, his arms wrapping around my shoulders.

"I thought you had left," he finally whispered in my ear. "I was looking for you everywhere." He clutched me tightly, cradling me in his arms, and gently kissed my neck.

"I was looking for you, too," I said, holding him tightly and holding back tears.

We looked at each other, locked in our warm embrace. His bittersweet smile gazed back at me as he swept my hair away from my face. I felt his smooth marble hands stroke my face, and as I closed my eyes, I felt the softness of his lips against mine.

The sensation rippled down my body and left my heart to flutter. I didn't want to hide anymore; I wanted all of what I felt.

Then he looked at me, his eyes fuzzy, drunk from the moment. "I am in heaven, Eleanor. I am in heaven with you," he cried as he held my face, and we locked into a deep and long kiss.

We moved to a lounge bench that was empty in a dark corner of the club. I leaned into his chest, and he stroked my hair.

"You are beautiful, you know that, Eleanor. I haven't been able to take my eyes off you from the moment we met." His arms around me, cradling me, and each slight touch sending a ripple down my back. "Shall we go?" he said. I nodded.

Neither of us wanted to end the night. I wanted more and he wanted me too. We made love, our naked bodies close together without any cares or fears. We scoured each other's bodies with our hands. His fingers pulled down my clothes and cupped my breast. I surrendered all my inhibitions, lost all pretences; anything else now felt like a lie. We were completely locked in the moment, that place where nothing else in your mind could enter. He brought me gently back onto the bed, his elbows above my shoulders. I felt his body, warm and heavy, all over me like a warm blanket.

Nothing can take this away, I thought. *I want all of you.*

We closed our eyes, our faces close together, warming up by each other's breath. Our bodies joined together in love, our souls united in a peaceful place. We were together; physically, mentally, spiritually, we were at one as we fell into a blissful sleep together.

*

I woke slightly moving. Rohit was asleep above me, gazing down. I felt embarrassed: I must have looked a mess, while he looked rugged and sexy. I saw myself in the mirror like a reflection of a zombie. He smiled at me warmly as he interlocked his fingers into mine. I suddenly stopped caring, because the look on his face said he was content. He took another deep breath, looking deeply into me.

"I don't want to go, but I better make a move back to the office," he said sleepily.

"I know," I said, smiling. "Me too!"

We both laughed. It was funny and weird but all too familiar all at the same time.

He kissed my hands. "I will see you in the office, then?" He smiled.

*

Things went on unnoticed in the office, or so it felt when I arrived. Rohit turned up later. I felt an instant rush of excitement from seeing him as I walked in. He gave me a sideways nod on passing my desk.

I wondered how we were going to keep this a secret. It was not that people didn't have relationships in the office, it just seemed awkward. He was matey with his colleagues, and I might just tip the balance. *Still*, I thought, *there's no point in thinking about it. The most amazing thing happened last night, and I cherish that. Nothing can be taken away from that.*

The rest of the week seemed a little obscure in our interactions. Rohit spent most of his time focusing on work, and I came to realise there was little or no conversation between us during the day. Our nights were filled with endless conversation on the phone on all sorts of topics, from books to music to the people at work. I loved Rohit's calls and anxiously waited for the phone to ring. I desperately wanted to see him and be with him again but didn't know how to express it. It was difficult to read whether he felt the same, as he made no advancements on meeting up.

I sat out my time in the office, watching his every move, wondering and waiting for some possible sign that all of this was true, but it was as though I had become invisible to him. Sometimes I would walk over to ask a question, and he would ask me to hold on. A week had gone by, and I became nervous and obsessed as to whether he still wanted to be with me. While our conversations were full of amazing stories at night, I couldn't help but wonder whether he had time for anything more. On Thursday night, when we spoke on the phone, I decided to confront him about it.

"So, I just wanted to ask," I said, interrupting his flow and trying to stay cool. "What are you up to this weekend?"

"I am not sure," he said. "What about you?"

"Well, I have nothing planned."

"Do you want to come and meet me? Some of my friends might be coming over on the weekend," he said calmly.

"Sure," I said. "It will be nice to meet them." I immediately felt a sigh of relief.

He still wants to be with me, I thought. *It must have just been a busy week, that's all.*

*

On Saturday night I dressed casually in some fairly flattering jeans and a long-sleeved burgundy top and drove over to Rohit's house. He lived at home with his dad and two brothers. Rohit's mother had passed away from cancer when he was twelve years old, and he helped support his dad with running the family. He was very close to his dad and his brothers. He had the house to himself that night, as his father had gone to the temple that evening.

They lived in a post-war semi-detached house, typical of Harrow suburbia. I knocked on the door and saw that glow of Rohit that I had fallen in love with. I gravitated towards him, and he pulled me in with a welcoming smile.

I gazed back at him, filled with that fuzzy feeling that loving gives you. "I am so happy to see you."

He took my hand, guiding me through the hallway and into the kitchen. It was a tired-looking house, as if everything had been kept the way his mother had left it, timelessly, as though everything had stopped when she had. The hallway had a dusty olive carpet and patterned wallpaper. There were faded pictures of his mother, garlanded around the frame with artificial flowers. Beneath it stood a small shrine with incense and a tray of candles, where they sat and prayed. Her presence echoed around each room with an everlasting imprint of how she ran things. Her belongings, shoes, purse and necklace mingled loosely on a shelf amongst car keys, cups and trinkets as if she would be back home any moment. I couldn't imagine what it would be like to lose someone like that, how one would deal with it, and I knew that it was hard for Rohit to talk about it. I didn't say any more: it became evident it wasn't up for discussion tonight.

"Can I get you a drink, Eleanor?"

I smiled. "Yes, please. I'll have a tea if you are making one." He poured water into a kettle and switched it on. Then he turned towards me, taking my hands to pull me nearer. I felt this amazing energy rush through me as he kissed me.

"I have wanted to be with you all week." He smiled.

Just then there was a knock on the door.

"Let me get that," he said. His friends had turned up, and I could hear a lot of hellos from a group of people huddled at the entrance.

I stood by the hallway and watched him embrace the group of guests who had arrived. They all seemed to love this guy just as much as I did.

Then they paused to turn and look at me. "Oh, guys, this is Eleanor, a colleague of mine from work," Rohit said, smiling.

My heart immediately sank. I wasn't his girlfriend, or friend even. I was just a colleague. It was a blow that my smile could not recover a response to easily. I nodded and tried to look calm. The rest of the night I spent hanging out with his many friends, although we didn't really gel. I didn't have a lot to say, and they seemed pretty involved in conversation with other friends and stories about their times together.

I sat the whole time on the couch, huddled into the corner with a cold cup of tea. Silently watching, silently observing. I felt out of place and no longer could justify what I was doing there. Rohit again didn't have as much time for me either, although I completely understood his friends were important to him. He obviously had a lot of socialising to do that night, and I was getting in the way of that. It was approaching 10 p.m., and I felt as though I had outstayed my welcome. In some ways, it felt no longer cool or right being there. Surely his friends didn't really want to talk to me. I was just a colleague, and maybe for Rohit, he should just be with them that night.

"Rohit, I am going to go now," I said, rising from the sofa. "It's getting late."

"Are you going? Are you sure? Why don't you stay?" he said, confused. I would have stayed the whole night just to be around him, but something was telling me that I should do the right thing by him.

"I don't want to drive home too late. Let's catch up some other time."

"Okay," he said, looking faintly saddened. "Will you be okay getting home?" he asked, concerned.

"Yes, of course!" I said, incredulously. "I will call you when I get back," I said, smiling at him.

And with that I left, feeling rather disappointed and out of place.

I thought about what this all meant driving home. It seemed odd that he didn't want to mention me to his friends. At the same time, it seemed okay to say that I was a colleague, as we had only just started seeing each other in that way.

When I arrived home and got settled, I called Rohit. It was almost midnight.

"It was nice getting to meet your friends," I said. "Do they know about us?" I asked.

There was a silence in his voice. "No," he said, hesitating. "I haven't told them anything yet."

I paused to compile my response. "Do you think you ever will, you know, tell them about me, I mean?" I asked, half not wanting to hear the answer.

He took a deep breath and paused. "This ... this isn't going to be easy, is it, Eleanor?"

I paused, silent. I couldn't answer the question with words, but I knew the answer. We knew where this was heading.

"My dad, Eleanor, he would fall apart if he knew. I can't afford to let that happen, not after everything he has been through with my mum." He took another aching breath and fell silent in thought and worry.

"I know," I said. "I have the same issues: my parents would be devastated, and they would cast me out and probably burn me alive!"

How silly of me. I had almost fallen into denial of these consequences. Speaking to him on the phone was a world away from the reality of it. Our voices locked into a melody of love for each other. I knew what I felt for him, and he knew what he felt for me. And in that time and space, we were completely immersed in that feeling of love. We didn't need to care for anything else. It felt timeless, being together; it was the kind of love where the physical reality of our love was so minor in comparison to what truly and deeply was felt in each other's presence.

After our long talk, I lay there on my bed and thought about how things were for Rohit and me, how our feelings were confined in a timeless bubble that was liberating, and we could love each other so deeply, yet how unwelcomed, how detrimental and precarious it was to the world around us. Rohit and I had a bond that was far superior to anything from where I stood. Very few words needed to be said; very few actions were needed to feel it. I just had to look at him, and I felt its warmth over me, mentally, spiritually, emotionally and physically. We had something that felt far beyond worldly things, and we knew that our feelings weren't bound to these conditions. But how long would we be able to sustain such love? How could we give to each other's needs if the world had forbidden it?

From then on, we barely saw each other out of office hours. We spoke endlessly on the phone until one evening I sensed something had changed. He was unusually quiet and distant in his responses on the phone.

"Everything okay, Rohit?" I asked.

"Well, not really ... It's my dad, Eleanor," he said. "He's ... he's trying to introduce me to some girls."

CHAPTER TWENTY-EIGHT
– *Love Lost* –

I fell silent for a moment. I knew what it meant, but there were no words to describe how it felt.

"Eleanor … are you there?"

"Yes, I am," I said, clearing my dry throat. "So … what are you going to do about it?" I asked, pushing down the pain.

"I don't know … I don't know, Eleanor."

"Maybe you should just meet them," I said hesitantly. I wanted the words to run back into my mouth, but it was the right thing to do, the right thing to say.

"I think … I think I have to … I mean, it doesn't mean anything," he said, quite matter of fact.

"Doesn't it?"

"I love you, Eleanor … I don't think you replace love; it's not a physical thing," he said. "That never changes; that will always be there."

It was hard to hear it. I felt close to him and far from him all at the same time. What did that mean? What was a future for us in all of this? My internal being toiled with these questions, and my mouth became dry of words. The harsh reality was that there wasn't one. Not in the worldly sense.

"I hope, Rohit, and this is the most important thing to realise in loving someone, that you will find peace in every decision you make. I just want you, more than anything, to be happy."

*

The weeks went by; trees glistened in the summer sunshine, the days longer, the warm nights, yet nothing seemed appealing to observe anymore. In the office, I could hear Rohit on calls with various potentials that his dad had put him forward for, and in the evening, he would call to tell me all about them. We both laughed about it, but inside I was cut open and bleeding from his casual and frank discussions about the meet-ups and awkward conversations he was having with potential women, one of whom could possibly be his future spouse. He complained about how empty it was, how dry the conversations about background and work were. Why sitting there was as meaningless as spitting out vowels and consonants. Underneath, though, I was crying: each one of these meaningless meet-ups was another blow to my ego, another scratch on the wall to mark that our time was up.

Our relationship was slowly fading into the meaningless territory. There was even less room for it now, as if it had no place on earth. At work we hardly spoke, and I watched him leave the office week after week so that he could be lined up for dates with complete strangers. Sometimes he passed my desk with a half-smile and an air of reluctance at what his father was arranging for him. I sensed he was coming to accept it, and he was drifting away from me.

At times I was livid; I wanted to kill him, hurt him, make him feel the poison he was drip-feeding me with. But I wasn't going to show it. It wasn't his problem. It was mine alone.

*

One afternoon I got an unexpected visit from a friend at work called Rickesh. I met Rickesh at boot camp, and we'd worked together for a while.

"Hey, Eleanor. How's it going?" he said, approaching my desk. "Fancy a quick coffee? Got something I need to talk to you about."

"Sure, let's go," I said. I felt a little perplexed by the abruptness of his request, as I had not spoken to Rickesh in over a year.

We headed down to the cafeteria. We laughed about the funny times we'd had on a kick-off and caught up on work before the pleasantries receded, and I sensed the real conversation pressing on his mind. "Actually, Eleanor, I wanted to ask you something," he said, looking down in thought at the coffee cup in front of him. "Do you know much about Rohit?"

"Rohit? Yeah, of course," I said. "I work with him."

"Yes, I thought so. It's just that, you know, I know he's Indian, and my family and I are looking for someone for my sister, so I was hoping you could help me get them together for a date."

I was speechless and nearly fell out of my chair. How could I possibly do this? As if it was not hard enough to be with someone who was dating other people, now I would be organising dates for him?

"I don't know, Rickesh. You know, it's not really my business. I am not sure I am the best person. I mean, I really only know him when it comes to work ... I am sure he would be interested in meeting her though."

"Hmm, I see," he said thoughtfully, and sighed. "I just thought, well, you guys hang out a lot and maybe there might be an opportunity for you to introduce her."

"Oh, right, I see," I said. I felt tense from the words, the weight of what he was asking me. Was I being selfish for not wanting to help? My mind whirled between guilt and kindness, between right and wrong, and as the air thickened, I felt the words pass my lips. "How about this?" I said. "How about we all go out one night, and if it works, it works, and if it doesn't, it doesn't?"

"Okay." He nodded in agreement. "Yes, that sounds good. I think that's a good idea."

My heart pounded, and I tried to find sense in my thinking. *What am I doing? Is this right? What if something happens? Yes, but what if there is nothing in it? It could be harmless. We could all just continue as normal, be friends, anyhow. Nothing has to happen here, and if he truly loves me, then there is nothing to worry about.* I tried to convince myself that the latter perspective was right: let this happen. After all, he had met many women now, and he hadn't been interested in any of them, so what difference would this one make?

*

A week later I had set up a night out with Rickesh, his sister and friends, my team, colleagues' friends, and of course, most importantly, the person I loved the most. Rohit.

Andrea wasn't sure when I mentioned what I had planned over dinner at home.

"Eleanor, this is just not right. You love Rohit. Surely you can't do this to yourself."

"He's doing it anyway. And I feel like I have to now, for Rickesh. He's put me in this awkward situation. I mean, he wants Rohit to meet his sister, and I didn't know what else to say to him. Just going out as a group seemed pretty harmless."

She sighed, reluctantly. "No, you don't have to do anything. Why are you putting yourself through this? It would be heartbreaking, wouldn't it, to see this unfold? And if it works out, then what?"

She tried to pull a response through my dazed exterior. It made complete sense, what she was telling me, and she was right, I didn't want to do this, and yet at the same time, I felt cornered into arranging a date for the person I loved the most.

"Yes, I know it will. It will hurt, Andrea, I know, but I think we have to learn to love without limits. Nothing changes about how I feel, and maybe that's the same for him. We know the outcome of us being together would hurt our families, and I have had to spend a lot of time working on accepting that. I have to learn to let go." I could almost feel my soul crying inside as I said the words.

Andrea could see how it hurt, and as one of my closest friends, she tried in her capacity to empathise. "I don't know, Eleanor; I think it's a mistake, but let's just see how it all plays out, then, shall we?"

We met everyone at the Club Bar in central London. A towering staircase with an overhanging chandelier dazzled and shimmered in the foyer. Much to my despair, Rickesh had already arrived with a clan of friends and headed towards where Andrea and I were seated at the bar.

"Hey, Eleanor," he said, patting me gently on the shoulder. "This is my sister, Nia."

I turned to my right, and there stood a stunning girl with large brown eyes, a slim face and a beautiful figure.

I felt like my heart had fallen out and was now flipping and palpitating on the floor when I saw her. I knew there was a big chance Rohit would be attracted to her.

"Hi," she said, smiling at me and turning to greet Andrea. Andrea nodded, looking bemused, switching glances at the pair of us while sipping her Martini.

Rohit hadn't yet arrived, and Andrea and I spent some time mingling with the three of them as we sipped on another round of Martinis. More of Nia's friends arrived, and they huddled round a bar table, giggling and laughing. I joined Andrea again at the bar, where she had sat observing the group.

"She seems nice," she said, observably. "She's very pretty, isn't she?" she remarked, as if she was trying to kill me with her words. She knew it hurt.

"She is, yes, isn't she?" I said calmly. "And she's Hindu, and vegetarian, you know," I said, smiling.

"Hmm, nothing like a good Indian vegetarian, is there?" she mocked.

Andrea could see right through it. "This is a mistake, Eleanor, but if this is what you need to do, then I guess I will be there for you." She pointed her head towards the door. "Looks like Rohit's here."

Rohit walked in through the bar area with Jay and a few other mutual colleagues. My heart skipped a beat as I saw how pleased he was to see me. How I longed to be locked in his embrace, to withdraw from the plan. He looked handsome in a black long-sleeved T-shirt and grey jeans. I wanted him to wrap his arms around me, feel his warm caress. Our eyes locked, and I felt a divine moment between us. But it was disrupted by Rickesh, who came over to greet us.

"Hey, Rohit," he said, shaking his hand. "I'm Rickesh, one of the grads on the programme, like Eleanor."

"Ah, good to meet you," Rohit said cheerily. He was immediately distracted by Jay, who had pulled him to the bar to order a drink.

"Sorry, will be back in a minute," he assured Rickesh.

Rickesh pulled me aside. "Hey, Eleanor, do you think you could introduce Rohit to Nia now?" he said, nudging.

Oh, please don't do this to me, I cried inside. *If only he knew what he was asking me to do*, I thought. "Of course!" I said excitedly. "Let me go speak to Nia now."

Nia was now over at the bar, mingling with her friends.

"Hey, Nia," I said coolly. "I just wanted to introduce you to somebody – you know how your brother wanted you to meet someone."

"Oh yes," she said.

"Well," I said, turning her to where Rohit stood talking to Jay, "he is over there."

She looked over, pausing for a moment as she saw him laughing with Jay.

"So, what do you think?" I asked her.

"Yes," she said, "he's nice. I really like him." She gazed over at him as though it was love at first sight.

Oh no! I thought to myself. *This is not what I wanted, but okay, she might like him, but it doesn't mean it's the same for him.*

"Come, let me introduce you," I said blankly, trying not to let my mind stir up the consequences as I walked her over to where Rohit stood.

"Rohit," I said, pressing his arm to get his attention. "This is Nia, Rickesh's sister."

"Oh, hi!" he said, shaking her hand. The three of us stood in awkward silence for a moment before I relented to making conversation.

"Erm, did you know Nia is vegetarian?" I said, feeling quite stupid.

Rohit looked at me like he could see right through me. He knew I was up to something, the way he looked at me silently and nodded just from that introduction. I tried not to get caught in the tension between us.

"Can I get either of you a drink?" I said politely, trying to change the subject.

"Er, no thanks. I have a beer right here," Rohit replied dryly.

"Nia, how about you, hon?" I asked. *Hon*, I thought, as if suddenly she was my best friend or something.

"Yes, I will have a glass of white, please."

I nodded and moved back to the bar. I felt light-headed and gutted for myself.

They hung out together for a while, and I just couldn't bear to look at them together talking. Nia made her way back to a lounge area next to the dance floor, where her friends and she rocked a little to the music. I sat alone for a moment, feeling cut open, knocking my gin and tonic back as though it had healing properties.

Rohit strolled over and sat next to me. We both looked on, watching the others cavorting on the dance floor.

"Eleanor, what the hell are you doing?" he asked.

"What am I doing?" I said, shaking my head and almost crying.

"You know more than me about where this is heading, don't you?" He looked down despondently into the floor.

"I just want you to be happy, Rohit," I said. "And," I said, shaking my head in defeat, "I am not the one who makes you feel like that. Maybe if you met the right person, you would feel complete. But I can't complete you. I said you might like her, and she might be the one."

He shook his head as if it was impossible to see it.

"And you would be happy with that?" he said, looking at me.

"I don't know how you can expect me to answer that," I said, looking down.

We both looked over at Nia dancing with her friends. She beckoned me over and then tottered over to drag me onto the dance floor.

"Come, Eleanor, I heard you are good on the dance floor."

I turned to glance at Rohit as I joined Nia in the crowd. He sat, head down, elbows resting on his knees, beer bottle in hand. Then Nia went over and sat with him near the lounge. A sea of arms rose above my head on the dance floor, where the music livened to a hit song, and I burrowed into the music, along with the dancing bodies.

It felt like my soul had let go of my body and I had become an empty corpse as I submerged in the crowd. I wanted to be out of here. I couldn't bear the feeling any longer and went over to say goodbye to Nia, who had returned to the lounge to mingle with her friends.

"Nia, it was nice to have met you, and hopefully, see you again."

She gave me a hug. "Yes, it was nice meeting you too, and hopefully, see you soon."

Rohit stood close by, looking at me.

I looked back at him as we breathed in a moment together, that face that I knew so well. I sent him a look of farewell, that I would see him in the next lifetime, that maybe one day we might reincarnate into other bodies that were the right race, caste, colour, vegetarian, had a great job and family. Maybe then we could fall in love and be with each other.

"Goodbye, Rohit. See you in the office," I said with a half-smile.

His face seemed grief-stricken.

It was almost 3 a.m. by the time I left the club. I hailed a taxi and managed to stop myself from crying all the way home. I had lost track of Andrea; she must have left earlier in the night.

Rohit didn't call that night, and I wondered whether it was just too late or whether things really had developed with Nia.

I woke the next morning, startled by a text from her.

"Hi, Eleanor, it was a great night last night, just to let you know, Rohit and I went back to mine. Nothing happened, he stayed over, and we just talked."

I felt like death had caught me and was now dragging my body to the funeral pyre. *Why would he have gone? Did he really have to?* I kept wondering what all this meant. Here I was, hoping that there was something left, that he would have no interest in anyone else, and now he was happy to pursue this?

I looked at the message over and over, and I couldn't get my head around what had happened, so I called him. Practising my lines to stay cool, I made the call.

"Hi, Rohit," I said nervously.

"Hi, Eleanor," came a calm response. "How are you? All okay?"

"Yeah, I am fine," I said calmly. "And you?"

"Yeah, good," he replied as if that was all that was left to say.

"Did you get home okay?" I asked.

"Yes, I did. Actually, I went back to Nia and Rickesh's for a smoke and fell asleep there." He paused. "Nothing happened, of course. We just talked."

"What does all this mean?" I said to him, almost crying.

He sighed into the phone for a moment. "Listen, Eleanor, you wanted this, didn't you? So, I don't know why you are asking. But you are right though, there really isn't a real way forward, and last night after we spoke, it made ... it made sense that it might be worth getting to know Nia some more."

I was speechless; it was as though I had laid myself on the funeral pyre, and now he was lighting it. A part of me wanted to beg him not to, tell him not to go ahead, not to let me go, but his words convinced me that I only had myself to blame. On the other side, I saw a selfish man, who did nothing but serve his own interests. He did have a choice, and he chose not to be with me. I felt like he had betrayed me and messed me around. I wanted to hurt him and say something that would cut him open the way it cut me. But on the other side, I wanted him to feel how openly accepting I was, how much I loved him, that love was endless and boundless. I could only feel pain whichever way I looked, as though love had turned into a double-edged sword.

I broke down in tears on the phone, unable to deal with the pain, and for once in our short-lived relationship, he heard me cry and was speechless.

I wasn't alone in this pain, but I had to face it alone. There would be no one there at this service.

"I better go," I finally said, breaking the long-endured silence and unable to speak anymore from the tears. Rohit didn't have a chance to say goodbye as I dropped the call.

I fell to my knees, curling into a ball on the carpet, trying to contain the thoughts piercing through me like shards of glass cutting into my heart. I wanted to stop breathing: it felt better when I didn't breathe. It seemed to suppress the agony.

What was I going to do with this empty corpse roaming around the earth now? Empty and lifeless, and how could I have let myself become so precious about Rohit when I had known the reality of it? That we could never become more? We had known where it was heading; we had known what would happen. Now I was just a wreck, a piece of driftwood floating in the sea. I was torn, and there was nothing, nothing, nothing that anyone could do to help me.

Rohit tried to call me throughout the day, but I couldn't bring myself to call back. I lay cuddled up in my bed, staring at the ceiling while the tears streamed down my face. I listened to my favourite songs that reminded me of him. I was grieving as if I was at my own funeral service.

*

I woke up on Sunday morning in the clothes I had been wearing the day before, my mouth dry, my hair a knotted mass, my eyes swollen like two puffed-up pillows. I could barely open them. It took a while then to recollect the tragedy that had happened. There were more missed calls from Rohit. I couldn't bear to look.

I headed downstairs to get breakfast. I couldn't fathom the idea of food, even though pangs of hunger lined my empty stomach. I hadn't eaten the day before, and now I felt weak and light-headed. It was early, 8 a.m., and Andrea had made her way down for some water.

"Morning, hon!" she said in a spritely tone. I had my back to her so she couldn't see my face.

"Morning, Andrea," I croaked in a hoarse voice. It felt as though I hadn't spoken in days.

She peered down at me to make eye contact. "Are you okay, hon? What happened, Eleanor?" she said, concerned, turning to face me.

"Rohit and I are splitting up," I said, looking at her with tears.

"Oh, Eleanor, Eleanor, Eleanor," she said, sighing sympathetically and giving me a big hug. It felt comforting; it released the pain. Speaking to Andrea made me feel less alone.

When I told her what had happened, she was horrified. She couldn't see why Rohit had to pursue this right now.

"You know what, Eleanor? I have lost a lot of respect for Rohit," she said, pausing to sip her tea. "I thought he was a really understanding guy, but this is really beyond what I thought he would do."

"It is partly my fault though," I said, trying to make her understand that I shouldn't have introduced him to anyone and that it was almost sending the message that I was consenting to it. Which I was, because I wanted him to be happy.

"I don't know," she said, sighing. "I still feel like he has a choice in the matter. It's not like you were forcing him. What he is doing is not really right either." She began processing her rationale further. "I mean, can't he see it isn't necessary? Isn't it hard enough that you are both breaking up? I don't get it. I mean, what on earth are you both doing to each other? Is this really necessary, Eleanor? Is it?" she said, finding the whole matter inexcusable and hard to understand.

"We can't be together, Andrea. Our parents would never approve. It would be my whole family disowning me, even at the mere mention. Forget even being caught together. My mum would probably try to kill herself, and his dad, well, he would be mortified, wouldn't he? So here we are, Andrea. That's why we can't do this."

It was hard for Andrea to understand this screwed-up Asian culture and the nature in which people have to behave. "Why can't you guys just be together? Will they really care that much?" She shook her head. "Look, let's go out," she exhaled with a deep air of resignation. "It looks like you just need to take a step away and a break from it all, and it will come clear eventually."

Andrea was amazing support. Even though it was difficult for her to understand what was going on, she always found ways to say the right thing.

*

Later that evening, after a couple of wines at the pub across the road and much-needed consoling from Andrea, I came home to an empty room and lay on my bed. I looked at my messages. Surprisingly, none from Rohit, which came with a feeling of contempt that he had moved on, and bliss that I had some distance from the emotional upheaval it brought.

It was Mrs Abbots who had left a missed call, and it immediately lifted my spirits up. I returned her call, and we talked for a while. I talked about my travels, and she talked about her teaching post in China, where she had taught English at a large school. Most of the conversation seems a blur now, owing to the two large glasses of red wine I'd had with Andrea earlier. I could have sworn that my speech was slurred.

But when she asked me how things were going at work, I remember breaking down in tears.

"What is it, dear? Tell me."

"Oh, Mrs Abbots, I don't know where to start, to be honest. I met a guy at work, and immediately I felt this connection with him. You know, it was like this magical, mysterious feeling of love where we barely needed to spell it out to each other. We were one in the moment."

"Well, then what happened?"

"We couldn't be together, Mrs Abbots. You must know where I am going with this."

She remained silent.

"We broke up, not because we didn't love each other but because ultimately our families would never agree; they would never allow it, and most likely, as you already know, the mere mention of it would cause an outrage and result in something brutal."

"Surely, Eleanor, surely not. Are you telling me that you are prepared to break up with someone you dearly love to conserve the honour of your family?"

"Yes, Mrs Abbots, that is right; that is what is tearing me apart. We love each other, but it would clearly be a sin in the eyes of our parents. He's Hindu, and I'm Muslim, and we wouldn't stand a chance of convincing them."

"Eleanor, I must tell you this, and I hope that you will take what I am saying to mean no offence whatsoever, but love, *love*, my dear, it can't be boxed. It can't be bought, and it can't be sold. It comes from within you. It is a gift, not a sin, and the only evil is what may surround it. Some people define love to be evil, to be something bad, because of fear, but remember what I told you a few years ago. Do you remember? Your word is golden. Be true to that gold within you, and everything will flourish around you. It will work itself out."

"But how will I know?"

"Eleanor, you already know. And now you are letting fears get in the way of the truth."

"But how, Mrs Abbots, how? How do I find the strength to go against my parents, their religion, their faith? How does one fight for the truth when it could be harmful to the people you love?"

"I know it will be hard: it takes courage and conviction, my dear, and believe me, I have lost in the weight of that battle."

"You have?" It became clear to me that in all the years that I had conversed with Mrs Abbots, I had barely scratched the surface of who she really was. So short were our encounters, and so selflessly consumed in helping me, we rarely touched on hers.

"Many years ago, yes." She paused as if hesitating to bring up such a delicate subject. "I fell in love with a young man. He was handsome and kind and attentive, but my father, you know, he wouldn't agree. There were many reasons, of course, like you are experiencing with your parents' approval. I was a coward of some sort, they might call it. Too afraid, my dear, too afraid. We both were consumed with the importance it held to marry the right person by our parents. How much guilt one holds to uphold face, and yet all I have learned through it is that love, such a golden essence of life, cannot be diminished by the mortal world of flesh and blood. It knows no boundaries. Suppressing it is like asking someone to carry a well of water around with them: it is heavy and was meant for life, and when, of course, the well is dry, the vessel itself becomes meaningless. Like Tagore would say, 'The water in a vessel is sparkling; the water in the sea is dark. The small truth has words which are clear, the great truth has great silence.'"

"Tagore?" I said. I remembered my father once quoting that verse from his books. I said curiously, "I didn't know you read his books?"

"Well … he is a famous poet," Mrs Abbots resumed with a short pause. "Anyhow, I can only pass on to you now what years of heartache and suffering could sum up in one sentence. That love is the only reason we are here, and above all else, it's the only truth worth fighting for. I hope in time you will learn to care less about what people think and more about what you think about yourself, because one day you will look back and be proud of yourself. Be proud of being true to yourself."

"Can you change it now? Is he still alive?" I asked.

"Oh, yes, very much so, dear. He has a family now though, and responsibilities, but love, my dear, is infinite. Cherish its gifts. Life is messy, I know, but what you love is clear as water, which is the essence of life."

I wished I could have asked more about this love of hers, but it seemed that she wanted to move on, and I for one was ready to sleep.

*

In the morning, I sat in bed, contemplating these words. There was truth in all Mrs Abbots's wise words. Yes, I loved Rohit deeply, and maybe in his missed calls, he was also trying to tell me. Maybe we should talk things through, work things out. It was possible we could work things out if we loved each other. Then it was worth fighting for. But would I want to endure all the pain and suffering that Mrs Abbots had faced?

I changed and slipped into a dark red work dress, freshened myself up with make-up and combed down my long hair. I felt like I had risen from the dead and was now breathing in new life.

I will hopefully see Rohit. Maybe we can get a coffee, talk things through, I contemplated as I walked through the car park.

When I arrived in the office, I found Rohit standing over at Jay's desk, reviewing some work.

"Hi, Eleanor," he said calmly.

"Hi, Rohit. Hello, Jay."

"Aye." Jay gestured back with a grand salute in his usual cheerful way.

I brought my notebook over, clutching it with both hands.

"Rohit, erm, I was just wondering, would it be possible to quickly go over that report when you have a moment?"

Rohit seemed fixated on Jay's screen and didn't seem to be paying attention. "Erm, yeah, sure. Bit busy right now. Could we try later?"

"Sure," I said.

I returned to my seat as both Jay and Rohit continued with their analysis. Then Rohit's phone rang.

"Nia," he called out in delight.

My heart sprang out as I sat behind the divider, staring intently at my screen.

Rohit continued on the phone, whispering and laughing. It hurt, as though he was crushing me with their laughter.

I couldn't bear it and decided to sit at a desk away from the others in another campus building. I was walking over to the building, deep in thought and feeling devastated at Rohit's nonchalance, when I bumped into a colleague at the door.

"Hi, Eleanor. How are you doing?" came an uplifting voice.

"Oh, hi, Matthew. How are you?"

Matthew was a colleague of mine who I occasionally worked with on some deployment projects. I enjoyed working with Matthew: his upbeat tempo and infectious laughter always had me in a fit of giggles or high-spirited. But today I felt void of any humour. I tried to return a beaming smile of surprise, but I couldn't snap out of the moment before. I stood in thought about Rohit's behaviour now as a whirlwind of scattered leaves formed around the front entrance and as the wind swept through my hair.

"I'm good, thanks for asking," I said dryly.

"Wow ... you look nice, Eleanor. Where are you off to?"

"Oh," I laughed. "Nowhere. I was actually just going to sit in another building." I gave him a thin smile.

"Wow, well, you look beautiful, as always." He smiled.

I shook my head. "Not sure what beautiful is, really," I said, sheepishly staring down at the dress.

"Well, can I just say ... you are one of the hottest girls on campus?"

"Thank you." But instead of smiling, I almost burst into tears. "I'm sorry. I have to go. I will hopefully speak to you soon," I said, looking down. I walked away, leaving Matthew looking baffled. *One of the hottest girls on campus*, I thought. *One man's treasure, another man's trash. That's what I am*, I thought. *If only he knew that I was the saddest girl on campus too.*

CHAPTER TWENTY-NINE
- Empty -

It was a warm summer evening. We'd taken a drive up through Richmond Hill, through narrow, dimly lit streets and where grand terraces overlooked the river. Rohit stopped the car, and we sat enjoying the view of the starry sky and the moon shimmering on the water.

"I love this song. Have you heard it?" Rohit said, raising the volume.

"No. What is it?" I asked.

"Coldplay. It's called 'The Scientist'."

We listened, and he locked my hand into his.

"I think it says it all," he said, looking down as he pressed my fingers gently.

I continued to listen.

"You know, I've never fully understood you. It's quite a mystery, and it's like a science trying to figure you all out. And then, when we are together, it's all perfect; there is nothing more to be understood. It's clear, and that is Eleanor, what makes it all so amazing." His eyes marvelled at me for a moment before he continued. "You know, I could sit and talk about a blade of grass with you. It's nothing but mindless conversation, I know, but ..." He paused for a moment. His eyes gleamed, though he was bursting with happiness as he looked out at the river in front. "It's with you," he said, turning to face me. "With you, it makes perfect sense." He smiled, shaking his head.

"Here, this is for you." He passed over the CD case, and inside the cover was a single blade of grass with a note: "With all my love."

I laughed, overwhelmed, feeling a little unworthy, I guess. "Well, you make me sound very dull and uninteresting, as a matter of fact! Hmm, let's see. Let's talk about this blade of grass now, hmm?"

He laughed, squeezing my hand, and I rested my head against his shoulder, then turned to look at him. "I do know what you mean," I whispered gently. "I do know that feeling," I said as we kissed for the last time.

*

Months had gone by since waking up from this moment, now only captured in a lucid dream. It was vivid, every detail crisp, sublime and real, only to be haunted by my waking moments, by reality. The sunlight seeping through the long, thin curtains in my room in the morning now only revealed what a hollow existence my life had become. Mrs Abbots was right. Without love, what remains is an empty vessel.

On the weekends, I wandered the streets, scouring it for something that might make the pain go away. The trees, once radiating green in the summer sun, now stood empty, lifeless and grey. I watched people enviably as the world moved on with their lives. People going to work, children going to the parks, the cafes bustling with the aroma of coffee and cinnamon, where waitresses wiped down tabletops. I longed to smile like them or swap roles with the cashier at the supermarket as she handed me the groceries, or with the woman taking her dog for a walk. Any state of being other than this would be better: to just feel human again.

But here I was in this empty, isolated world, submerged in anguish that nothing could salvage me from. My evenings were now spent in the comfort of my room, swirling red wine, the temptation to call Rohit lingering at my fingertips, in tears when I couldn't bring myself to do it and with balls of tissue piled up high by my bedside when I found the courage to resist.

Any comfort from my friends seemed short-lived; it was like taking a painkiller, and the effects wore off eventually. I sought counsel from Mrs Abbots, whose advice, although wise, was often harder to implement in practice.

"Don't shroud yourself in darkness, dear," she would say on the phone. "Look ahead. Tomorrow comes with a new beginning." It seemed hopeful, there were no doubts about that, but this shroud of darkness felt like a thick blanket I couldn't shift.

I fought this war in my heart and mind. Battling the darkness and turning it to light. In the light, I was doing this for Rohit because I loved him, because it was the right thing to do. It didn't matter whether he was with someone or not; I still loved him. And although I ached and yearned for him, I could imagine his life being blissful now: he could make his father happy, uphold his family's pride by marrying someone who was accepted in his society. But in the darkness, I could only feel what an easy decision it must have been for Rohit. She was beautiful. Her face perfect, those large, dewy eyes that fluttered long lashes, her neat and short, silky hair. Who would resist? Rohit didn't need to, of course. It hurt so much hearing about the holidays, the engagement plans, the little giggles in between conversations. On a daily basis, I swallowed these reminders of reality, one by one, chewing them like dry bread in my mouth, harsh and tasteless as they scraped my throat. They hurt like pangs of hunger and felt heavy inside. I wished more than anything in the world that I could get over it. Where his life was thriving, mine was stuck in a grave, dead to the world, dead to him. I longed to be alive. I just didn't know how.

*

My parents saw my vacant stares on my weekends at home. I barely spoke, lost in my world of misery. I couldn't care for the food or for the small talk. I lost weight; my face became hollow, my eyes grey and deepened from tears and lack of sleep. It didn't matter where I went, whose comfort I sought, I felt alone, and there was nothing anybody could do to cure me of it.

One weekend back at my parents' house, I sat watching the dusky sky grow darker over the hills. The door opened with a jolt, and Mamajee came into my room.

"What are you doing, sitting here in the dark?" she asked. "Why don't you turn on the light?"

She flicked the light switch and snapped the curtains shut.

My eyes were puffy from tears. I hid my face away from her.

"So, who was it?" she asked.

I was stunned that she had been so direct with her question, and my silence only confirmed her suspicions.

"I told you, *told* you, about bringing shame to our family. You said you would hold your end of the bargain. Where is this boy from?" She demanded answers in her usual pose, hands on hips and pointing accusingly at me.

"There is nobody, Mamajee. I have nobody, okay?" I sniffled.

"Must feel good now, hmm? It's like being bitten by a poisonous snake: once it's in you, it will slowly kill you. I bet you thought he loved you, ha? Didn't you? Hmm?"

I shook my head dismissively at her need to antagonise, to provoke a reaction.

"No man ever really loves you. Just remember that. They just take what they can from you. I bet he never looked back once when he laid his eyes on another woman, did he? He solved your mystery and was ready to solve the next. A man conquers only what a woman cherishes. They are only interested in material things. You gave him your treasure, and he walked away with every ounce of dignity you could hold on to. Left you valueless, didn't he? Now you are wounded, lifeless, treasureless. Did he look back once? Hmm? I bet he didn't. I tried to teach you this, didn't I? Hmm, and you chose not to listen, and now look at you. He's filled you with self-pity, turned you into a pile of crap on the floor. I thought you would have been better than that. I thought you would listen to me. We are not like those English hell worshippers. In our culture, no man ever deserves your treasure unless he can pay the price for it. A dowry. Otherwise, you are worthless. Well, you are worthless now. There have been many, many proposals for you. Many, and you have countlessly declined them all. Time will not stop as you get old. To a man, your value drops even more, and people are talking already. Tongues are wagging; we can't even show our faces to people. Who's going to want you when you are old and haggard? Ha? Hey? Who? It's already proving difficult. Nobody wants a girl who is gallivanting off travelling, away from home, working, socialising with men. It's not our culture. It is not respectable for a girl. You tell me where your future is now. Do you see any other girl of your age behaving like this?"

I sat staring into the blackened reflection of myself in the window where the curtains hadn't shut properly. How ugly I looked. Mamajee was right. I was worthless. I had reduced myself to this low and pitiful state. I couldn't imagine anyone wanting me, and maybe she was right. Rohit had only thought about himself. I had given my all to him, and where did it leave me? He hadn't even looked back once at me when he met Nia. To him, I was just another glorified one-night stand. I had no more tears to cry and stared emptily out at my reflection in the darkening window.

"If you let me," Mamajee continued calmly, "I will find someone who will treasure you, provide you with everything."

"No, Mamajee," I refused bluntly.

"Listen to me, just listen to me. What are you going to do right now? You are going to sit endlessly in the dark? You can meet these people; you don't have to say yes. Just speak to them. That is it, simple."

"And what if I don't like them?" I asked.

"Then we just tell them. It's simple. I am not going to force you anymore, but you do have to think about your future. You are not getting younger, are you? What do you say?"

I didn't respond, and I knew Mamajee would interpret that as a yes.

*

It was as though I was watching my wedding playing out before me and I had become invisible to the world around me again. The house was filled with unknown aunts who had come to help Mamajee fuss. In the kitchen, there were four pots of curry bubbling away on the stove. Two other women clambered over each other almost as they busily prepared, cooked and cleaned. I stood awkwardly watching as they fussed over how thinly they should cut the cucumber or how much rice they needed to boil. Mamajee seemed upbeat as they sang songs and cut patterns into pastry dough for the coconut samosas.

The house looked as though it belonged to someone else. Immaculately tidy, with ornaments placed on shelves in height ascending order and knick-knacks, odds and sods cleared and stowed away. It looked as though nobody had lived or sat on any furniture in years, as if it were meant for display purposes only. Mamajee had laid down a set of doilies and embroidered coverings on the sofa. And plastic flowers had been dusted and placed as centrepieces on tables and windowsills. A rose-scented air freshener was sprayed regularly to prevent the odours from the kitchen lingering in the lounge room. I observed it all with mounting pressure.

"Mamajee, please don't think I am going to marry this guy."

"Don't worry," she said. "Nobody is asking you to marry him just yet. Just meet him. There's no rush."

"Of course not," my sister scoffed as she winked and nudged past me. "As if anything Mamajee says is worth believing. You know there's no going back now: she's already announced it to everyone as 'There are talks of a big wedding.' Which would only suggest to anyone this is a formal engagement."

"What? No!" I said. "No, I haven't even met this guy yet. How could she do that?"

"Well, good luck trying to keep shtum. She's already been inundated with calls from relatives from across the country and overseas."

Nashira Khala had arrived especially for the occasion in the morning and had begun fussing over the choice of saree.

"Do you think this is the right choice of colour on her?" she asked Mamajee. "She has such fair skin. Surely a darker colour would flatter her more. She has golden skin, and the saree is golden."

"No, she can wear gold. It's only the Chini Paan [*Tea and Sweet*] ceremony. We don't want to appear desperate."

"Hmm, true." Nashira Khala gazed at me. "Eleanor, you are going to look beautiful. Let me put your hair up."

"Wait a minute. Chini Paan? That's like an engagement ceremony, isn't it?" I said.

"Oh, well, yes, but you can have it before or after the engagement. I think your mum was just talking in general, you know, how you would have tea and sweets."

Mamajee busied herself as if avoiding any further interrogation, pulling out the blouse, petticoat, sandals, jewellery, bracelets, bindis, jumkhas and a whole array of necklaces. They had the full Indian bridal couture spread out in front of me.

"What? I am not wearing all of this!" I screamed.

"Eleanor, this is the first time they are going to see you, so of course you have to," Nashira Khala said with a frown, and began the makeover.

My hair was pinned up in various barrel curls. My skin was bronzed and golden with shimmering powders. Eyeshadow cascaded in multiple tones on my eyelids to the brow. A large, ornate hair clip rested on the side of my hair, along with a central bindi chain, which draped down my forehead. There were layers and layers of gold necklaces that were then placed on top of my saree. As stunning as it all was, I couldn't help feeling concerned that this was my family going a little overboard.

There was a slight change of plan for the lunch venue, to be now Babajee's restaurant, despite the number of hours Mamajee and the women had spent cooking and fussing at home. It later became clear why there was a sudden change as we approached the venue in my brother's car. To my surprise, what had been planned for the meeting was nothing near discreet. Ahead of me was an entourage of people heading to the restaurant. It seemed as though Mamajee had invited everyone and his monkey to this meeting.

It was no longer my family with his family; it was now his entire family, consisting of his two brothers, sister, niece, dad, mum, his brothers' two accountants, accountants' two friends, plus Babajee, his friend, Mamajee's friend, Mamajee's friend's son and daughter, my sister, two brothers and my aunt. I could only seethe at Mamajee's indiscretion.

Everyone was seated at the table as I entered.

"Make sure you walk slowly," whispered Mamajee as she continued ahead. My aunt and sister both walked along with me as though they were dabbling with the idea of being bridesmaids.

My gold saree jingled, and the bells around my earrings chimed to the sound of my footsteps. The silence aroused a sense of awkwardness and shook me with distasteful nerves.

Mamajee and Babajee beckoned me over. I greeted everyone coyly, going 'round the table with a quick nod and jingle sound that came from my earrings. They all seemed to gawp back at me, and I was left not knowing what else to do but nod back, plus the sound effect. Then everything went very still, quiet and uncomfortable again. Babajee ushered my brother Karim into the kitchen to start serving the food.

The prospective suitor was seated four people away from me on the opposite side of the table. I called him "Mr Man", as I still didn't know his name. Mamajee refused to tell me, as it was considered impolite for a bride to ask the name of a prospective husband, and also for a mother-in-law to call him by his name. His character, mannerisms and demeanour came exactly as depicted in the picture provided by Mamajee: polite, reserved, quiet, conservative, nothing loud, nothing wild, nothing adventurous, a regular guy, nothing out of the box, and there wasn't any outward evidence of deviation. A pure breed of Bangladeshi class. Undoubtedly, a perfect selection for a spouse in my parents' eyes, a good son-in-law, respectable, reserved, polite, impersonal. "Mr Straight and Narrow", let's just say.

His mother, who was now sitting next to me, looked me straight in the eyes, assessing me as fit for the role as a dutiful potential daughter-in-law and sealed her approval of me with a kiss on my forehead. I could smell the betel nut and paan from her mouth as she inched closer to me. Then she smiled at me, marking her affection by piling food on my plate. It is a strange custom in Bengali culture that one serves food as a mark of one's affection or liking towards another. My sister sat next to me, nudging me every so often and smirking at the events that were taking place.

Then my brothers came through from the kitchen, attentively serving drinks with the occasional ill-humoured grin at seeing me dressed to the nines in bridal wear. My aunt and sister continued with their bridesmaid roles by prodding me in the mouth with grilled chicken pieces that had been generously served onto my plate by my potential mother-in-law.

"Make sure you don't eat any of it," Mamajee whispered in my ear from behind my chair. According to Mamajee, it was considered discourteous for a bride-to-be to enjoy the luxuries of eating. Apparently, it comes across as impolite to do so. So, I sat, holding onto my fork, looking down coyly while the family made small talk.

After the frenzy of food and feasting carried out by the entourage of guests seated at the table had finished, Mamajee moved my sister and me to a booth.

Potential Mother-in-law came over and sat opposite me, staring directly while rolling paan in the side of her mouth. She finally conjured up the ability to speak without spitting paan at me.

"Do you speak Bengali?" she asked slowly in Bengali, as if it was unknown to me.

"Jee. Yes, I do," I said without eye contact, which was also considered impolite (a bride-to-be should never make eye contact with her seniors).

"And you live in London, I hear? What do you do there? You are working?"

I consolidated my answer with an affirmative to the three questions. "*Han jee* [*Yes*], I do."

She paused, thinking about my answer.

"Do you go home to your parents regularly?"

"Han jee, I do."

I did as Mamajee had trained me in the art of being a Bengali bride. It wasn't that I wanted to please them, it was because I wanted to please her. To somehow acknowledge the years she had been put through. Many protocols came with the tea ceremony, such as not making any conversation with people, sitting quietly and only answering with short and simple answers. A bride is considered the centrepiece of the ceremony. She is gazed and marvelled at, and to remain demure during the ceremony is what gives the bride her status and dignity.

Mamajee then joined us with an aunt who was a close family friend. More dessert and paan was brought to the table, and the three women carried on talking for another twenty minutes.

I sat quietly, looking down. *What am I getting myself into here?* I thought. *I do hope that Mamajee knows this is going nowhere, that her efforts are all in vain.*

The potential groom's father then came to the table with Babajee. He was a weary-looking old man with a long old beard, the kind without the moustache, and looked somewhat of a religious type with the white Punjabi suit and matching white prayer cap. He topped the look with a beige V-neck sweater.

"Do you pray, dear?" he asked, chewing on some paan.

To which Babajee interjected before I could reply. "Oh, my daughter can recite the whole Quran, you know. She even won an award for it when she went to the mosque."

I couldn't help but fume quietly at Babajee's excessive sales speech. I had memorised one chapter of the Quran, not the whole Quran. That would have been somewhat of an accomplishment by any means. His father seemed quietly impressed. Babajee's eyes gleamed as though he had answered a million-dollar question.

"Shabash, Beti, shabash," said the old man, nodding slowly and raising one furry white eyebrow. "Then you must know chapter twenty-one, the most significant of all of what Allah has written for us."

I felt the blood rushing to my head, and a single pulse throbbed in my temple as if it was screaming at me to run and hide.

My dad quickly stepped in. "Oh, no, no, that was a long time ago." He chuckled sheepishly. "She won't remember anymore." Thankfully, for once, Babajee was doing me a favour.

However, just when I felt the vein in my head stop throbbing, he started embarrassing me even more. It was as though he had to clutch at straws to find anything successful about me and use anything to sell me.

"My daughter, she is, er, er, very good at poetry, you know. She came first in the UK in a poetry competition."

Please shut up, Babajee, I thought to myself. *I was sixteen. So what?*

The groom-to-be overheard, and I quickly glanced to see him giggling silently.

Then it went all quiet again. Babajee ushered my brothers over.

"Hey, boys, go get everyone together. Get to know one another; you should all get together for a while and have a chat." Chairs shuffled, and my sister clambered awkwardly into the booth seat next to me. Everyone looked awkwardly at each other for about thirty seconds, waiting for someone to make a move in starting the conversation.

Then Mr Man's brother stepped in and introduced himself. "Hi. I'm Rahim, and this is my brother." I sensed he was younger than the groom, and that meant another nameless introduction. Traditionally, as a sign of respect, a person of lower seniority is forbidden to call his or her senior by their name. There was a geekish look about him, thick-rimmed glasses, a thin, sharp face and a smile that suggested that he was enjoying playing centre stage for once.

"I work in London, and my brother works in investment banking."

Mr Man nodded, agreeing to his brother's statements. I continued to look down but often took short glances to observe the commentary and expression.

It seemed as though Babajee had an egg timer, because no short of three minutes, he came back. "Okay, that's it, times up. We will all go home now and have some tea." His eyes lit up from his wide grin, as though he was introducing the most exciting part of the day.

We all stumbled out, myself being the last one, because, of course, I was just "the most significant one". I guess it was good in a way: at least they wouldn't see the effort it took to stumble down the restaurant stairs with that heavy gold sequined saree. Walking to the car was like another banal Southall Street scene, a whole convoy of black Mercedes and BMWs pulled off to the house.

I rushed straight to my room as soon as I stepped into the house. I couldn't bear to put up with any more pretences. Who was I becoming? What was I getting into here? I thought the whole point of this was to meet the guy and just see him, but this had become a fanfare. I looked at myself in the mirror, and I saw the face of a typical Bengali bride. The girl I once knew, unrecognisable.

The grips in my hair cut into my scalp and felt like a crown of thorns. I wanted to get out of here. It was 6.15 p.m. on a Sunday, and I still had to make my way back to London by train. I called the enquiry line, but just as I hit the call button, there was a knock on my door.

"He's in the other room," Mamajee whispered quietly. "Go talk to him, but remember, don't say too much."

Mr Man's mother stood outside my room. I bowed my head down courteously, and she held my chin affectionately. "Don't be shy, my dear; my son is a good man."

Mamajee stood behind her and mimed the word "No" to me. "Remember what I said," she glared.

I found Mr Man sat in the next room, relaxed in a chair. It was as though I was being interviewed for a role at the bank. This role, though, was for a dutiful Bengali wife who would serve her husband for life.

"Come, sit down," he said, relaxing into his chair with manspread legs and one foot resting over his other knee.

I fumed; he was already irritating me. *He better try harder than that*, I thought.

I sat perched on the edge of the bed. He looked down at the floor, bobbing his head as though he was agreeing with himself on what to interrogate me about. His hands now clasped in front of him, he moved into detective mode, leaning both elbows now onto his knees. I observed the melodrama that came with this individual's body language, with bemused dissatisfaction. And so I continued, silently, embracing and cringing at what his first move would entail. So disgusted by his attempt to even make conversation, I decided I wanted to end the enquiry.

"So, what is it like in Edinburgh?" I asked.

"Yeah, it's okay," he said, tipping his head forward. I am sure he was relieved that I was able to start the conversation.

"And do you like it in London?" I added to break the silence again.

"It's okay. It's not that great. I'd eventually like to move back to Edinburgh."

I felt relieved knowing this. I wouldn't want to move to Edinburgh and had no further questions. I could sense an air of awkward silence becoming nauseatingly uncomfortable for him.

He hesitated. "Er, so, do you have pets?" he said hastily.

"No, but if I did, I would love to have a dog." I looked him straight in the eye, knowing full well this would provoke some disgust towards me when I said it. It was a deliberate response to annoy him. Muslim families don't keep dogs, and I wanted to repel, destroy any effort he made to connect with me.

He looked straight back at me and gave me the answer I was looking for. "Erm, yeah. I don't like dogs."

My face radiated a tiny shimmer of a triumphant smile. I think he took it as a hint.

The conversation didn't pick up any faster than the slow train to Waterloo from Richmond. When it stopped, it took a long time to pick up again, or it didn't move at all.

Luckily for us, we didn't have to scrounge around, racking our brains for any more topics of conversation, such as pets: my brother came up shortly after our brief exchange. He peered through the doorway.

"They want you both downstairs, as they are getting ready to leave now," he said gruffly.

It turned into some money-laundering service in the living room, people yelling friendly things at each other and at the same time refusing cash. Both families were now offering backhanders to one another of fifty-pound notes, for the trouble, hospitality and the beautiful introductions that had taken place. Each refusing politely.

"No, no, brother, this is for you."

"No, this is for you."

Yet pressing it down into each other's hands, all part of the camaraderie and hospitality that accompanies this Bengali Broadway show.

The sibling audience looked on in awe at the tennis match going on with the wad of cash from one side of the room to the other. No one gained any more from it: the five hundred pounds given to me became a backhander to Mamajee, then to my dad, who then gave it back to his parents.

My family saw them out through the front door. I decided to stagger and jingle in my saree and heels all the way back upstairs while I heard the engines starting and the loud farewells going on outside. I unravelled myself from the wretched saree, let my hair down and got myself ready for the train back to London. It was a huge sigh of relief. Finally someone had let the caged bird free at last, and I could run back to my idea of reality.

*

When I finally arrived at my humble houseshare, I dived onto my bed. It was comforting to be in the calmness and solitude of it. The fresh smell of my room, and the whiteness of the space that was my own world. I looked up, relieved that I had managed to be set free again, but the bliss didn't last long. The phone rang; it was Mamajee.

"Hope you got home okay. The other family also mentioned they got back home."

"Oh, good," I said. "Glad they all got home okay."

"They also accepted you, and they are happy to proceed with the engagement."

CHAPTER THIRTY
– Searching for Mr Right –

"No," I said. "There is absolutely no way, Mamajee. I can't be with him."

"Why? Why can't you? The whole world knows about this meeting now. All the family in England and overseas knows about it. What do you think that's going to look like? Hmm?"

I shook my head in disbelief at her manipulations. How could she lay so much guilt on me?

"Mamajee, no. I can't see how this will work. And you said, remember? You said it was just a meeting, it doesn't mean I have to go ahead!"

"It's not allowed in our culture to meet and date people. They will look down on us for this type of arrangement. And anyhow, why do you think it will work with anyone else? He is a good, decent boy from a good family. They came all the way from Edinburgh to see you."

I felt the guilt and disappointment rising in me slowly from Mamajee's persuasion, and the seven-year-old me gave into a chant. *You promised too, remember? You promised!*

I shrugged her away.

"Mamajee, no. I don't want to go ahead with this. And anyway, you organised this. It wasn't meant to be an entourage, it was meant to be just a simple greeting. You went way overboard and turned it into a full-blown wedding!"

"So, you want me to tell them, do you? Tell them that my daughter is not interested?"

I went silent on the phone, could hear the panic that I was stirring up in her.

"You want to see the end of me, don't you? That's why you are refusing. I spent my whole life—"

"Oh, okay, Mamajee, spare it. Look, I honour what you have done. I just can't do this. Anyway, the guy wants to move back to Edinburgh, and that wouldn't work, would it, if I lived in London?"

Somehow that seemed to calm the uprising in her. "Okay, look, fine, I'll explain that you work in London so it wouldn't work out. Well, there are a few in London. It wouldn't be easy for us to get down that way, so I don't mind if you just meet them for coffee, but please, don't tell people. And also, spare us some dignity by dressing appropriately when you do. I don't want to hear from people that you dress inappropriately in front of their sons."

I guess there is no harm in this, I thought. I should do this for Mamajee. After all, that was the whole point, right? To make her happy.

I went on several fifteen-minute coffee breaks with people who looked nothing like their pictures nor sounded like their profiles. I started to understand now what it had felt like for Rohit.

First of all, there was "Mr Exclamation Mark". I called him that because he described himself as "such an exciting person". All the emails were written with exclamation marks after each sentence.

"Hi, Eleanor! My name is Raji! How are you! I got your email yesterday! I am really excited to meet up with you!!"

When I read his emails, I pictured a really bubbly guy who was interested in travelling and going places. He had his own place too, which made me feel he was a little more independent.

We met at the tube station in Oxford Street. At first I could not spot him. I was too busy looking for a smiley, excited face, and to my disappointment, there he was, standing with a grim face at the corner of the station. His face showed little expression when I introduced myself.

"Hi. I am Eleanor," I said with a smile.

He looked to the floor. "Hi. I am Raj." There was no exclamation mark from the expression on his face. He didn't appear to ever smile, even at other people. And over coffee, he continued on in his dreary, monotonous voice about his line of work and the things he enjoyed doing in his spare time. I couldn't wait to finish my coffee and be back home. It was clear this wouldn't work. I politely declined his offer to meet again.

Then there was "Mr Philtrum". I met him in some Thai restaurant after another email introduction. Bangladeshi, tall, medium build, he had that spiky, gelled hair that possibly wouldn't move in a blizzard. I couldn't stop staring at his hair at first as I approached to meet him outside the restaurant. It was Saturday afternoon, and he was dressed in his best pinstriped banker's suit, coupled with a pink shirt and the snootiest woven tie. *Oh no!* I thought. *My mind's in bitch mode again. Eleanor, wake up. Open your heart to this guy. He could be nice.*

I took a deep breath. I couldn't get away from his large philtrum (the vertical cleft between the nose and lip), and as he pondered over his order, I became more and more distracted by it. The idea of kissing him horrified me. I desperately tried to keep an open mind, mute the bitch inside, who was closing in on me to the point where I could no longer hear or comprehend what he was asking me.

"Eleanor? Eleanor?" he said, waving the menu at me. "Would you like a drink?" He nodded, amused at my blank expression. The waiter, having paused, then took it on himself to pour water into each of our glasses.

"Oh, er, no, I am fine with just water."

Eleanor, get your head in gear, came a voice from inside my head. *Remember, you are doing this for Mamajee.*

I fired a question, which came out completely inappropriately. "So, do you normally work on the weekends?"

He smiled, thinking I had presumed so from his suit. "Well, no, I am not working today." He laughed unflatteringly, baring all his teeth and saliva strands.

I gulped my glass of water to distract myself. I could only engross myself in one thought: how superficial I had become, how I was forcing myself into love, and yet love, as Mrs Abbots had said, can't be boxed, can't be bought and can't be sold. It comes from within. It is a gift, not a sin, and the only evil is what surrounds it. It wouldn't have mattered if he had a large philtrum or wore a banker's suit. It wouldn't have mattered what he did for a living, or what religion or culture. Love does not care about these things. And even if he did come close to matching all of my superficial desires, would I really feel love? Would it satisfy that contented inner being in me? It wouldn't have even mattered what I was doing right now, or talking about. Love wasn't there, and just as Rohit said, "You know, I could sit and talk about a blade of grass with you. It's nothing but a mindless conversation, I know, but it's with you. With you, it makes perfect sense."

After departing from this date, I realised I wasn't empty of love; I still felt it. It was filled inside for one person, and every time I thought about it, it only infinitely expanded with that feeling. It was only for Rohit. And although I had come to terms with knowing that we both could not share that path together, we shared the same meaning of love and that there was another meaning that was preventing us, that had taken precedence over everything. Our love for our parents.

The true reason why Rohit and I broke up wasn't because we didn't love each other; it was because of the commitment we had, to honour our families, their pride, their sacrifices, the commitment from our respective parents to raise us. That seven-year-old girl had made a promise to Mamajee. I had vowed that I would spare her the indignity of dishonouring her name, that I would live by her word, how it was written. I owed it to her, for the sacrifice, for the pain she faced. I felt that in the core of me.

As I walked home that night, I could only recall the events that had taken place. That day on the floor, when I sat crying, begging

Mamajee to stay when all she wanted was to leave. I knew that what she had done for me was selfless; the child in me felt it, and now that child was revealing itself. I had been the selfish one; I had put my own selfish needs first. I recollected the pain I had caused by holding her back: that selfish seven-year-old had been prepared to have her suffer at the hands of Babajee's cruelty and endure more pain all because of fear. Fear of how we would survive without her, nobody to look after us, clean us and feed us. I could only recollect that at the time, losing Mamajee had been equivalent to losing everything that was needed to roam the earth. My hands, my feet, my sight, my breath, and if losing her was everything, then I would have given everything for her to stay.

I realised that this had echoed in my subconscious throughout my adult life, that I was paying the price of that sacrifice, of her commitment. And if I were to redeem myself from this closely harboured guilt, then I must honour my word, to uphold her honour. I had to spare her the indignation, so that her commitment and her sacrifice was not in vain. I owed her that vision to be seen through to the end. If I couldn't be with Rohit, then I would find the perfect gift of fulfilment for Mamajee – that was that I married someone who they would love and be happy with.

*

I called Mamajee that night when I finally arrived home.

"Well?" she said, demanding the verdict on the two proposals.

I remained silent, the crackle on the phone more resonant. It was enough for her to assume that I could not agree, and I could hear her disappointment brooding.

"I just knew, I knew it," she said disappointingly. "I knew you would be this type of girl. Even raising you was hard. I spend most of my time on earth unable to show my face, and then I will burn in hell for not raising you well enough."

It made me want to cringe, hearing her say this, the disappointment, the failure. I knew I didn't make my parents proud. I was their biggest failure.

"You are twenty-five years old, Eleanor. Girls your age are all married and settled now. It's hard to even find men who would even accept you. No decent family with any class, education or status would look twice at a girl like you. Off gallivanting around the world, living away from home, and Allah only knows what you are up to there. People don't agree with that. That's why it has been so difficult to even find people who would even consider you."

It made me sick to my stomach hearing this. The insinuations that I might be classified as loose by others, that I could be deemed not suitable or worthy of marriage to these families. That I didn't stack up.

"I guess I am not good enough, then," I said, relenting.

The seven-year-old me joined in at the pity party. *You are not. Just look at you. You can see why it didn't take long for Rohit to move on now, can't you?*

"Listen, I am giving you one last chance. There is one more proposal," she said. What followed was a long pause of hesitation. "I am not even sure they will even consider you, because they are from quite a respectable background. His family knows the Ahmeds who the boys hang out with. I was speaking to Khalid's mum the other day about all of this, and she mentioned that this family is very respectable and that the son works in a bank. The boy's father has asked for your email so that you and the boy can exchange. Please do not tarnish us with a bad name here. He will email you, so make sure you respond appropriately."

I remained silent, although I wish I had asked more questions. There was a feeling of guilt, a lack of self-worth and a resignation that trampled all over my self-esteem. I felt like the lowest form of life.

She's right, said the seven-year-old voice inside me. *Who would want you?*

*

That night I received an email.

Hi Eleanor,

I got your email off my cousin who knows your brother, that sort of thing ...

Where do I start?? Well ... I'm a British-born Bangladeshi, 26 years old, I work for an investment bank, I'm based in London, and I have one brother, who is at university.

I've completed my bachelors and masters in economics at UCL. Oh, I'm 6 foot tall, slim, athletic build and play tennis on a regular basis. What else do you want to know?? Just ask!!

Ciao,

Syed

We exchanged pleasantly on email at first. There were no photos, and we mutually agreed to meet at my office's lobby, since we both worked in the city.

I found Syed sitting sunken in a leather chair in the lobby area, peering over a large broadsheet and pretending that he had not noticed my arrival down the escalators.

With the numerous failed coffee dates, I had surrendered any belief that this might lead to something, and as I came down the escalators, I had given up any expectations that the person behind the broadsheet had to match any criteria. I could only hope that he was pleasant enough in character to hold a conversation with.

Finally the broadsheet lowered enough to catch his eyes smiling back at me upon my approach towards him, and Syed rose from the seat to greet me.

"Ah, you must be Eleanor," he said delightedly. "Mwah, mwah," he said, pecking me on both cheeks with an air of sophistication.

"Hello. Nice to meet you," I said calmly.

"Shall we go across the road and get a drink?"

"Yes, that's a good idea."

He continued to chatter as we crossed the road, and I noticed that his mannerisms were different from the other men I had been introduced to. He came across as well spoken, and there was something a little more elitist about him. His hair was neatly cropped, and his suited attire gave the impression that he was someone who took great pride in how he presented himself.

He also did all the talking and voluntarily brought up details about himself. How he and his father were in the property business. That his father had worked for a charity for the disabled and had met the mayor of London and received an MBE from the Queen. How they lived in a large house in Hampstead Heath, and although it didn't concern me, it came as a refreshing change to talk to someone who wasn't necessarily assessing me for my validity as a wife.

Our meeting was cut short by his father, who called relating to a business matter, and after a five-minute phone call, pacing around the bar, Syed returned.

"I'm so sorry about that … er …" he said, peering down at his phone and writing a text message. "Er, would it be possible to meet again? I have quite an urgent matter to attend to right now, and I do think it would be nice if we … er, had a little more time together."

"Sure," I said. "I can't see why not."

"Let see here," he said, looking now at his diary on his phone. "How about tomorrow evening? Would that work? Would you be free? I know a great little spot upstairs in the British Museum," he said, smiling.

"Sure. That sounds lovely," I said, and smiled back.

He shook my hand, which came across as a little peculiar, as if we were signing a business contract.

"Nice doing business with you," I said mockingly as we shook hands.

He smiled and turned to walk away through the bar, but to my surprise, as I picked up my handbag, he turned back to hug and kiss me on both cheeks, then looked at me straight in the eye deeply and said, "I will see you tomorrow."

"Yes, I will see you tomorrow," I said, feeling a little overwhelmed.

There was something very charming and refreshingly different about Syed in our brief encounter, and I could only look forward to learning more about him.

*

"I am quite intrigued by him," I explained to my close friends Andrea, Sonia and Lenna over drinks that evening.

"Eleanor, I think it's weird that you are going through an arranged marriage here," Lenna declared as she clinked her wine glass.

"Well, wait. I wouldn't go as far as marriage just yet. But I do think, you know, so far, that he seems nice. Which is a change from the usual weird crowd my parents have set me up with."

"Hmm, we'll see, won't we?" Andrea nudged as she peeled some pistachios to throw into her mouth.

"Do you think you will see him again?" Andrea asked.

"Actually, as a matter of fact, I am meeting him tomorrow," I said to all of them.

"What? That's a bit keen, isn't it?" Sonia replied, looking a little surprised.

"Well, you know, we didn't actually get to speak for very long today, so he suggested maybe we meet for dinner at the British Museum tomorrow evening."

"Don't rush anything, will you, hon?" Sonia warned with a pained expression. "I mean, you never know, he could be an absolute nutter."

I shook my head at the absurdity of this remark. "It's just a dinner. I am sure it will be fine!"

My phone beeped with a message alert.

"Oh, look, I just got a message from him," I said to the girls. "'Hey, beautiful, great to meet you today, still thinking about you, sorry it was rushed and hope I can make it up to you tomorrow.'"

"Quite a charmer, isn't he?" said Andrea.

"Nutter, more like." Sonia shook her head, taking another drag of her cigarette.

"Sounds like we won't be seeing much of you from now on, Eleanor."

"Oh, come on, guys, let's not get carried away with ourselves here now."

*

The following evening, I met Syed at the British Museum. He was dressed casually in jeans and a sweater. I marvelled at the great domed ceiling as we made our way up the stairs.

"This is beautiful," I said. "You know, I have never been in here before."

"You are kidding me. What? In all these years that you've lived here? You know I live across the road from here, don't you?"

"Oh, really? I thought you mentioned that you live in Hampstead."

He hesitated for a moment. "No, no, that's where we live on the weekends. See, it's quite a long commute for my father, so we tend to move between the two."

"Nice," I said. "Must be wonderful to have two places."

"Are you hungry?" he asked, interrupting my flow and abruptly changing the subject.

"Yes," I said. "A little." I hadn't eaten all day. "How about you?" I asked.

"No," he said. "I ate before I came out."

"Oh?" I said, surprised and feeling a little disappointed, as I'd thought we would have dinner together. Nevertheless, we were seated at the restaurant, and a waiter came to take my order. I ordered soup with some bread while Syed stirred a mug of tea around and continued talking away. It was awkward now to eat, given he hadn't ordered anything.

"Are you sure you don't want to order something?" I asked politely.

"No, no. There's nothing halal here. You do subscribe to eating halal only, don't you?" he said sternly.

"Well, yes," I lied. I was slightly overwhelmed by the confrontation and could only assume he practised religion enough to warrant asking.

"So, how are you, beautiful?" he said, looking at me with his arms folded and resting on the table. He peered down at my hands. "Sorry, do you mind if I have a quick look at your hand?"

I opened up my palm.

"That's a funny line. Is that a scar?"

"Oh, yes. I cut myself once on the dha when my mother was teaching me how to use it."

"Oh, wow. You must be, like, proper housewife material."

"Ha! You wish!" I said, joking.

"Gee, that must have been a deep cut to have scarred so long."

"Yes, well, I was trying to hack a fish in half before my hand landed on the blade."

"Well, my mum would be impressed if she heard about your war wounds."

I smiled, slightly coyly, at his praise and bundled my napkin over my face.

He leaned back, looking at me admiringly, shaking his head in disbelief. "So, where does a beautiful girl like you hide? Who would have thought! All this time, you have been living here in London, and our paths never crossed once."

I admired the fact he could express his feelings openly, without hesitation. He had a different personality from Rohit, who would not be so direct in his expression, and it had often been difficult to decipher what he was thinking or feeling about me. It was flattering to receive compliments for once, something that I had not received in a while, since Rohit and I split.

We talked for a while in an endless flow from one topic to another, although it seemed that he was doing most of the talking and I the listening. The conversation seemed passively about wealth, holidays, cars, business deals, status and upbringing. I kept an open mind, but from what he described, one could only picture that his parents were of high society and were abundantly wealthy, although

I had no anticipation or concerted interest in meeting someone with such credentials.

The waiter came over. "Sir, just as a note, the restaurant will be closing at 10 p.m."

"Oh! Is that the time already?" I said, surprised that we had been there so long.

"Wow, yes, time flies!" exclaimed Syed. "We'll just get the bill, then," he said to the waiter.

"Yes, of course, sir."

Syed paid the bill and continued talking as we walked out. "So ..." He paused outside the entrance of the museum. "So, what should we do next?"

"I am not sure. You must know London pretty well, since you have lived here all your life. Where's good to go?" I asked.

He thought a little. "Have you ever tried Arabic food?" he asked.

"No, I haven't actually," I said, opening to the idea.

"Okay, I've got to take you to this place; it's one of my favourite places in London."

He hailed a taxi, and we arrived at a bustling restaurant on Edgware Road. The atmosphere was ecstatic, with people sat at tables packed tightly together, and in close-knit conversations, puffing shisha.

The interior had a very Arabic feel, and a kaleidoscope of mirrors glittered on the walls and shimmered reflections on the ceiling. Tiled mosaics dotted the tables. Brass ornaments and furnishings wielded a regal appeal throughout the restaurant. The ceiling lingered with smoke and filled the air with the aroma of rose, mint tea and apple shisha. At the end of the room, a large TV screen played contemporary Arabic music where stunning Arabic women in Western clothes danced and flirted with the camera.

"This is amazing!" I said to Syed as we were seated. We sat at a small table for two.

"Yeah, I knew you would like it. Hey, Ali!" he said, raising his hand and ushering over a waiter.

The waiter came over, shaking Syed's hand in an overfamiliar and brotherly way.

"Could we get one shisha, some mint tea and some humus and pita?"

"Certainly, brother, certainly," said Ali, who then repeated the order loudly to the kitchen staff as he rushed off.

"You must come here often," I said. "You seem right in your element."

"Yeah, yeah, of course, I have been coming here a long time. You know we don't go to clubs and bars. That's for the English, not for the Muslims, you know. This is the halal way of life."

He talked a little more about his father's work and the lavish party they had held after he was awarded his MBE. And their big house somewhere in Hampstead and how his parents were well known in London. I couldn't really comment on any of it. I couldn't help but notice that while he volunteered this information about himself, I couldn't understand why he never asked about me.

So, I asked him, "Well, is there anything you want to know about me?"

"Well, there's no need to ask questions, is there? What good are questions when you surrender to the will of Allah anyhow? I know everything I need to know about you."

He smiled at me admiringly, and yet his remark seemed intimidating and overconfident.

"Ah, here we are," he said, immediately distracted by the waiter who brought over tea and shisha. I watched as he puffed away, detaching the nozzle from the pipe and puffing thick clouds of smoke around us. The air between us became dense, making it difficult to see each other.

He then passed the pipe to me. I put the nozzle back on and started with a light puff. It smelled sweet and felt choky when the tobacco became a little intense.

"Take it easy," he said as I coughed.

I passed it back to him, and he began puffing away and looking at me.

"I will make you a good Bengali wife one day," he joked.

CHAPTER THIRTY-ONE
– *Telltale Signs* –

Things really picked up the pace with Syed. We spent long hours on the phone with each other at night, a whirlwind of conversations on so many levels. Within the first two weeks, we saw each other almost every day. I'd meet him at the South Bank or somewhere in east London after work. I had started working from the city office more to avoid Rohit, and it also helped with meeting Syed earlier, who always seemed in a rush to get home.

Syed was your typical alpha male, with an air of chivalry about him. He made a point of opening doors or helping me into a taxi and carrying my bag. He would often take me shopping and would ask whether I would like anything, encouraging me to buy while insisting he paid. And often he would be annoyed if I attempted to pay for anything, which always made me feel uneasy. In his view, women shouldn't have to carry anything; that was a man's job, and often when I insisted, he would feel emasculated. I didn't think anyone had cared for me in this way, as I had always lived so independently. He was extremely generous and romantic, and in our meetings, he would often present a small trinket of jewellery, a gift or a flower. During the summer, he also sent bouquets of roses to my office, which raised some eyebrows, including those of Rohit, who found it awkward to ask who they were from.

He refused to call me by my name; it was always "janu", which means "sweetheart". One evening in a restaurant, I pulled out my purse when the waiter came out with the bill. I wanted to pay; we had been dining lavishly at his expense, and I had not yet returned the favour once. Perhaps I had taken my insistence on paying too far on this occasion, as no sooner had I pulled out my purse than he grabbed my wrist firmly on the table and gave me a reproachful look. "Janu," he said, "what are you doing?" His tone was very deep. "Please don't embarrass me again like that in front of the waiter."

"Sorry, I didn't mean to offend you—" I said before he interjected.

"Yes, yes, I know your type," he continued. "Miss Independent," he said, placing the quotation marks above his head with his hands. "Janu, I am here to take care of you. When you are with me from now on, let me sort everything, okay?"

I was comforted by his words. It felt right; he was only trying to look after me, that was all.

When we came out of the restaurant, he placed his jacket over me and pulled me closer to him. "You are so beautiful. You don't know how much I want to be with you, but if you want to carry on, you are going to have to trust me and take everything that I have to offer you. Make sense?" He was being very firm, and that was okay: it was important to him. But something about it seemed forceful and intimidating all at the same time.

We spent more and more time together, to the point where Syed and I saw each other every evening, and if it wasn't us seeing each other, we would be on the phone. Most of the time, he would drive me around, showing me places. One evening he took me around Hampstead, where we had dinner at a Lebanese restaurant.

"Let me take you around my neighbourhood," he said casually.

"Sure," I said. *This will be the first time that I get a glimpse of anything concrete in his world*, I thought.

So far, I had heard about his parents meeting with high-society officials, diplomats, mayors and MPs. I'd heard about his investment business with his father, how his mother worked for a charity organisation, and his father was the managing director of another, but really, I knew nothing about Syed, not in any depth, and strangely enough, he didn't ever ask about me.

We drove uphill to the top heights of Hampstead. It was a dusky summer evening, and the street lights were starting to come on. We had driven through Hampstead Heath, through woody forest roads where the trees were so densely arched over, the evening sun barely peeked through. We approached a narrow country lane that was for private use only.

"This is where I live," said Syed.

We drove through the private estate. It had mansions the size of three houses. I was so in awe I became speechless. "Wow, this is amazing, Syed," I said, peering out.

He pulled over in front of one house, a large mansion with a neo-Georgian-style front. It had a large double oak door in the middle. On the front were two Greek-looking pillars.

"Do you want to say hello to my ammu?"

"Sure," I said.

He paused. "No, not today."

"That's okay. Let me go and introduce myself." I walked out of the door.

Syed called, "No, janu, no."

I carried on walking to the front door. I could hear Syed in the background, telling me to stop. I knocked on the front door. It was 8.30 p.m. I waited. Syed had now driven off. What I found really strange was that there was a pig in the window. It was a money pig. I knew, I just knew that all of this was pretence: Muslim households would not have a pig or any animal as an ornament.

A voice came from behind the door. "Who is it?" It was a very English-sounding man's voice.

"Hello there. I am here to see Syed's mum," I called out.

"There is nobody here of that name," came a rather direct remark.

"Oh, apologies," I said. "I must have the wrong house."

I walked away feeling quite proud that I had been forthright in finding out the truth, returning slowly to the main road. It was now very dark, and Syed's car was nowhere in sight.

Within a minute I saw a set of car headlights. Syed pulled up. "Get in," he shouted. "Janu, I am very disappointed in you," he said as if I were a child. "Why did you go off like that? I told you not to leave!" His tone was heated, and I could tell he was resisting the urge to shout his head off at me.

"I thought you wanted to introduce me to your mum," I said calmly.

"If you had any decency, you wouldn't invite yourself over like that, would you?"

"Well, if you had any decency, you wouldn't lie," I said.

He didn't answer. And I felt the shudder of the gear shifting as he forced down the pedal. "No respecting woman would do that. Why would my mum want to meet you at this time of night?"

"Well, as it happens, she doesn't even live there," I pointed out.

Suddenly he started accelerating at great speed. The car swerved down the country lanes, his steering was jerky and off-centre. I felt immensely intimidated and could only sense it would be better to remain quiet.

"You disrespected me!" he said. "I am beginning to question the kind of woman I am seeing."

I almost wanted to laugh, but the speed at which he was driving and his anger and rage at the events made me discontented about doing so. I waited for him to calm down. He drove to the hilltops of Alexandra Palace, where the landscape glimmered with a thousand street lights before us. We got out of the car, and he thrust me towards him, turning me by the hand to face him.

"Why don't you trust me?" he said, looking at me. He held my neck, stroking it.

"Why did you lie?" I said.

"I didn't lie," he said.

"Well, the man behind the door didn't know anyone by that name."

"That was my brother you spoke to, and, no, he wouldn't open the door to strangers at this hour."

I had nothing to come back to on that, because I didn't see the need to prove him wrong, even though I had my reasons to doubt him.

"Janu, I love you. That's the truth, and I want you to be a part of everything, and if you want to be a part of my family and me, you are going to have to do things the more traditional way. You know, not randomly turning up like that. There are certain protocols and etiquettes you are going to have to follow."

"Then why did you ask me if I wanted to see your mum, in that case?"

"Oh my God, it was figuratively speaking." He raised his head up to the dark, starry sky incredulously, then looked back at me. "You are not that intelligent, are you?" he said, tugging the collar of my coat affectionately.

I raised my eyebrows with surprise at his put-down.

"I am kidding," he sighed, smiling. "Janu, janu, what am I going to do with you?" he begged, giggling helplessly as though he couldn't find words to describe the events that had unfolded.

"And why don't you ever ask anything about me?" I remarked. "I find it strange that you don't want to know anything about me." I confronted him again, as I hadn't yet got a clear answer on this.

"Janu," he said, stroking my hair away from my face. "Do you think I would date you if I didn't know anything about you?" He looked at me straight in the eye affectionately. "I know more about you," he continued, "than you even know about yourself."

"What?" I said, shocked at his response.

He shook his head with disbelief and began heading back to the car.

"What do you mean?"

He didn't answer.

It was quiet on the drive home. He looked calmly on at the road. I looked out of my passenger window. I thought about what he'd said, what he knew about me and the strange charade he carried on about where he lived. And furthermore, more disconcerting than that, the aggressive behaviour he'd displayed in the car. If he knew me that well, then he'd know I didn't care about wealth and money. It didn't add up. I couldn't wait to leave the car. *I am going to end this,* I thought to myself. *This is too weird. I don't think I can be with someone so controlling.*

We approached the front door of my house, that normal life I had with Andrea, Sean and Dave. It was almost 10.30 p.m.

"Do you want me to walk you in?" he asked.

"No, it's okay." I smiled awkwardly. I just wanted some breathing space now; I wanted to think about how I would call him later and let him know that I didn't want to see him anymore.

But just as I opened the door to leave the car, he grabbed my hand firmly and said, "Janu, you do know that your family, relatives and family friends all know that we are seeing each other, don't you?"

I was speechless; I couldn't imagine why he would need to make such a declaration. He gave me a wry smile as I made my way out of the vehicle, and then I watched him speed off down the road.

That night, the safeness of my room and the comfort of my bed were not enough to remove the unsettling feeling I had about Syed. That brief exchange had left me in a state of fear and paranoia.

Firstly, men and women are not supposed to date in Bengali culture. Mamajee and Babajee would probably kill me if word ever got out that I had. I knew this because of the way Mamajee and Babajee responded when they heard of the terrible atrocity of honour killings. In Mamajee and Babajee's eyes, it was quite justifiable for a mother and father to murder or beat their own child, should their daughter deface their honour in courtship before marriage. In one case, a very wealthy business associate of Babajee's had ended up in prison after the father found out his sixteen-year-old daughter had been seeing a local Bengali boy. The father was furious and had ordered a hitman to kill the boy. He then proceeded to beat his daughter and locked her up in the house for days. When Mamajee heard of what the Qureshis had done to their daughter and her boyfriend, she had given no sympathy to the girl at all.

"That bitch should have been killed along with that boy. He should have killed the daughter. Oh, if that were my daughter, I would have killed her by now." I could see her boiling up with rage as if she was experiencing it herself. Her gritted teeth to withhold her anger and resentment over what she had described as an unforgiveable act were enough to assure me of her response if ever I betrayed her.

It was for this reason that most young, unmarried Bengali couples were not seen out in public, holding hands, kissing or even talking about their relationships. It is why such relationships are kept in secret, and within young Asian girls' circles, the underworld of love and courtship, secret letters and exchanges, meetings about their love lives, was expressed and discussed in code, such as "I am meeting you-know-who" or "*she*" (which referred to the boy she had planned to meet) or "I am meeting *her* at the library."

Love was a social taboo and a treacherous game of lies that most young people upheld for the sake of honour. Only the trusted amongst us would ever be made privy to such relations, and it begged the question as to who Syed had told. What had he mentioned to my family? And what did he know about me? There was only one thing that would prevent the backlash, uproar – if they knew that I intended to marry Syed. Then, and only then, would it be less frowned upon, and although it was considered less favourable, it wouldn't be dishonourable. The grapevine and gossip wouldn't spread so wildly, and the community would accept that we had intended to marry.

It was as though Syed knew this would make it hard for me to leave. Or was it that he just assumed we were ready enough to openly acknowledge our relationship? I recollected a moment where I'd wanted Rohit to acknowledge that we were more than just colleagues to his friends, how it had hurt when I was nothing but someone he worked with, and here I was now, wanting my relationship with Syed to be hidden, to be unknown. Now I could only feel pressure to make this work, that there was no turning back.

I wrestled with my inner thoughts. *Could it be that I am just getting ahead of myself? I did upset him by going off like that. Everyone reacts differently, and just think, Eleanor, this might be a good thing, if he knows your family and he has a good family background. That would really please your parents.*

The seven-year-old me was smiling again. *Finally, you will make them proud. Finally, you will be in an open and honest relationship with someone who the whole family will respect.*

My thoughts derived pleasure and fear all at once from this notion. On the one hand, there was a promise that I would finally make my parents happy and proud, and on the other, I couldn't fathom whether Syed was the right person for me. It was difficult to say; it had only been a few weeks, although intense, and what troubled me even more was that the choice had already been taken away from me. I couldn't make that phone call to tell him it was over. I needed to understand this situation more.

*

The following day I met Syed after work at a restaurant not far from his office in Canary Wharf. His eyes fixed on me with that wry smile again as he approached the table. There was a look of confidence in his expression that loomed over me, causing fear and trepidation.

"Hello, beautiful," he said, planting a wet kiss on my cheek.

"Hello," I said calmly, avoiding eye contact.

He sat down and immediately began looking at the menu.

As I watched him deeply engrossed in the menu, I began cumulating questions. I desperately wanted to find out who he had talked to and what he had told them about us.

The waiter came over to take our order. "Now, what can I get you to eat?"

Syed peered over at me from the top of the menu.

"I hope you eat only halal," he said.

That was quite suggestive, I thought. Was he insinuating that I wasn't religious? To be quite honest, I wasn't religious at all. I didn't practise it, even though Mamajee had raised me to be a fully practising Muslim, to carry out the five daily prayers, to fast during the month of Ramadan, to eat only halal and not drink alcohol. Admittedly, I no longer upheld those habits, and I knew in the eyes of the community, for a Bengali girl, this was frowned upon.

I knew that tongues would wag if they ever found out, that of course, it would propel Mamajee's closely guarded honour to a lower place in society. I could almost hear the backchat she would face if I disclosed the truth to Syed: "Oh, did you hear about so-and-so's daughter? Despicable behaviour, not a practising believer, disgraceful, doesn't eat halal meat. Oh, I wouldn't want to associate with that family: the children are so wayward. The daughter doesn't even pray."

Such a facade I had to uphold just to keep the peace. While I was sure some people genuinely loved practising, I knew a handful of people who were just pleasing the community. The ones who would go upstairs and pray, but their minds were elsewhere and not really into it. The ones who didn't really want to wear a headscarf when they walked around town and would prefer to wear Western clothes over Islamic attire. The ones who would happily eat pork sausages and dine at non-halal restaurants.

Yes, that person was me all right, and I knew in my head that Syed was already suspicious that I wasn't into any of this. But the seven-year-old me took over. She wanted to please him, Mamajee and my family (who I knew weren't really all that into it either). So, I pretended, feeling it was better to preserve my parents' honour, it was worthier than my own worldly rights right now. But there was a part of me that grieved at these hollow pretences as it shadowed over my real life. That world of freedom that I had painstakingly created, where I worked, travelled the world, met who I wanted, ate and wore what I wanted. I was losing sight of all of that. And the greatest paradox of all was that I was losing sight of this for the sake of vanity, because being who I was would be denting someone else's ego. I could see all my efforts to gain freedom, the challenges in doing so, the hours studying, the hurdles through university, the coaching and priming by Mrs Abbots, were now all in vain.

There was only voice that was tearing me apart now. The voice of the seven-year-old me, frowning inside. *You better not mess this up. After all, you promised Mamajee.*

"I think I will have the vegetarian curry," I finally said, looking up at him and avoiding the question. "What about you?" I said.

"I am going to have the chicken pad thai. It's halal chicken in here."

He is religious, I thought. This was going to be tricky, but then, maybe not so bad. You know, life was about compromise, and eating just halal food wasn't so bad.

After we had ordered the food, Syed sat back in his seat, looking back at me with a suspicious smile.

"What are you smiling about?" I asked.

"I was just looking at your dress."

I looked down at my clothes; I was wearing a short-sleeved, fitted black T-shirt and fitted long black trousers. "What about it?" I asked, looking over at him.

"You know, if you wore that in front of my parents, they would – how should I say it? – not be impressed."

"Why? What is wrong with what I am wearing?"

"Well, the top is low-cut, and you are not wearing a scarf."

"Oh, I see," I said. "No worries, I will keep that in mind."

He nodded at me. "You see, I don't care. You could wear a bikini in front of me, but my parents, you will have to make sure you dress appropriately in front of them."

My heart sank. He was coaching and priming me already. Was I losing my identity again, or was this facade a small compromise? After all, I did still have to change what I wore in front of my parents too. Still, this was early days, and perhaps things wouldn't be so bad, I thought.

"Syed, can I ask you something?" I said nervously. "You mentioned yesterday that my family knows about us. Who knows about us?"

"Oh yes!" he said, grinning. "I was wondering when you were going to ask! Do you know Muhammed from Adderington?"

"Yes," I said. My mind began to process the connection. Mohammed was a close family friend, and my brothers hung out with him almost every evening. He was also very entrenched in the community life: he regularly attended mosque, got on with my parents and was well liked by everyone, although he was also the biggest gossip because of his closeness in the community.

"Well," continued Syed, "Muhammed's father and my father are related, and we visit them a lot, so when I heard you lived in Ashcroft, I couldn't believe it! I only mentioned that I had seen you to Muhammed, and he knew instantly who you were, of course, because he's very close with your brothers." He laughed in disbelief. "Small world, hey? Small world."

Oh, God, I thought, *everyone knows. There is no going back now.* It was possibly why Mamajee had not chased me about where things were heading. She probably knew the ins and outs of my interactions through the grapevine. Why was she silent? Muhammed was a real gossip, and I knew that my brothers would have already found out, which meant, of course, my family knew.

The seven-year-old me came back to haunt me again. *You are already soiled goods in their eyes. If you have been frolicking around, it will surely look bad. Mamajee's reputation is now on the line; she wouldn't be able to show her face if the whole town knew that you were seeing someone and decided to flake out. Do you think people would be inclined to meet you after that? You would already be known to them as that wanderer who goes off with guys.* The seven-year-old me was right. I had better go along with this. After all Mamajee had been through, I couldn't let her down now.

*

As Syed and I progressed, things started to become stricter on dress codes and protocols. I stopped wearing my skirts, fitted dresses and jeans. I started hanging around with Syed's high-society Bengali friends and turning up at Bengali high-society events. Syed wooed me, wined and dined me romantically. For one of these events, he bought a stunning dark red saree with red embroidery for me to wear.

On the outside, I felt like a strikingly beautiful woman as he introduced me to his friends and associates. I felt reincarnated as an elegant Asian woman. On the inside though, I was losing myself. I felt empty, ugly and soulless.

At first I felt warmed by the compliments and praise. "Oh, janu, you are more stunning and beautiful when you wear shalwar kameez. Don't give up who you are to that fickle Western world. Your culture is you. Be proud of it." Or how he would kiss my hand romantically, then present a box tied in silk ribbons, revealing jewellery. Or between layers of tissue paper, he would reveal an embroidered saree or a shalwar kameez with stunning embroidery. I felt overwhelmed, and in some ways, it felt right to be heading in that direction with Syed. After all, this was going to make my parents happy, regardless of how disjointed my world was becoming.

When I faced my other reality though, people were noticing changes in me too. It raised a lot of suspicions when I wore an Indian tunic to work.

"You look nice," said had Rohit on entering.

"Thank you."

"Are you off to a wedding later?"

"No," I said bluntly.

Which left him looking blankly on at me.

My colleagues had also commented. "What's with the long skirts?"

"Oh, I dunno. Just a change," I said, slightly flustered for words.

"Very, er, bohemian," one of them said. I could sense they knew what was going on, and often the comments sounded remarkably the same.

"Don't go changing too much, will ya? We like you just the way you are."

And these comments resonated the most when my friends noticed my change of appearance.

"Feels like I haven't seen you for ages, and yet we live in the same house," Andrea said in the kitchen one day.

"I know, it's been a crazy couple of months. I have been seeing Syed a lot, of course."

"Yeah, blimey, you don't say?" she said. "Sounds like this guy has really swept you off your feet, Eleanor."

"Yeah, sort of," I mumbled, feeling disconcerted by her observation.

"Sort of? I've never seen you wear those what-do-you-call-ems before," Andrea said, looking at me suspiciously.

"Shalwar kameez."

"Yep, those. Nice though."

"Oh, yeah, I know. He's very generous. He bought all of these outfits for me, and things." I chuckled, trying to reassure her that this was positive.

"Hmm." Andrea looked at me suspiciously. "So, when are we going to meet this man of yours? Sounds like you two will be heading down the aisle in no time at this rate."

"Yeah, you guys should definitely meet him. Let me arrange something."

CHAPTER THIRTY-TWO

– Rules of Engagement-

The following week I arranged a night out with all my house-mates and friends to meet Syed. He had no hesitation in meeting with them and had decided the best place for it was at the shisha restaurant we had now regularly dined at on Marylebone Road. I was a little nervous about how all of this was going to turn out. My friends were all Westerners who had very little understanding of how things operated in Asian cultures. It had been a couple of months now that Syed and I had been dating, and at some point, undoubtedly, these worlds were going to collide if we were to continue. I came dressed in a handmade maroon shalwar kameez with a small embroidered vine that grew all the way down the dress. I had already primed my friends about Asian customs and cultures on the way to the tube station.

"Andrea," I said. "Please don't mention that I drink and go out clubbing. Honestly, it won't go down well."

Andrea looked at me with a dubious smile. "Oka-a-ay," she said, "but why do you have to pretend? Shouldn't you just be open and honest?"

"I know, Andrea, I know, it's wrong. But if he finds out and then things go wrong between us, I don't know what he is capable of, and if my parents find out, this would be devastating for them."

Andrea looked disapprovingly at me. "Eleanor, you are having to lie about who you are. If you have to do that, then he can't possibly be the right guy for you. I mean, if you don't feel comfortable with him, how can this be the right relationship?"

I knew what she was saying was right, that I was setting up false pretences and I was living a white lie, but my countless attempts at finding someone who came remotely near to westernised had been really difficult.

It was easy for Andrea to say: she didn't have the same worries; she had a Western upbringing; her family would let her marry whoever she pleased. English society was open and accepting of anything. It didn't matter what you wore, or the caste, the colour, the type of person you were, the culture and background you came from, and race was also not questioned by the majority of Western parents. They didn't mind who their child dated or married, as long as they were happy.

Meeting someone for me was much harder. They didn't just have to be Muslim, they had to be Bangladeshi. They also had to be from the same district, a specific set of villages, a certain caste. Their parents had to have a good business or some level of academic status. The potential suitor also had to have been educated to degree level and be in a respectable career, something like law, medicine, engineering or finance. The criteria was a long list, and in amongst all of this, the chances of meeting someone who you might fall in love with or even find remotely attractive was yet another hurdle. And although I hadn't developed a relationship with Syed, and I wasn't certain I loved him yet, I could see in some ways how this would work. I could see my families getting on. It was now a case of if I could.

We arrived at the restaurant, where Syed had already busily ushered the waiter to arrange a long table for the seven of us. Syed and I sat in the centre seats, surrounded by my housemates, Andrea, Sean and Dave, and my two other friends Sonia and Lenna. Before anyone had sight of the menu, he ushered the waiter over. "Some mint tea to start with, please, and three apple shishas, brother."

Lenna rolled her eyes at this. That normally came with a silent remark of "What a prick!" and Sonia immediately averted her eyes to stop herself from laughing.

Lenna was always quite headstrong. The torments of previous bad relationships had left her with a lot of war wounds. She had already made her mind up when mentioning Syed. "Eleanor, this sounds like a real no go. Can't you see this guy is a prick?" But in Lenna's eyes though, everyone was a prick. Anyone I dated had to be, because they were men. The only exception to that was Rohit, who later, in her mind, became a prick because he didn't stand up to what he really wanted. There was something very endearing about Lenna in all her feistiness. She was the kind of person who wouldn't let anyone take advantage of me. Sometimes in clubs, for example, when a guy wanted to talk to me, she would be quite happy to move them along. "Okay, prick, move along; show's over," she would say without hesitation. She protected me and made sure that nobody used and abused my trust.

Syed rambled on with small talk, entertaining the men with a full explanation of the culture of shisha. Lenna looked at me from across the table and shook her head disapprovingly. The rest of the evening, she barely said a word except when she was talking to Dave, who sat next to her and had not really said much to Syed. I turned to Sonia, who sat silently opposite me, puffing away at the shisha, and indicated with a sideways smirk, as if to say, "Eleanor, what the fuck are you doing? But okay."

The food that Syed had ordered on behalf of the table arrived, and the group went along with that for fear of ordering something inappropriate. "It's all halal here, so no one has to worry. Just tuck in." He laughed greedily at the large platter of meze, mixed grill and lamb kofta. There was a selection of olives, pickles, naan bread and yoghurt. In the centre arrived a large gold tray of chicken kabsa, a slow-cooked rice dish that had a whole chicken in the centre. It was scented with cloves, cabbage, garlic and topped with almonds. Andrea and Sean sat next to each other on one side of the table and had managed to pick up some conversation with Syed on food.

"This is really good food, man," Sean praised with a belch as he sipped his coke. "Could do with a beer though." At which everyone froze. Indifferent, he then continued. "So, how did you find this place?"

Syed looked a little perturbed by the comment but then became smug with praise. "Oh, you know, Sean, it's never a case of how you find something, it is how it finds you. I only attract the best of things." He grinned with his gummy smile that displayed his crooked teeth like a jagged, rocky coastline.

Lenna rolled her eyes at me as she ate, as if to say, "Prick. He didn't even answer the question."

"My family always comes here for dinner," Syed continued, "and as you can see, this place has the best Eastern food."

Dave looked at the menu despite the food already arriving. "Eleanor, you getting a drink?" he asked me.

"Oh! There's no alcohol here, guys," Syed said firmly, looking in my direction. I felt like I had hit a wall with words.

David loosened it up. "Oh, I will have a mint tea. Should I get you one too, Eleanor?" he said softly.

"Yes!" I said, feeling a little embarrassed by Syed's stern look. "That would be perfect, David." I could feel the heat on my face from the glare coming from Syed's direction, and it subsided as the conversation changed to something else.

Other than the one slightly heated exchange, I was relieved that nothing particularly eventful happened that night, but in my friends' eyes, they had already drawn their conclusions.

*

"Why are you with this guy, Eleanor? He is a complete dick," Lenna explained the next time the four of us met. Sonia concurred silently as if it were the sum total of her encounter with him.

And my housemates, who were normally less opinionated, reserved their comments to "I am not sure about him, I must say." I had only managed to squeeze that much out of Andrea when I quizzed her later one night after dinner. Even David had skirted around the issue by busying himself.

I became deeply unsettled with their feelings about Syed. I knew deep down inside there was a lot of truth in their perceptions. I could only silently admit them to myself, but I felt compelled to make this work. I needed to be married. I needed to be happy, and the only way I knew how was through making my family happy, most importantly through making Mamajee happy and removing all those wounds that tormented her past from the countless and vivid issues she had had with Babajee.

*

One afternoon I had met Syed at Canary Wharf again. It was a sunny, breezy day, and we walked across the square to a car showroom to look at the new cars on display. I wore a long black dress, over it a mid-length coat, and had wrapped a scarf around my neck.

Syed was busy showing me the large, exclusive Land Rover four-by-fours. "I think you should buy a new car," he said. "I don't think much of that Audi you drive. It's too ..." He paused when he noticed somebody in the crowd. He pressed my elbow. "Cover your head," he said.

"Why?" I said.

"Don't ask questions. Just do it," he said abruptly.

I unravelled my scarf, pulling it over my head.

A man he knew walked towards him, giving him a quick nod. He then stopped and approached us. "Assalamualaikum," said the man to both of us. Syed shook his hand, and the pair had a brief exchange in Bengali.

I turned away to face a large silver estate, as I didn't think this was something I needed to be involved in.

Syed then came back to me. "That was my dad's business partner," he said. "I need to make you aware of a few things here. Firstly, you are going to have to wear a scarf when you are out. People know my family, and if they see you like this, they are going to talk."

I was confused. "Like what?" I said. "I am wearing a long dress. I am covered up. What more do you want?"

He crouched down, leaning in and bending into my face. "Listen to me. If you want this to work, then things are going to have to change. You are going to have to start dressing more appropriately for starters, not this English, Western crap. If my family saw you like that, they would be horrified by you!"

I was silently fuming. "First of all, I am not going to change anything. If you don't like what you see, you better start looking elsewhere, as it's not me. I am not going to change who I am."

I started walking off, but he grabbed my arm from behind with a firm grip.

"Do you have any respect and dignity for yourself? What kind of girl gives away so much of herself? Do you think any respectable Bengali man would accept you the way you are? The way you dress and hang around with English friends, going out to bars and sitting next to Englishmen?"

I suddenly felt like crawling into a shell somewhere, the insinuation that I was out of order and that I was some kind of filthy societal reject for living my life the way I did. Perhaps he was right though. Who would accept me like this? I thought about whether I would ever meet someone like Syed again. Someone who did like me and, more importantly, who I came near to liking or wanting to be with. I stopped to think, mulling over the words in my mind as I looked on at the canal we had walked along from the showroom.

"Janu, look at me," he said calmly now and holding my hand. "I just want us to be happy and to find true happiness. Sometimes it comes with a little compromise."

I calmed down. "I do understand that Syed. It is just ..."

"Shh," he said, "no more." Gently pressing his fingers against my lips. "Let's move on, okay?"

I smiled at him submissively. One part of me felt secure, but the other part of me ached.

*

Six months into our relationship, we were having several arguments. It would start when he discovered something new about me that he didn't like, and it would lead to me walking off.

The rules of engagement were getting tighter around everything. Syed would get angry at all kinds of things, and I felt like a snag list of things that needed fixing. From clothes to make-up, or the things I would talk about, such as the places I had travelled to on my own, or the languages I wanted to learn, I was being restricted and edited out. I found it hard to let go of some of these requests where he would ask that I no longer made mention of certain topics, such as my perspectives on culture or education, or the things I wore and the places I had been to. These would often result in heated conflicts. Other things I would let go of or try to compromise and accept things would have to change. He didn't like, for example, that I wouldn't speak in Bengali with him when he was talking in Bengali with me. And when I did, my Bengali was not good enough. He would correct me and put me down in such a condescending way that I could only feel insulted. "I am embarrassed by your inability to speak your own language. Didn't your mother teach you anything?" Which I would take personally, and a fire of rage would light up inside me. There were other petty arguments about the books I read and how he disagreed with me reading them, such as *Life of Pi* by Yann Martel or *The God of Small Things* by Arundhati Roy. While he never read books nor understood why one would want to, he insisted that I didn't insult him with Western or non-Muslim authors. There were arguments about my friends and the people I lived with. He didn't want to hear about my friends, and within six months I was no longer allowed to mention their names with him or meet them.

On the good side though, when it was just him and me together in isolation, without the rest of the world to contend with, things were good. He would take me on dates to the park, where we would sit together, enjoying the ducks or the boats swaying past in the lake. He enjoyed taking me to fine-dining restaurants, such as Benares in London or the London Hilton on Park Lane for afternoon tea, all halal, of course, and with each encounter I found myself slipping away from my reality into his. At times I loved meeting the sweet and romantic side of Syed, but it felt as fragile as a glass bowl. I knew it would take only the smallest thing to shatter it into pieces.

I felt uneasy and was always torn between two worlds. On one side, I had the world I had made for myself, full of creativity, freedom and being myself, and on the other side, there was a world full of promise that I could finally make Mamajee happy, one where I could finally be free of the seven-year-old-me guilt of that promise I had made to Mamajee. That her sacrifice in raising me was not all in vain. The question remained whether I could see it through with Syed and how long we could continue getting to know each other before Mamajee's patience wore thin. If she already knew, was she silently waiting? And why?

*

One cold evening in November, after dinner with Syed, he pulled over the car at a lay-by in a country park a couple of miles away from my home. The frost glistened orange off the grass and trees by the lamplight. The engine hummed softly as he placed it into park.

"Have you heard this song?" he said.

He turned up the volume. It was "The Scientist" by Coldplay.

"Yes, I have heard of it before," I said with a straight face. Of course I knew it, and I convinced myself that it was only a matter of coincidence that he should ask about it.

He started singing mockingly, as if he knew the lyrics, and faintly followed the words in a high-pitched hum.

I smiled back calmly. Syed continued humming.

"You know, my mother and father have been getting a little worried," he said, nodding his head.

"Oh, right. Why?"

"Because I spend most of my time seeing this madam over here." He nudged me, laughing as he did. "They are all talking, Eleanor. Everyone knows."

"I know," I said.

"My parents have asked multiple times."

"About what?" I asked.

"Well, the main question is, when? When are they going to meet your parents?" He shook his head. "You know what that means though, don't you?"

I nodded.

"So, tell me, then," he said, pressing his lips together and pausing for a moment. "Are you ready to go ahead? Because once we do, there's no going back."

I paused for a moment, the music playing in the background.

He looked at me, waiting for an answer. "Well?"

"I guess so."

"You guess so?" he said. "You guess so?" he repeated with a cackle. "I am about to make you my wife, and you guess so?"

"No, I just mean—" I tried to rephrase the words, but before I could bring the words to my mouth, he laughed louder.

"Oh, shut up!" he shouted, and threw something that landed on my lap.

It was the plastic CD case for the Coldplay album, and on the back, underlined by the song, were the words "With all my love." The blade of grass was windowed inside the case.

"I found this in your glovebox. I just want to know one thing. Did he fuck you? Hmm? Did he?"

I remained silent.

"WELL, DID HE?" he shouted.

There would be consequences either way now. If I told him the truth, he probably wouldn't want to see me, and this would all end miserably. If I didn't, then I was pretty sure we'd continue miserably, and he'd want to know eventually.

"It was a long time ago, and yes," I said.

"Well, it couldn't have been that long ago. This album was released just over a year ago."

He's quite a detective, I thought.

I stayed calm.

"Yes, that's true."

"Here I was, thinking you were fucking innocent," he said, shaking his head and pounding the steering wheel.

"Are you telling me *you* are?" I said in an act of real courage while dreading the response.

"Yes, if you want to know, yes."

I found that hard to believe, but I didn't press it further.

He hung his arms over the steering wheel, taking large, deep breaths. Then he drew himself up from the steering wheel to face me.

"If I hear anything, ANYTHING, about this in front of ANYONE, then you better expect something far worse than hell. If my family ever hear about this, this is going to be hell. So, you better make sure you don't tarnish my name. If you want this to move forward, then you better not disgust me ever again in this way. When you and I enter this marriage, we are tightly bound in a cocoon. Do you hear me? A cocoon. It's just me and you, no one else. Do you hear me?"

I nodded.

He sighed, calming himself down. "Okay, I just wanted to make that clear, that was all."

He drove me quietly back to my place, and I left the car silently. I looked up at my sleepy house as though I was at the junction of two worlds. Was this the end of one and the beginning of another? I wasn't sure. I didn't have the will to fight it, and all I could see was that this was something I forced myself to accept. This must be how it was written for me.

CHAPTER THIRTY-THREE
– *The Proposal-*

A s far as Bengali weddings go, there's no such thing as a man on bended knee, proposing and devoting his life and soul to a world of marital bliss to the one he loves. There's no such thing as a ring; that's all taken care of by the family, but I could have at the very least expected a ring of the phone call sort. As far as Syed was concerned, he didn't need to ask me. He just had to ask his parents to ask my parents. So it came as a surprise when I discovered that our discussion in the car the night before wasn't just to clear the air, it was to clear the path of any debris and set the conditions straight for a lifelong commitment of marriage, and I was to hear of this from no other person than Mamajee.

"Yes, you must come up this weekend; it's something important." She sighed on the phone.

"Important? Like what?"

"Aye, hai, hai, tut, they are coming this weekend."

"Who?"

"You know, the boy's family; they want to meet us, have a cup of tea."

I was stunned into silence. I thought there would have been some mention of it from Syed.

"How did this come about?" I asked, perplexed and confused.

"You know your uncle Sabur called, and he mentioned that this family want to see you, and of course, given we need him as an intermediary between the families, we've asked him to come along too. Otherwise, it looks bad. We can't have people knowing what you guys have been up to, can we?"

Oh, she is finally admitting that she knew, I thought. It also confused me as to why she'd allowed it. She had been against even a five-minute conversation with anyone before, and here we were, knowing that I was dating him. *Still*, I thought, *they must really like him, or they wouldn't have allowed it. Who knows?*

"They are only free this weekend. So make sure you come up," Mamajee added.

*

I called Syed back.

"Hey, janu," he said casually.

"You could have mentioned it," I blurted out, annoyed.

"Ohh! Ha ha! Well, it was a surprise. Thought you'd be happy, no?" He chuckled.

I went silent.

"Oh, come on, it had to be done this way; otherwise, people would talk."

"People already know, Syed. You've told me everyone knows. The only person who doesn't seem to know is me."

"Oh, janu, janu, come on, you are overcomplicating things now. Yes, it's just a bit of a facade, I know, but what will you say to people when we tell them how we got married? That we were dating? That our parents introduced us informally? I think you will need to think about how appalling that would be to our community. They would be utterly disgusted. You have to do this for your parents and my parents, that's all."

I took a deep breath. "None of this seems right, but okay," I said.

"Janu, the only thing that's important here is us. We are co-cooned, remember?"

*

An electric charge ran through my hands as I made my way down the stairs, the chatter and laughter getting louder as I approached the door with my sister. Upon entering the room, an air of silence cascaded across it. Mamajee, Babajee, Syed, the intermediary, Uncle Sabur, and Syed's parents were sat at the dining table amongst a clutter of china teacups, plates and half-finished sweetmeats and snacks. Syed's brother, Sufyan, and my brothers were sat in the living area of the room, watching TV on mute and talking. They also looked up to see me.

Ammujee (as I call Syed's mum) rose from her chair and beckoned me in.

"Come, dear, come and sit down with us." She smiled lovingly at me as my sister guided me across to join Ammujee where she sat at the dining table.

It felt so plastic and manufactured that this meeting had been arranged, the hair, the coy, demure pose, under the pretence that I had never met Syed before. The idea this arrangement had all been contrived to steer off any gossip, so that our families could define this as an arranged marriage.

I was expecting a lot of questions to be thrown at me from his parents, similar to previous arranged-marriage tea parties, but Abbujee (Syed's father) took one glance at me and turned to look at Babajee sitting on his right side. "So," he said, "Rabbani Saheb, we know, you and I know, that we are against time. We have now met your daughter; you have now met our son. We have met you and your wonderful family, and we are very happy and delighted with the outcome of today. And of course, you and I know, it is difficult to come up here that often from London, so the first thing I would like to do is book a date for the wedding."

I gasped inside.

Wedding? I thought to myself. "Hold on," I said, "we never talked about wedding dates."

Babajee nodded in agreement.

Abbujee continued on. "You know in London it is very difficult to get a hall at short notice. Sometimes people are booking venues over a year or two in advance, so I made some enquiries before I arrived and booked a hall provisionally for the walima [reception held by the groom's side] on the eighteenth of July. Obviously, the wedding day itself would have to fall sometime before that, and I am sure you will find something in Manchester that you will be able to host suitably before that date."

I sat looking down, speechless. *They are talking about a wedding? Already?* I thought.

Quite contrary to my reaction, it seemed that Mamajee and Babajee were looking pleased with the idea.

"July." Babajee began counting with his fingers. "Hmm, only seven or eight months away; it seems okay." He nodded slowly, thinking it through. "July, er, yes, I don't see any objections to that."

"Yes, of course, that works for us," Mamajee added.

It does? I thought. *Since when?* I had turned invisible again and was muted out from any discussion.

The intermediary stepped in. "Okay, it looks as though we are all settled on going forward. I guess there is only one small element that remains to be discussed; it's the question of the mahr [*dowry*]," said Uncle Sabur, pressing his round glasses up against his nose.

"Mahr? Who in the name talks about mahr anymore? Oh, don't be so old-fashioned, Sabur Miah; these things are just wasted formalities, surely," retorted Abbujee. I noticed with a quick glance that Abbujee's face shook side to side, making the rounds of his dark, speckled face wobble.

"Yes, yes, maybe so, but it's still a tradition we must abide by. In Islam, the mahr is set to the husband's income, property and any assets that he will provide for his wife upon divorce, and of course, it is obligatory to provide an agreed amount on the day of the wedding for the marriage to be consummated."

Babajee stepped in after much deliberation. "Well, normally, it is in the region of ten thousand pounds, I would say."

"Hai, Rabbani Saheb, this is only a formality. The kids both work and earn a living. If they have their own house, eventually it will be legally settled in the courts, anyhow. No need to make this into a big song and dance. I am sure they will not even bring up such a matter of divorce. For formality's sake, let's make it five thousand pounds. Two thousand five hundred of that will be given on the day of the wedding. The rest – Allah forbid – never needs to be provided."

Ammujee, who had remained quiet the whole time on the matter, stroked my back gently.

"She will be looked after, Bhai," she said, addressing Babajee.

"Oh, no, no, of course, I wouldn't doubt that for one second," Babajee laughed nasally.

"Just formalities, of course. Yes, let's call it what it is, of course. I cannot disagree when in such fine company, of course."

"Then it's agreed," Abbujee exclaimed, his voice raised as he rose from his seat to embrace Babajee from side to side.

"Alhamdulillah, praise be to Allah," Abbujee muttered.

"Alhamdulillah!" they all joined in together, rising from their seats to embrace each other.

I caught a glimpse of Syed, sitting opposite. He smirked directly at me as he rose, with a look of victory and jubilation. I felt deeply unsettled. I thought I would feel overjoyed; it was as though I had only come to sit on the shore and had somehow been swept into the sea.

Ammujee held me in an embrace and kissed my forehead, teary with joy, as the men reconvened on politics and other matters in the living area.

"Here," she said. "I had this ordered for you." She opened a red velvet box containing a ring, then placed it on my ring finger.

"So beautiful," she said admiringly at me. "Did you put on your saree by yourself?"

Mamajee interjected, shaking her head.

"No, no, Bhabhi. Girls these days don't usually wear sarees; she is not very good at tying it round her." Another undersell by Mamajee: she knew I'd donned the saree by myself, but in her eyes, it was shameful to say anything good or brag; it was always more gracious to play down any compliments.

*

It was late, almost 10.30 p.m., by the time Syed's parents had left, following tea and dinner. We saw them off from the front door, Mamajee and Babajee standing by the front gate, Suraya shivering behind her scarf and waving. My brothers hovered around the hall-way, and I stood behind them all, watching as the black Mercedes pulled off from the pavement and dark silhouettes in the car waved back at us.

Mamajee shut the door, and I was speechless and overwhelmed by the squeals of excitement from Suraya as she jumped for joy. "Sis! You are getting married!"

Mamajee also beamed proudly and hugged me tightly. It felt as though it was the first time that I had ever seen Mamajee happy, her face elated, and for a moment I felt years of weight, guilt and anxiety slowly being lifted.

Babajee walked past passively up the stairs as Mamajee contin-ued to rock me side to side. Then he turned to look at me. His face saddened; something seemed to be pressing on his mind, and he de-liberated over whether to say it.

I felt such happiness and warmth from Mamajee's affection that when I next glanced up, Babajee had gone.

Later, when I had a moment to myself and Mamajee was busy announcing to the world the big news, I became deeply unsettled by the events of today. Something didn't feel right, but I couldn't ex-plain it. Could I really make this work?

*

"I have some news," I said to Mrs Abbots at the cafe near the library the following morning. She was back from her long placement overseas, and I wanted to tell her in person, given she seemed to be the one who managed to breathe life into my soul through all the obstacles and hurdles that came my way. I smiled, recalling a time it had been difficult to meet her under the reign of Mamajee's control, and I hadn't been allowed out. How far things had moved on in Mamajee's eyes since; how easy things were without constant scrutiny. I wish I had asked more now about her time in Shanghai, but it had all been overshadowed by my news.

I noticed Mrs Abbots looked a little aged now since our last meeting at my graduation. The skin under her eyes was sallow, and her face a little withdrawn, but on hearing my declaration, her expression glowed with life.

"Oh! Good news, I hope! Well, I must say you've taken me a little by surprise with that. Go on then, do tell!" She chuckled as she placed her teacup down on the saucer, and I paused to admire her.

"Well, do tell, my dear. Do tell. I am brimming with curiosity!"

I sighed deeply, looking out of the window that faced the main road.

"Well, I am getting married."

Mrs Abbots looked shocked, if not a little disturbed, by my statement. Her mouth opened, and she paused to take a deep breath.

"Oh, heavens. Well, I must say that has come as a surprise to hear! May I ask to whom, perhaps? To that gentleman you mentioned over a year ago, I presume."

"No, not him. It's kind of through my parents."

"Kind of?" Mrs Abbots said.

"Yes, well. Mamajee introduced us through a family friend."

"Oh, I see. Well, I don't remember you mentioning it last summer when we spoke."

"No, it's only really happened in the last six months."

"You mean to say, you barely know him, Eleanor, and you are already getting married?"

"Well, I have been getting to know him," I said, trying to convince her. Mrs Abbots's face seemed to be more horrified than happy.

"I thought, Mrs Abbots, you would be pleased for me," I said, feeling slightly perturbed.

"Well, you see, it is quite surprising … only in that you sounded deeply troubled by your last relationship, and here you are now, in the process of getting married. Are you sure, Eleanor, that you have thought this through?"

I sighed. "You are quite right, Mrs Abbots. Yes, I am a little nervous, you could say."

"So, tell me, dear, tell me, how did this come about?" she said, placing some sugar into her cup.

"We've been dating over the past six months, and well, yesterday it was decided."

"Decided? Yesterday?" She placed her teacup down heavily on the saucer, rattling the spoon.

"Yes, his parents and my parents met, and there were all these formalities, and before you knew it, they had agreed to it."

Mrs Abbots nodded slowly, trying to process it all. She took a sip of tea and shook her head profusely.

"And tell me, dear, was this something you wanted? You know, we have talked about arrangements in the past, haven't we now?"

I took in a deep breath, looking at her concerned expression.

"Honestly, Mrs Abbots, I don't know. Yes and no, I guess."

"Well, what feels right and what doesn't, dear?"

"You know, after splitting with Rohit, I did feel empty like you said. It was too late though; things had moved on. Mamajee persuaded me to look ahead, and I still owe her in a way."

"You owe her?" said Mrs Abbots. "For what, may I ask?"

"For being born."

Mrs Abbots seemed to have gone pale from the words and remained speechless as I continued.

"You know, I made a promise to her. You know, when she was going to leave after Babajee beat her up. If she stayed, I would spare her any dishonour, so that all the years of sacrifice she has endured would not be in vain. Well, I guess I will be finally giving her that back."

I started to cry, and I could see for the first time that Mrs Abbots had tears with me.

"Oh, my poor dear," she cried, leaning over to hug me. She searched her handbag for a handkerchief, trying to hide her face behind it. She paused for a moment, holding the tissue over her eyes. In all the years I had known Mrs Abbots, I had not seen her cry. It seemed that this had touched her.

She looked out through the window, breathing large circles that formed against the glass.

"Eleanor, you cannot offer yourself as a pledge of honour. I am deeply concerned that you are compromising yourself for the welfare of others."

I shook my head. These were easy words, I thought. Easy things to point out. "It's not easy; you know that, Mrs Abbots."

"I know it's not easy, but remember what I said? What feels golden, that's what is right. You know what feels right, don't you?"

I shook my head. "No, Mrs Abbots. Truth be told, I don't. I don't know what feels right anymore."

"Then you must wait until you feel certain, Eleanor. You mustn't commit to this."

"It's too late. I already have."

"What do you mean?"

"The wedding date is finalised."

"For when?" She seemed astonished.

"They've booked the venue and everything. It's on the eighteenth of July."

She shook her head. "You are making a grave mistake, Eleanor. Please tell me you will think things through. You mustn't enter into something like this unless you feel certain you are happy."

"Maybe if everyone is happy, it will make me happy."

"Love doesn't work like that, Eleanor. It starts with you loving yourself. Everything else will start falling into place around you, but you have to value yourself first. Only then can you fix everyone else around you."

I shook my head.

"I can't see it. I am a societal reject, a malfunction to them in many ways. I only seem to have cast shame on my family."

"Oh, Eleanor, please."

"No, Mrs Abbots." I rose from my chair. "Please, I don't want to be confused anymore."

She rose up with a pained expression.

"Here." She held me close. "I want you to know I am always here, always. I always care, and you must think about what I am saying to you."

"Thank you, Mrs Abbots. Of course, I do consider everything you say. I will send you the details about the wedding in due course, and I hope you will be there."

Her thin smile only gave me assurance of one thing: she was not convinced.

*

As the weeks rolled by, my relationship with Syed became more intense. My world became closed in to the two of us.

"You and me," he would say, "we are in a cocoon from now on."

The reality of this concept was far from bliss. Anything outside this shell seemed to disrupt it. There were countless arguments about the wedding arrangements, where we went on honeymoon, the demands and expectations he had on my family. In traditional Bengali weddings, for example, the clothing worn by the groom was gifted to him by the bride's family, but there were no compromises on Syed's part on the expectations. My parents, through no fault of their own, were unable to meet such grand and ostentatious requests, and needless to say, I couldn't ask them to provide the costs for the wedding, as traditionally expected. I watched the credit card bills slowly mount, with Breitling watches, Savile Row custom tailored suits, Indian groom's outfits, flowers, jewellery and outfits for the whole family, all stacked up on my expense.

Our arguments would start with an insult that I couldn't bear to hear, a jeer at my expense on how my family were beneath his standards, which would lead to me walking out on him. Then came his long-drawn-out vicious cycle of apologies: "I am sorry. I didn't mean it."

He would win me over by taking me shopping, buying me amazing flowers or telling me affectionately how beautiful I was. He would open doors, carry my handbag or shopping bags, find a nice place to drive and park up so that we could sit and talk things through. I was dazzled by the highs, and crippled by the lows, and when the question came up over and over as to whether we were right for each other, it was simply put down to wedding pressures and that soon these things would settle down.

"Janu, it's only because I love you," he'd say in one of these long talks following an argument. "I don't want to lose you."

I would succumb to the belief that these transgressions would dissolve if I learned to forgive him and believe the promise that things would change in time, but ending up back in his arms was almost a trap. Each time, the insults became harder, his arguments stronger, and the act more merciless.

I tried at all costs to avoid conflicts or conversations that sparked arguments, such as my past, travel experiences, male friends, shops that I may have perused before and restaurants I had dined at.

I would avoid talking about any interactions with my friends or housemates, and conversations about work would only consist of the work itself, not the people I interacted with, unless somehow it was unavoidable. Yes indeed, our relationship only yielded enough spark between us when the conditions were right, and in the space of six months, things had changed dramatically. I barely saw my housemates unless we bumped into each other in the hallway, and Lenna and Sonia had almost given up on inviting me out for drinks.

We were now only seven weeks away from the big day, and the stress of wedding plans had us both run-down. I had lost a lot of weight from the lack of food and sleep, and Syed had been ill all week with the flu. In his absence, I had gained a little time, and found Andrea in the kitchen one evening.

"Hey, Eleanor. Feels like it's been an age since I last saw you. I haven't seen much of you, my dear. How is it going?"

"It's okay. It's been a little stressy, with the wedding and all."

"Well, you look a little worse for wear, I have to say. Have you lost weight?"

"Yeah, I guess so. It's been so busy I wouldn't even know."

"Why don't you come out with us? We are going to grab a bite at the pub."

I hesitated. I knew this would definitely come to conflict if Syed ever heard. "No. Maybe some other time."

"Come on, Eleanor, we've hardly seen you all year."

"I know, Andrea. I just think this would unsettle things, that's all."

"Well, you don't have to drink; you can just have food with us. Go on, you'll be fine."

I smiled, still a little reluctant.

"Okay, I suppose it has been a while, and yes, it would be nice to catch up."

"Yay!" cheered Andrea.

"But, erm, I do have to be back by nine."

*

Andrea and I headed to a pub in Richmond, where we met with Lenna and Sonia. It was only 6 p.m., but I was tense with keeping a close eye on the time so ordered food immediately. If Syed knew I had met my friends, I could only imagine the arguments from it.

"Eleanor, this is crazy! I can't believe you have to hide all this. You are not doing anything wrong. It sounds like this guy has got you under lock and key. We don't even see you anymore," Sonia explained.

"You are right, it's difficult to see you guys, but he loves me, and maybe he's just, you know, worried."

"Worried? I think you need to be worried about him, more like. He's the dangerous one."

"Listen, there's just ... there's a lot going on, you know, with the wedding. I just don't want to rock the boat too much."

Although it was great seeing my friends, I wasn't completely feeling comfortable. I left at 8 p.m. and headed home by bus.

When I arrived home, Dave was standing by the door of the living room, waiting for me.

"Hey, Dave."

"Eleanor, the phone has been ringing non-stop, and the landline rang a few times. I think Syed has been trying to get hold of you."

"Oh? What did you tell him?" I said, feeling quite nervous.

"Well, I told him I didn't know."

"Oh, okay," I said calmly. "Thanks, Dave."

"Everything okay?" he asked.

"Yeah," I said. "He's probably just trying to get hold of me about something."

I called Syed straight back on my mobile, which now displayed eleven missed calls in the course of two hours. I regretted that I hadn't brought it with me. *How stupid of me*, I thought.

"Hey, janu. Where have you been? I have tried ringing you loads of times."

"I am sorry. I fell asleep and had my phone on silent," I lied.

"Well, I rang the landline, and your housemate said you weren't in."

"Oh, no, I just spoke to him, and he said he tried knocking on my door, but I must have been in a deep sleep, as I didn't hear him knock. Anyway, how are you feeling?"

"Yeah, could be better, I suppose," Syed explained with an emphasised cough.

I felt relieved that he hadn't pressed it any further.

*

The following day I went to meet Syed before I headed up to Manchester. It was Friday, and I had planned to meet with the caterers and discuss the wedding arrangements.

We met at a shopping mall near his house and, after lunch, made our way around the shops.

I had been fumbling around in my handbag as I paid for something when Syed offered to help with my belongings. "Here, let me take your handbag," he said politely. Then something fell out onto the floor. He picked it up. It was the receipt from the night before.

"Here, let me have that," I said calmly, but he turned away so that he could closely inspect it.

"You went to Bar One, it says here. That was last night."

A wave of panic hit me. I could see that he was seething with betrayal; his eyes prickled with anger.

"Why did you lie to me?" he said.

"I just went to see my friends."

"You fucking lied to me!" he shouted, and immediately dragged me by the hand through the shopping mall to the outside car park. I was crying, and people were watching.

"You fucking betrayed me? And we are supposed to be getting married? Why? Tell me! Why?" He then slapped me around the face and pushed me with great force into a wall. I could feel the rage in the force, which knocked my engagement ring off my hand, and it rolled out into the car park. I tried to pick it up from the floor, but he pressed my hand down onto the tarmac with his shoe to prevent me from getting it.

"You don't deserve to wear this ring anymore. You are a fucking liar! This is over!"

I cried, the tears filled with fear. "Well, then, we best finish this. Just let me go if you don't want this."

"No," he said. "No, you don't get out of this that easily. Your parents will hear about this, so you better get ready for the downpour."

"I am leaving," I said.

"Oh, you are not going anywhere, bitch," he said, blocking my path.

People watched as he pushed me around outside the mall, his breathing heavy, his eyes bulging with rage, his face and mouth frothing like a savage dog.

"Just leave me alone. I just want to go home." But that only aggravated his rage more.

"Oh yeah? You don't get to do what you want anymore. It's up to me now!" he shouted, snatching my handbag, which had my car and house keys inside.

A couple of hours went by outside the mall, where he interrogated me about every detail about my evening, with rhetorical outbreaks of abuse and insults that I was some whore meeting up with other whores. This subsided into an apology from him. "I just love you, and I don't think you love me, do you?"

"I do," I said.

When he had exhausted all angles of the conversation with me, he finally relented.

"Look, this isn't going to get sorted out today. Just take me home," Syed said, exhausted.

He sat in the car like a zombie, breathing and seething every so often at me. His eyes rolled back to the point where I could only see the whites of his eyes, which concerned me. How could things have got out of control like this? When we arrived near his home, he left the car without saying a word, and I decided to go to my gran's house instead that night. By the time I arrived, I was shaking, crying and very distraught. I collapsed in a pile at their door and told them word for word what had happened.

This was the first time Syed had laid a finger on me, and it questioned the boundaries of what I would tolerate. Yes, there were conflicts, there were arguments and raised voices, terms and conditions, but at no point had he raised his hand to me. Was this a sign of more to come? Or could it have been a one-off encounter? Perhaps I had pushed the limits. Of course, anyone would be upset at being lied to. I admitted it wasn't right to have lied, but had it needed to spiral into violence?

My whole family were in an uproar at first.

"How dare he raise a hand to my unmarried daughter? He doesn't have the right to be anywhere near her, let alone touch her." My dad demanded his whole family come up to Manchester and explain themselves that weekend.

*

"Listen, Rabbani Bhai, I know my son acted out of order. Yes, you are right that is deplorable behaviour, but—"

"I am concerned whether this is suitable now," Babajee interjected. "If this ends in divorce, then we will have bigger problems on our hands. What assurance do we have from your son that he is responsible enough to look after her?"

"Oh, come on now, Rabbani Bhai. Surely you can see this is something that got a little out of hand. Your daughter lied, and that would obviously have upset him. I think they need to learn to respect each other; these are all lessons in life. We've all been there, haven't we now? You know this is only a slight raise of hands. This sometimes happens between two people; we've all seen it."

Babajee paused and looked at me. "Before they are married though? I don't want a divorce on my hands. If your son cannot tolerate her, then he should be with someone he can remain in a stable marriage with. Such violent behaviour ahead of the marriage makes me very doubtful that this could be successful. What guarantee can you give me that this won't happen again?"

"Rabbani Bhai, that is up to Allah. He's the only one who knows what is written. I can't guarantee you anything. All I can say is that they both need to learn from this and move forward. Look, we are weeks away now; we should be celebrating and enjoying it now. Surely you are not going to let one mistake disrupt things. The whole family knows; there are people flying in from America and Dubai and India. We are a family now, and if something goes wrong, we'll work on it together. Think about it, Bhai. It's up to you, but just think about it."

A couple of weeks went by engrossed in one thought: whether to continue with the wedding or not. Syed had tried all methods of persuasion: phone calls, messages, cards. There were bouquets of flowers dotted around the living room now, which even Andrea didn't have enough buckets or vases for, and in the office, even Rohit raised his eyebrows when he looked at the collection of flowers mounting around my desk. But all the flowers in the world couldn't remove the clouds of doubt hanging over me, and the longer I deliberated, the closer it got to the wedding date.

*

Many people passed all kinds of advice to me. His parents told me that their son had learned not to do this again and convinced me round to the idea. Babajee, on one hand, wasn't convinced, but on the other, he couldn't bear to face the community and the collective total of two thousand guests who were to join the wedding celebrations. Mamajee could only be upset. "I can't believe this. The whole world knows now. How are we going to show our face? All my life I have been waiting, all my life."

Meanwhile, my friends spent hours convincing me not to go ahead. "Eleanor, it's like putting your head into the lion's den. It is just obvious what will happen next," Sonia said one night.

"I can't understand it, Eleanor. I just can't see why you would want to be with him."

"Once they strike, you can't tame them. They will always find another excuse."

"Eleanor, please, you mustn't go down this road. Please listen to me," Mrs Abbots begged on the phone.

"I can't. I can't get out of this easily."

"Why, dear, why? All the possibilities, all the choices are available to you, dear. There is nothing you can't do."

"I just can't. Have you ever given your word to someone, Mrs Abbots? Have you ever felt compelled to do right by others?"

She remained quiet.

"I watched her that day on the floor, loose limbs and almost lifeless. There was nothing left of her. She didn't want to stay. I begged her to stay, Mrs Abbots. I begged her. I satisfied my own selfish seven-year-old needs for my mother to stay with us. She had a choice; she could have left, but I stopped her. I couldn't see how I could survive without her and raise my younger siblings. How can I go against this now? Do you remember how you said that, Mrs Abbots? Do you remember? Be true to your word."

"This is not the same thing, Eleanor."

"Well, whatever it is, it doesn't feel right. This has to go ahead."

CHAPTER THIRTY-FOUR
– *The Wedding* –

The house looked like a sea of corpses. I walked over sleeping bodies belonging to my three aunts, my sister, Mamajee and Nanni on the living-room floor to get to the window, where I wrestled with the handle to open it. A wave of cool air seeped through as though the world had been waiting for today and had finished holding its breath. I heard snoring in every direction I looked. It seemed everybody was a little too tired to care that I had tripped over half their calf muscles amid the struggle to the window. I stood watching them all sleeping for a moment. It was only 5 a.m., and I was supposed to be a bright-eyed bride-to-be, but I could only feel exhaustion from the lack of sleep. The house looked a tip. Paper garlands, balloons, fairy lights strewn across the table. There were boxes piled high with miscellaneous items and luggage cases in every direction belonging to my aunts, who had come to stay over to attend the wedding.

I turned to look at myself in the mirror, trying to make the idea sink in. Was this what I was supposed to feel on my big day? Nervous, jittery, exhausted and with a sinking feeling, as if it were the end of everything I had once known. I tried to shrug it off. After all, Mamajee and the entire population of Muslim female relatives had said they had all felt the same when they had got married. Surely there was sanity in there somewhere; surely there were reasons for accepting all of this. But no matter what assurances I had been given, it came to no good. I kept thinking about Mrs Abbots, about what she had said before that last meeting: "Be true to yourself, and everything will come good." But I was in a way being true to myself, wasn't I? If this was what made Mamajee happy, then this, in turn, would make me happy. And anyhow, it was too late to change my mind now.

Everyone has settled on this idea. I have to look beyond. I am here; I am about to start one of the most important days of my life. At least as my parents know it. This is what they have been waiting their whole lives for. For this precious moment to be fulfilled. Oh, think how wonderful this will feel, Eleanor, when you can share that oneness with them on something. Oneness, yes, that's what it is. In oneness they are happy, and I am at one with that. No more pain for being the black sheep, the whore or the embarrassment to them. I can finally live in harmony and be at peace with that.

I took a shower and washed my hair, rinsing the sleep from my eyes and restlessness from my thin body. What I saw in the mirror was a sad, thin body now. There was once a time when I remembered being thin or losing weight was something to be proud of, but this scrap in front of me looked like a corpse. I looked like I was dying. Perhaps, in a way, I was. The real me was dying in preparing for my new life, my wedding day. In the six months leading up to the wedding, I had lost two stone in weight. One might think this wasn't a huge amount, but I was a slender figure already, and losing just a few pounds made me look gaunt and emaciated. I could tell from the look on Rohit's face one lunchtime that he was concerned.

"I don't know what's happened, Eleanor. But I have never seen you like this. Is everything okay?"

"Yeah, I am fine," I'd said, shrugging. "You know, I sometimes lose my appetite, that's all."

"You will tell me, won't you? You will tell me if you need anything, right?"

"Yeah, sure I will," I'd said, pressing my fork into my chips. My skin tight, dehydrated. My eyes grey, hollow caves. My body a skeletal structure of thin limbs that horrified anyone who knew me, except, of course, Mamajee, who waved any concern away as it being down to the stress of the wedding.

What a sad day, I thought. *How could I feel this empty of joy and excitement on my wedding day?*

Still, there was no time to think like that now. *You are getting married, Eleanor, today, and you are going to be a bride.* That was the voice of the seven-year-old me. I knew she had won over me.

I wondered what was going through Syed's mind right now. Perhaps excitement, joy and celebration were the sensations experienced in his world. We hadn't spoken the night before. He wanted us to build up to the big day, and he had planned an evening with his friends at a shisha club, which may have persuaded him not to leave me the normal twelve dozen missed calls obsessively when I hadn't picked up. I was surprised that I didn't feel short of breath or nervous at the thought of getting married to him anymore. There was enough on my mind to let myself collapse into the idea. It didn't feel like my wedding day; I didn't feel like a bride – just somebody organising a party for seven hundred people. There was far too much to prepare, organise and think about before I could feel like a bride walking down the aisle. *That feeling will come once I am dressed, I am sure*, I said to myself.

The doorbell rang, and the hair and make-up artists arrived to transform me into a bride.

It took two hours to complete my hair alone, each strand twisted into barrels with pins piercing into my skull uncomfortably. And as the torturous transformation continued upstairs, downstairs I could hear life continuing as normal, Mamajee charging around, ordering people about. The clink of teacups, the stomping of a hundred feet coming up and down the stairs. I heard laughter and giggling as aunts and other relatives got ready in the room next door. This moment felt more like theirs than mine. Perhaps that was how it was meant to be, how all those years it was explained countless times by Mamajee, how it was expected.

Mamajee came into the room to see how things were getting on. I had hoped that she would bring a smile or say something reassuring or look a little happier now. But she seemed to stare neutrally back.

"Make sure they hurry it up; otherwise, we will be running out of time. The limousine will be here in an hour." That only brought on my anxiety more. Time was ticking as it approached the final hour.

"Okay, darling," said Shamila, the make-up artist. "Your hair and make-up are done. Let's get your wedding gear on, lovely." She laid out the heavily embroidered wedding dress. A deep velvety red lehnga skirt and blouse sparkled with Swarovski crystals embedded amongst gold embroidered vines and patterns. It glistened in the light, causing dots of colour on the ceiling. I climbed into the skirt.

"Oh my, you've lost a lot of weight, haven't you?" Shamila observed. "I am sure this fitted perfectly at the fitting." She looked me up and down suspiciously as she chewed her gum and neatened my hair with her red-polished fingernails.

"It's been a little stressful, I guess," I said, looking down with my back to her.

She sighed deeply. I could see her expression in the mirror as she chewed her gum, processing, thinking things through, as she straightened out my blouse.

"Listen, whatever happens, happens, but if there is one thing I have learned it's don't change anything about yourself, darling, because it doesn't matter what you change, you won't be able to change him. Take that from someone who learned the hard way."

"Thank you. I will remember that," I said, looking down.

The beauticians then placed forty thin red bracelets, which were capped off with two large twenty-four-carat gold bangles on each side of the bracelets, on each arm. They felt heavy and restrictive, as if I had been chained in handcuffs. They then placed ornate gold chains around my neck. The largest one went all the way down to my breast and was centred with a large pendant. My earrings were then gently placed into my ears, two heavy bells that pulled down, cutting into each piercing. Another chain that went down the middle of my forehead was placed right into the centre. Shamila pressed it down to steady it on my head. It felt cold, and the sharp surface made my skin prickle. Then the two women fussed over the pleats in a heavy shawl that they pinned in place on my shoulder. It took many pins to secure it around my body; some cut into my bra strap, jabbing into my skin as though it was deliberate torture for the ceremony.

Mamajee and my aunts all gathered by the door to watch, and the women carefully placed the veil over my head. They all watched intently, and I saw two familiar faces peering through the doorway amongst the crowd of women. It was my friends Lenna and Sonia. Their faces were sad and expressed their deep regret for my choice. I looked back at them, mirroring their thoughts.

"You can still change your mind, you know," Lenna whispered.

Sonia continued to look at me. "Please think about it," she begged.

The women continued dressing me with the veil, shrouding my forehead, which prickled like thorns as the wiry embroidery cut into my skin from the weight. My aunts sighed, taking pictures as I sat shrouded underneath it. I could hear the clicks of a dozen cameras, and family members squeezed into the hallway to get a glimpse. I lost Lenna and Sonia at this moment as more people squeezed through to get pictures. I moved slowly, with every step weighed down, as they shuffled me around for various poses. And through the chains, bangles, the skirt and veil, I caught a reflection in the mirror of a woman I no longer recognised. My face as pale and white as a porcelain doll's, my skin thick and heavy with foundation. I had large smoky eyeshadow, like dark, thundering clouds, which faded into golden arches below my eyebrows. On my forehead was a large ornate chain piece that hung from the centre parting in my hair. Layers of gold chains rested on my neck, contrasting with my blood-red gown, which shimmered with Swarovski crystals. *Does God only wish that I be turned into an ornament? Surely, then, this is vanity!*

"Mashallah, you look beautiful, Eleanor," my aunts cried. But these compliments seemed empty of meaning. I didn't feel it.

The video cameraman then asked to move to the front door so that he could take more pictures and film footage. The women in the family all marched outside as quickly as possible so that they could get ready for the big shot. My sister escorted me out as though I had no idea how to navigate to the door. It was frowned upon for a bride to do this by herself, and so any movement required my sister's aid, whether to sit down, stand up or walk. Moving, eating, talking was also forbidden or frowned upon for a bride, and so it was the companions' or bridesmaids' role to assist with every move. She led me out to the front, like a stone being moved from a static surface. I shuffled my weight of gold, bangles, veil and heavily embroidered skirt through the gawking crowd in the hallway.

I walked slowly along to where a long white limousine parked in front of the driveway, and a crusty-looking chauffer came out from the driver's seat to open the door for me. The video cameraman inched his way before me, following my every footstep. Suraya stood next to me in a gold saree that matched the gold embroidery on my red wedding dress. Her hair tied up in a barrel-curled bun, complete with glittering earrings to match her saree, could only be described as beautiful.

We entered the limousine, followed by an entourage of aunts and female cousins. It must have been exciting for them, riding in a limousine, but it only felt achingly empty to be seated there.

I could leave somehow. Maybe I could still take up Lenna and Sonia's offer? There is still time, I thought. Tempting as it seemed, the seven-year-old me stepped in again.

No, you can't! You know this would be frowned upon. What would people say? Today you are going to make Mamajee and Babajee proud, proud that you are married, that you can give them the respect they deserve. Today you will stand up and give them that. You watch, Eleanor! You watch!

As the girls in the limousine laughed and giggled, I looked outside. I saw the path through the church leading across to my old primary school, where once upon a time that seven-year-old me had run home, collecting stones, hearts and petals. I passed the main roads that I used to walk down from high school. I saw the hills I had once dreamed of going beyond, and I saw the house on the hill. The house that Babajee and I had looked out on frequently. Clouds brooded above it now, and as we approached the venue, I could feel them loom heavily over me. I had that sinking feeling that it was going to rain on my wedding day.

As I paced my way through the entrance of the venue, there was no respite from the heat emitted from the glaring spotlight of videographers and photographers' flashing cameras. Another ten minutes passed at a snail's pace, manoeuvring between greetings and guests who had spotted my arrival.

I felt a rush of excitement when I caught a glimpse of Mrs Abbots standing there at the entrance, her neck reaching out to catch my attention. My view, though, was overshadowed by Mamajee, who had pushed her way through the crowds and onlookers like a security guard and grabbed my arm, pulling me into a powder room. I heaved through the hustle and bustle, my red embroidered ensemble pressed into the sweat, as if I had been thrown into a bed of nettles and left to swell from the stings.

Naheeda Khala fanned me, aware my make-up was starting to melt. "Oh, your eyeliner is starting to smudge. I knew she should have put a waterproof one on."

These seemed trivial matters to be concerned with now, considering that the rest of my body was suffering a fire of hell. I pretended in my head that Naheeda Khala really cared, given my last encounter with her had proven almost fatal. I could only see her role as being of cosmetic value.

My sister began neatening the pleats of my veil and untangling the threads that had caught on the shimmering set of red and gold bangles weighing heavily on my arms.

I thought about how difficult it would be to run. The dress, the shoes, the gold – the veil alone weighed five kilograms, and my full ensemble felt easily like another ten. If I made a dash for it, I would be grabbed, pulled back screaming, possibly surrounded. I would only be looked at like a madwoman. *Still, I still have a chance*, I thought. *I still have a chance.*

Mamajee heaved, her breathing heavy. Something about her looked nervous and uneasy.

"Now listen," she said. "They are going to do the nikah [wedding vows] in a few minutes. Your boro mama will do the nikah from our side. You must look down; don't smile or look at people or the camera. Remember, you are meant to be graceful and respectful. Make sure you bow at your uncle's feet when you have said '*kabul*' [agree to the marriage]. But don't say it straight away. You don't want to appear too eager: that would also be shameful."

My sister held my hand, Naheeda Khala dabbed my forehead. Suddenly there was a knock on the door. I hoped that it wouldn't be the cameraman or the videographer, and to my relief, it wasn't. A kind and loving face appeared. She looked nervously on, peering through the small crack in the door.

"Mrs Abbots!"

I wanted to embrace her, hear her soft voice tell me something lovely and calming, but the thought was bolted by Mamajee's voice.

"You! No, not allowed in here," Mamajee barked at her with broken English.

"It's okay, Mamajee," I said, disappointed with Mamajee's reaction.

"Please, Mrs Abbots, please come in."

"No!" Mamajee retorted.

Mrs Abbots tried pushing the door past Mamajee. "Please, I just want to have a word," she said awkwardly.

"No, no! You go away! You do not belong here," Mamajee expressed displeasingly.

She seemed to be heaving furiously, and her behaviour confused me.

It was as if she knew Mrs Abbots, but I couldn't understand how.

"This woman is not allowed here. Who invited her?"

"I invited Mrs Abbots, Mamajee," I barked, confused at Mamajee's rudeness.

Mrs Abbots stood, demure, her face down.

"Why? Why did you let her in here?"

"Mamajee, no. Mrs Abbots is like a teacher to me." I smiled at her.

"I just wanted to see you, that's all," Mrs Abbots added.

Mamajee shook her head. "Teacher?" she cried. "This woman ruined my life, and I am not going to let her ruin it again. I spent my whole life suffering because of her."

"Suffering? Mamajee, what are you talking about?" I asked as she crouched into her chair with her hands over her face.

Mrs Abbots said nothing, a look of guilt burdened her face heavily.

"Please don't do this," Mrs Abbots begged, looking at me.

"What is she saying?" Mamajee asked. Mamajee stood up, enraged, her hand trembling as she pointed at her. "Don't you dare listen to this woman; anything she says is a lie. I have been the victim of her torments. She is a liar. She made an oath, and she broke it several times."

I looked at both women, baffled by their hostility towards each other.

What is going on here? I thought. My mind searched for an explanation as I looked at their faces and listened to the severity of Mamajee's words.

"Naheeda, go get your brother, and tell him to hurry," Mamajee said, sniffling.

Naheeda clutched my hand before vacating the room.

Mrs Abbots shuffled forward as Naheeda Khala left, closing the door behind her.

Mamajee broke into tears, and Mrs Abbots looked down. I sat looking at the two women.

"If something happened between you, then tell me."

"You can't let her do this," Mrs Abbots said to Mamajee. "You can't. She is—"

Mamajee looked up. "She is what? Don't you ever mention it. You promised, and now this is my day."

Mrs Abbots broke into tears. "But you can't do this. You can't, not to a child!" Her voice cracked into a large gasp.

"Suraya, call your mama," cried Mamajee.

Suraya edged her way out, awkwardly passing the two women.

"Mrs Abbots, tell me what is going on. What's happened here?"

"No. Come on, you must go!" Mamajee yelled at Mrs Abbots.

"No, you will not make me go!" Mrs Abbots shrugged Mamajee's hand away from her shoulder. "Please don't do this, Eleanor. Don't marry him," she yelled over the kerfuffle of Mamajee pushing her closer to the door.

"Don't marry him. Please don't. It will ruin you. They are manipulating you!"

"Oh, I see. Now you have come, have you? After you ruined me, my husband and my life. You have no right to be here now!" seethed Mamajee. "Get out!" Mamajee screamed at her, pushing her towards the door.

Then the moment forced it, and the words echoed out something that had been passing through my life.

"Don't do this, Eleanor. Don't. I am—" cried Mrs Abbots.

"Get out! Get out!" Mamajee interjected. "Allah, help, help! Somebody, get this woman out of here!"

Mrs Abbots shook her head. "I have every right to be here! Eleanor, you are making a terrible mistake!"

"Mistake? Mistake? Oh no, it was not me who made a mistake all those years ago; the one who had us all suffer was *you*! You, you selfish woman! Don't tell me what is wrong and what is right when you slept with my husband, and then come meddling in everyone else's affairs. Don't tell me what a mistake is. Get her out of here!" Mamajee cried and tried to push her through the door.

I was stunned and horrified.

"Mrs Abbots." I turned to look at both of them. "Is this true? Is it? Why? Why would you—?"

She started crying. Mrs Abbots cried and nodded her head at me as she was pushed away. "I'm sorry."

"Is that what you have come to tell me? On my wedding day?" I cried.

"No. I just don't want you to make the same mistakes. I want you to feel that you have the right to be loved and not go against it!"

I shook my head. A mixture of sickness, disbelief and anxiety churned inside, turning my stomach sour. I thought I knew this woman, but I realised I was far from knowing her. I couldn't make head nor tail of the exchange between the two women, and in a split second, I felt separated from all I knew and loved, and all I hated and despised. What was the truth? What was a lie? What was right? And what was wrong? Nothing was clear, and nothing felt real anymore.

"I don't think I can deal with this right now. I'm sorry, Mrs Abbots, but I think it's best that you leave."

Boro Mama reached the room.

"What is this?" he yelled crossly at both women.

"Bhaiya, get this bitch harami woman out of here," Mamajee yelled.

"You do as your mother has told you," Bora Mama ordered me, "and you, miss, don't ever come near my family again, do you hear?"

I still remember the look on her face vividly, aged yet beautiful, but shadowed by a look that harboured years of guilt for something, something that had sparked enough fury in Mamajee to warrant her dismissal.

Mamajee turned to me as Mrs Abbots was escorted out. "You see that woman?" she said in Bengali. "Don't step two feet near her. If you do, you dishonour me. It will ruin me, your father; it will ruin you. Do you hear me? My honour is your honour. Remember that. Come, let's go. They are all waiting!"

*

More people swarmed around me, and the cameraman tried to move back to make way for my grand entrance. I suddenly felt a surge of panic race through me as I entered the foot of the hall. The room darkened; the spotlight shone from the camera; and a sea of people glowed back at me.

I could turn back, I thought. There was still time.

I caught sight of Mrs Abbots amongst the crowd. I cringed now at the sight of her: the humiliation she faced seemed underserving for a lady of such grace. But a glimpse of that pained expression culminated a look of guilt not just for the mistakes she had made but for the ones that I was making. I wanted to cry, but it was too late. The music began, and the DJ announced my arrival on the microphone. "Ladies and gentlemen, please rise as we welcome our bride, Eleanor, and her family."

The hall lighting dimmed, with just the spotlight through the aisle as music played an old Bollywood song of love to serenade me. The light from the video camera glared on me, along with hundreds of faces and flashing cameras through the corner of my eyes.

I stole another glance at Mrs Abbots shaking her head slowly as I proceeded with the slow march down the aisle. I had to forget her. After all, this was my choice, wasn't it? Or had I chosen to surrender my life to the pleasures and joys of others? That was all I could see now from the seven hundred people smiling back. Before me, on the centre stage, was where my final journey ended. Walking down that aisle was as though I was seeing all that reminded me of my previous life pass before me. I occasionally looked across the hall, seeing those familiar faces looking back, aunts and uncles, friends, teachers, colleagues from work. They were all smiles as I walked down the aisle. If only I could take them with me. I could only see darkness now, even though all the light was shining on me, and there ahead, my destiny, a spotlight shone upon his face. There, seated on an ornate throne, was Syed.

Suraya and my aunt assisted me onto the stage, to stand before Mamajee. I bowed gracefully at Mamajee's feet to honour her presence, then sat beside her, together with my sister and aunt. Mamajee seemed calm and content now but remained with a neutral expression. I looked demurely down at the floor while all my relatives shouted and shoved to get pictures of me. A cameraman stood at the base with a large flashlight glaring in my face. The heat from the lamp felt intense and was further intensified by those gathering around the stage to look at me. Mamajee brought over a tray; it had two small Venetian glasses with sweet milk, and a tray of Indian sweetmeats, which was presented before me.

"We are going to do the engagement now, Eleanor," my uncle declared as he seated himself in a chair beside me. A microphone was handed to him by the DJ. He cleared his throat and read out the vows on a piece of paper. "Do you, Eleanor Rabbani, of Village Kandeshwor, take Syedul Hamid, Village Marohar Kandi, to be your husband. Say '*kabul*.'"

Mamajee had primed me that it was not seen as good manners for a girl to say yes immediately, and that she should pause and hesitate before saying so.

I had no intention of hurrying this, given that I had been avoiding these very words my entire life. The struggle to avoid being married at sixteen. How I had sacrificed my real feelings of love for the love of honour, how when it came to meeting with any potential spouses, I had turned them away whimsically, superficially, over the suit they were wearing or the smirk on their face or any physical or outward appearances, so that I could avoid being married. Now though, I felt no further from the truth than when I had been a seven-year-old wanting a mother's love. Would this really buy my mother's affection?

So plagued was I by fear and doubt that I only felt contempt for these very words now. What had happened in that room before with Mrs Abbots and Mamajee had only induced further doubt. What was the truth? What was a lie? Everything in this room before me seemed a fallacy, and had I now shaped my reality into one?

I looked across at the seven hundred people in the room, waiting for my words, and only felt a stranger to all of them. I didn't know my father, my mother. I no longer knew who Mrs Abbots really was, and I didn't know who the person was who I was marrying, and the biggest stranger in that room was me. *Who am I?* I thought. I could only think that surrendering to all this was my only hope of sanity.

"*Kabul.* I agree," I said vacantly.

Life moved on as quickly as the words left my mouth. The music continued, and the guests' murmurs became louder. Suraya guided me up from the seat to where my parents stood. I bowed again at Mamajee's feet, and she seemed transactional and emotionless to the events that her life's ambition had led her to. I then greeted Babajee in the same way, who blessed me by gently placing his hand on my head.

In traditional Bengali weddings, the bride and groom exchange vows separately, and since Syed had made his vows before my arrival at the hall, there were no further actions required of him, other than to sit on his throne and look the part of a nobleman. It was seen as disgraceful to make eye contact, and we were both escorted off the stage separately and seated on separate tables for the wedding lunch.

I could easily have been a guest at someone else's wedding; observing it for the very first time, everything seemed to be running as planned. The flowers had arrived for the head tables, and the guest tables dazzled with centrepieces, tea lights and wedding favours.

I sat exhausted, emptily staring into space while my siblings, aunts and parents busily ate. A large platter of grilled meats, steaming rice and a dozen different dishes arrived and were served out. It seemed foreign to even have such a desire as I watched the guests dishing up their plates with rice and extra servings of marinated meat.

My aunts came over, fixing my veil and fussing over my earrings. "You look stunning, Mashallah. Here, have some food," said a now heavily pregnant Nashira Khala between mouthfuls. "The kebab is really good."

I looked down at my hands covered in mehndi patterns, the colour a pale yellow, recalling a time when Nashira Khala herself had been the one worried about her future after the mehndi had not turned out the colour it was expected to on her wedding day. "It didn't turn out very well, did it?" I commented as we both looked at my hands.

"You know, Eleanor, you were right, what you said on my wedding day. You won't ever know how strong the colour will be until it's on your hands. Sometimes you have to let destiny take its course." How ironic that she would be reminding me of these words. Acceptance was now the fate I had also surrendered to.

I scanned the earth beneath my feet, trying to stop myself from the dreaded fear of my decision. As I held back the tears, I heard a familiar voice in front of me. "Good luck," he said with an air of calmness.

Standing in front of me was Rohit, with Nia. He smiled, and I suddenly felt awkward: it seemed strange seeing them together at my wedding. A year ago, I was watching theirs, and here they were: the man I loved and his beautiful wife. But I felt only one truth in that moment. That loving someone doesn't mean being with someone romantically. I no longer felt romantically in love with Rohit, and there were no physical desires. I had only hoped that one day I could tell him that I loved him regardless, that whatever I felt belonged purely to the soul.

"We brought you a present," Rohit added. They both smiled at each other in agreement.

"You look beautiful, Eleanor. If you ever need anything, then do keep in touch, won't you?" Nia said.

"I will do, of course. Thank you, Nia," I said, solemnly looking at them both. I sensed the air had filled with some deep sadness, as if they were offering me condolences.

"I will see you back in the office," he said to lighten the mood.

I nodded courteously. How different our lives were now, how far we were from each other.

*

An hour rolled by, and most of the guests, who had now finished their meals, were heading over to greet me and feed me customary sweetmeats that were fed to the bride before the send-off. "Good luck," they would say, or, "May your life be blessed," or, "You look beautiful, and Mashallah, may your life be blessed," while placing the sweetmeat into my mouth.

If only they knew, I thought. *If only they knew*. How ironic it felt: the sweet on my tongue weighed heavily, like a bitter pill, in my belly. I could only have likened it to being fattened up ready for the slaughterhouse.

I immediately felt guilty for such negativity. I took a deep breath and looked up to see Matthew, my colleague, seated at a table with colleagues I had also invited. His beaming smile lifted me for a moment as he mouthed the words "You are still the most beautiful girl around. You look beautiful." There was sanity in all of the chaos. At least seeing him made me feel a little safer, somewhere a little more familiar.

Mamajee then came over with a glassy smile, holding my face affectionately for a brief moment as we posed for the cameraman, and then, without any notice, she walked me down the aisle, which prompted the cameraman into action. He hovered over, wading past children, as guests gathered around me to watch and capture a moment all Bengali mothers waited for, for their entire married lives. The moment they give their daughter away. They steered me through the hallway. The cameraman skipped in front, the light burning into my face as the traditional send-off song was played by the DJ:

When that day is here,
And she is near,
Fear not, my dear.
There will be tears.
She was by your side,
And all your pride,
And now no longer near.
There will be tears …

It seemed the cue not only to begin the send-off parade but also for the howls and tears from Mamajee and the rest of the mourning parade. She hugged me and cried into my veil. I felt her chest against mine as she sobbed, but I couldn't feel it. It seemed as though she had switched it all on for the cameras.

A strange crowd of dark, unfamiliar faces surged through the banqueting hall to make their way through the exits. Suraya leaned on my shoulder, crying. I felt empty and cold, as though I couldn't cry. I heard the sound of a bell from my earrings, and it immediately brought on a distant memory of the day Ali Akbar's cow Lackey was sacrificed. Unknowingly, she had accepted her fate, and as mourners angled in from each side, I could only feel them sealing my fate in the same way for something greedy and vain.

More guests threw their arms in an embrace at me. Babajee looked emotional as he stood and watched from the side, and

Mamajee stood by the door of the wedding car, alongside Syed, to lead me into the car. I climbed in. Syed went 'round to the other side. He heaved as he closed the door. More onlookers took pictures from the outside, and the sounds and murmurs were all muted. I looked down.

"Now it begins," he said, locking the car door with a wide grin. "Finally, you are locked in." He cackled.

I ignored the comment, turning to look outside, only to see the rain come crashing down on the window, washing away my view of the guests, who waved their final farewells as the car pulled away.

CHAPTER THIRTY-FIVE
– Dead than Divorced–

Bang went the door. My heart pounded; every beat struck with the thud. Bang went the door again. The door hitting my back, the force of which resonated through my spine. The yelling louder from behind the door with each kick. "Open the door!" My feet deep in the carpet, restraining the pressure of it being opened.

I wanted it to stop. Soon enough the door would be forced open, despite all my efforts to keep it closed. I wedged it with my scarf. Only moments from now, I would feel the terrifying effects of that door being thrust open. Bang went the door again, a larger kick this time that pounded in my chest. The door almost came ajar as he pushed against it.

"Open the fucking door, Eleanor!" Syed yelled at the top of his lungs. I could feel rage, his voice grizzly. "Don't get me mad. I just want to talk."

Talking never worked; it only gave him more ammunition. It was as if every response led to something that provoked him, justifying his hands and feet in some manner on me. It had been a few months now, and I had learned the hard way to silence myself or face being kicked down the staircase or beaten with a heavy, wet towel or almost defaced with a wire coat hanger. He was feeling bloodthirsty today,

I could feel it. It seemed to be a cyclical pattern of behaviour that brooded every two weeks.

This was not the first time we'd had an argument about not following his instruction or protocol. There were many reasons that set the flames of fury in him, that later only made me regretful of my own actions. If I had only worn the saree his mother had wanted me to wear, then perhaps he wouldn't have pushed me down the stairs, landing inches before a glass shelf. Or if I hadn't refused to wear the earrings his mother had given me, would it have avoided being defaced with a wire hanger? If I hadn't been talking on the phone for more than ten minutes to my family, would it have made him more trusting? Or if I had just not woken him in the morning, could it have stopped him pounding that heavy, wet towel on my naked body? I could change, but each time, it only raised the stakes, and the punishment was more severe.

Yes, silence, I had decided, would stave off his hunger to hurt me for a while at least. Sitting by the door would hold him back for a few minutes while I put my thoughts together, but I knew that in each minute, the anger grew more ravenous, and with that, the pain that would be inflicted on me, more severe. *What happens when the door flings open is as yet unknown, and each second feels like a blessing.*

The door hinges creaked, bursting with the force, the scarf now rolling under the door with each push. I could feel my feet losing grip against the carpet as he heaved from behind. Syed was trying to push the door open, and I was sliding farther into the room.

I noticed the phone on my desk. Perhaps I could call Mamajee. When I was married, she had said, she would be there to support me no matter what, as long as I married someone they approved of. That was the idea: I wouldn't face this alone. They would be there. *Now's the time*, I thought. *Haven't I endured enough? I just have to call her, and she'll put an end to this, at least prevent this from spiralling out of control.*

The phone receiver, though, was too far to reach. If I moved, he'd have the door flung open in seconds. I kicked the receiver cord, and the phone tumbled down to the floor near me. Syed was pounding the door down now, and the scarf curled under the threshold. I dialled the number frantically, hoping desperately not to dial it incorrectly. It rang; each long ringtone felt like a lifetime passing in front of me as the door banged continually.

Mamajee finally answered. I felt almost home hearing her familiar voice. "Hello," she said in a low, calm tone.

"Mamajee, it's me!" I cried. "I need help. He's breaking down the door, and he's going to kill me. He's breaking down the door!" I cried that helpless, weak cry when your stomach muscles can't hold it together anymore.

The kicks against the door were getting quicker one beat at a time.

"Hmm, yeah, so what are you calling here for? How dare you call us when you have your own mother-in-law and father-in-law now?"

I couldn't process her logic. Why was she mad at me for calling her?

"I can't do this anymore, Mamajee. Please, he's going to kill me. He's trying to break the door down."

"No. You stop, you stop, and you listen to me," she said. "You've got a real nerve calling here now. How dare you think you can just up and leave? How dare you! You are calling us when you have your own in-laws there to bring things to justice. You mark my words: you bring that kind of shame on our family, then I would rather you were dead than divorced." She hung up. The phone went dead.

Her words echoed somewhere dark and hollow, and it felt like I was falling into a dark hole. The banging got louder. The door flung open, and I dropped the receiver. Syed's face looked fierce, his breathing deep, and his fists were tightly clenched.

"Who were you trying to call? Hmm?" he said, panting deep breaths and slowly inching towards me.

My lower back leaned into the desk, and I shielded myself with the office chair.

He leaned into me, his face right up against mine. "WHO – WERE – YOU – TRYING – TO – CALL?" he repeated, shouting into my face.

I tried to look down. I knew what was coming, whichever way I answered the question.

He grabbed my neck. His hands felt hot and sweaty. My head raced with the thought that strangling might be less painful than the blow to my head that I had received last time. He held my throat tight, and I felt the blood rushing through to the side of my head, my veins pulsating. His overbearing presence was now pushing me farther onto the desk. "I'll ask you one more time: who did you call?" His hands now wet on my skin. He was holding on so tight I couldn't answer.

"Oh, fuck you, then." Still holding me by the neck, he flung me across into the wall near to the door. The force hit the corner of my head and part of my shoulder bone, leaving a splintering pain. Cowering into the ground, I regained my balance. Holding my shoulder, I crawled nearer to the door.

"Oh, you are trying to leave now? After all the effort it has taken to get in?" He flung the door to close it, which caught my fingers.

"Aargh!" I screamed. Excruciating pain travelled up through my right fingers and sent a shock wave into my face. I curled up into a ball, leaning into the wall by the door, cupping my left hand over my right to soften the pain.

"Planning on leaving, were you?" he demanded as he towered over me.

"Leave me alone," I cried, tears flowing from my eyes and into my mouth. "Why can't you just leave me alone?" I sobbed, trembling from the shock and pain suddenly besieging my body.

"Leave you alone? 'Leave me alone,'" he repeated mockingly. "You sit in my house, and you answer to me," he shouted. Suddenly it went dark as the door slammed onto my head. Subsequent blows followed, with the light fading out.

*

My head swirled, and I came into being from a panicked voice.

"Eleanor, get up, off the floor." It sounded calm and nourishing, and I felt the comfort of a soft scarf and hands that shook my arms gently. "Eleanor, Eleanor, you must get up, dear."

Through my slight blinks, I saw the familiar face, and then my senses came alive with the pain. It found its way back to my hands, my neck and my head. I looked up and found that I was still in the office, by the door. It was Ammujee, my mother-in-law.

"Oh my! What happened?" she asked, heaving and picking me up to my feet. They had just got back from dinner. I felt dizzy being raised up in a rush, slowly bringing myself to balance. My face felt glazed with something sticky; it had encrusted itself on the side of my head. I wiped my face, trying to work it out from touch, but the skin felt sore and tender. "What happened, Eleanor? Tell me."

I looked down at my hands, and there were dried blood marks on my fingertips.

"Not again. Is this what you both do when we are away from you?" she barked. "We have a dinner with family tomorrow, and this is how you want to look in front of our guests? You are a newly wedded bride now, Eleanor. How am I going to show my face?"

This was all my fault, of course. It wasn't about my state, it was about hers. How it would look if any member of their family saw me like this. She continued to harp on about how disappointed she was that we were fighting and that I seemed to lack reservation. But I could no longer hear her words; I could only recollect that something far worse had happened that night. It wasn't the fight, Syed's pounding kicks or the pain from being thrashed into the wall. Something far worse came into my recollection. My very own mother would have wanted the same. Those brief words that had passed her lips echoed during that brief exchange. *Dead than divorced. I would rather you were dead than divorced.*

It sent a fresh rush of pain from my chest and into the pit of my stomach. Tears rushed down, stinging my bruised face. The thought travelled through my body, numbing it from pain. I no longer felt alive. Ammujee continued. Her mouth made wide, meaningful movements, but I wasn't listening. She handed me my scarf, which lay strewn half-wedged beneath the door.

"Well, you are not listening to me, then. Are you going to tell your ammujee what happened, Eleanor?"

I looked blankly back at her. *What does she want to hear?* I thought. That her son beat me up, pushed me down the stairs, chased me down the hallway and knocked down the office door, where he found me and repeatedly beat me, all because of an argument over which saree I should wear to tomorrow's dinner party. I was tired and jittery from the ordeal, the physical pain growing unbearable in my shoulder and head. If I did explain then, it would hurt to hear the explanations, the justifications for his behaviour from her, and I wasn't going to blame her for protecting her son.

"Ammujee, is it okay if I go to bed?" I begged through my tears.

She looked at me uneasily, grappling with the thoughts of what must have happened tonight. "If you must, go get some rest, then," she said wearily.

I slowly headed towards the stairs, through the hallway, dazed, weak and stiff. I passed the first room beyond the office, which had an open-plan, casual living area. The Greek columns dividing it from the dining room gave it a faux palatial appearance. I looked down at the cold, pale tiles with the blue-veined marble effect running through it. How false it all seemed. The cold on my feet sent goose pimples down the back of my legs. I carried on walking slowly towards the hallway.

Ammujee had now set herself to rushing around in the kitchen, which adjoined the dining area. As I shuffled past, a dark shadow formed around the sofa. It took a few seconds, as my eyes were still stinging and blurry.

"Bhabhi," whispered a voice in the dark. I turned to the right; it was my brother-in-law, Sufyan. He was sat cross-legged in the semi-darkened living room, rolling some prayer beads.

I quickly wrapped the scarf around my head, but the manoeuvre was harder than I'd thought, as my shoulder felt bruised and sore. I winced with the pain.

"Bhabhi, are you okay?"

I couldn't lie to him, but I couldn't bring myself to answer in words. I nodded and looked down and moved on quickly back down the hallway and towards the stairs. He looked concerned but seemed powerless to pursue it any further. Some more Greek columns stood at the bottom of the stairs, forming a shelf or picture frames. I glanced at the pictures, recollecting where they were from.

A picture of Syed with his father holding a medal to mark his MBE, awarded by the Queen. Another picture with all the family and Syed's extended family on our walima, and then the picture that really cut me open into tears was the one of our wedding day, my mother-in-law on one side and my father-in-law on the other. Standing proudly on each side of them were my own parents, and although everyone else seemed to be smiling, it appeared that the only person who hadn't smiled was the only person I had done all this for. My own mother, her face expressionless in the picture. Her lips, pursed together, seemed void of any joy or pleasure. I had anticipated that the outcome of that day would have been her biggest achievement and that she would have indulged in some personal satisfaction victoriously for her long and arduously fought goal in getting me to this point.

Why didn't she want to help me? I thought. *My own mother. How could she have said those words in my hour of need?* I tried to stop my tears. The pain was unbearable, and when my face tensed near my eye, the stinging emblazoned the sensation further.

I went into the bathroom directly right of the stairs. Cold and echoey, it had the same blue-veined marble-effect tiles as downstairs. I looked at myself in the mirror, and I burst into tears, that horrible face looking back at me, my eyes puffed and swollen. There was a large scuff with thinly torn skin on the left corner of my forehead, along with the right side of my cheek, where several scuffed lines had been etched into my face. There was another open wound on my left cheekbone, the blood had trailed its way down my neck and left a watermark stain. *What a mess!* I thought, but this was something of a small factor in what was really cutting me up inside.

I washed my face, the water cool on the wounds across my bloodstained cheekbone. The skin pricked from the pain but numbed slowly as the water cooled it down. My eyes felt thirsty and became clearer from the fresh burst of water that trickled on my face.

I patted my face gently with a towel and looked back at the mirror. The wounds were still large and swollen on my cheek, and the side of my forehead where the skin had grazed and torn was now slightly pink.

I didn't go back to the bedroom, where Syed lay asleep, snoring. He hadn't lost any sleep, of course. I couldn't bring myself to set foot in the room or let the disappointment and rage build up for what he had done. I crept back downstairs, the lights off in the open area and kitchen. Everyone had made their way to bed. I lay down on the cold leather sofa, reaching over for the thin throw draped on the armrest. It felt safe here now, calm, dark, peaceful. In the solitude, I could be me again. My mind, body and soul as one. I could release my sense of self, something that, when surrounded by people, I could not have. I was not alone here in solitude, but I felt alone around the people who all of this was manifested for. I was not at one with them, and that is the truth about loneliness: it's not the physical aspect of being alone that hurts, it is the feeling of isolation, that feeling that you are different from everyone else or that you are not at one with the world around you.

*

I woke from the sound of the front door shuddering. I looked at the living-room clock, a gold picture frame of the holy Kaaba with pilgrims surrounding it. It was 8 a.m., and Syed, Abbujee and Ammujee had left for work. It seemed that they had all skipped breakfast this morning, perhaps to avoid me curled up there on the living-room sofa. I could only be pleased with that outcome. I couldn't bear any more false pretences.

"Make sure you eat," Ammujee would have said, as if it mattered more than being safe, or "Take lots of care" were usually the words from Abbujee. Their silver-tongued sentences only left me tongue-tied.

I gradually rose up from the sofa; my body felt stiff and corpse-like. I hobbled up the stairs to the bathroom. I pulled up my kameez top; my ribs still had the graze marks, slowly forming into a pale yellow bruise. I slipped it off to look at what remained underneath it. *This is what God had destined for me, had written for me? This is what he wants, and therefore, I am? Or is it that this is what everyone believes he wants, and therefore, this is what is?*

I turned my slight frame in front of the mirror, observing the weak body, the skin tightly wrapped around my bones. My jawline, thin and pointed; my cheeks, hollow, blushed only by the bruising; and the large graze on my forehead, where a scab was forming. I used to be a healthy seven stone before I met Syed, but here in the bathroom, standing my skeletal corpse of bone and tissue on the scales, I weighed five stone.

I took a quick shower, the soap stinging the cuts as the warm water pelted down on my open wounds. Wrapped in a towel, I made my way to the bedroom. The bed unmade, the blankets dragging on the floor, the stale air of sweat and heavy breathing, ripe with the stench of the man I had married.

I opened the wardrobe for something to wear. Gone were the days of cosy sweaters and tracksuit bottoms to lounge around in. My mother-in-law wouldn't have approved, in case anyone sprang up at the front door. She wanted me dressed appealingly, appropriately. Before I had moved into the family house, she had already prepared my wardrobe. A large array of colourful sarees arranged in ascending tones was placed neatly on the top-tier hanging rail. They were pinned with matching blouses, sandals and handbags. These were prescribed to me by her on occasions such as dinner parties. Often, she would instruct me and lay them all out for me the night before.

"Here," she had said before we went for dinner with Abbujee at a relative's house. "Tomorrow you will wear the red saree, the heavy bridal one. You are still a new bride; they will want to see you in it. Of course, the handbag, sandals, bangles, blouse and shawl are all here on the chair. Don't forget the earrings. You must wear the earrings that the guests gave to you on the wedding day. Otherwise, you never know, they would be offended if they never saw you in them."

It was the red saree that had spawned the attack yesterday. I had offended Syed when I had challenged him on the reasons why I was still dressing up as a bride three months after our wedding day.

"Are you questioning my mother's request?" he'd asked.

"No. I just wanted to know why I had to wear the bridal outfit over and over again. It seems to have been worn a lot."

"Like I said before, don't ask questions; be respectful. It's your mother-in-law, for God's sake."

I didn't like that tone; I didn't like the remark, of course, and I couldn't leave it. But I should have let it go.

"It's not that I don't respect Ammujee. I just wanted to know why."

"Listen here, don't push your luck; show some fucking respect," he'd said, pushing me against the wall.

I looked at the sarees now, beautifully adorned with crystals and fine embroidery. Anyone would think I was a princess in a Grecian palace if they saw my wardrobe and the home I now belonged to. At least, if they had only glanced, they would be fooled into believing it, through the thin veneer of polish-sprayed glass tables, faux columns and blue-veined tiles, which were all a display for cosmetic purposes, as I had now become an object for their vanities. At least with their eyes, they would have been deceived into thinking it the truth.

Mamajee saw it as such. She was proud that my in-laws had expensive taste. She couldn't believe my luck with having a man like Syed. "So generous with gifts and flowers. At least if he hits you, he does say sorry. That shows that he cares. At least he loves you. It's more than I got."

Perhaps I was ungrateful; I had yet to accept these as blessings, that after every fight, every pounding of the fists, I would be rewarded this way, with flowers, sarees, pendants and charms.

The bottom rail of my wardrobe had been filled with shalwar kameez suits in an array of bright colours, some handmade, and others bought ready to wear. I tried to avoid garishly bright colours, although Ammujee's favourites were always in cerise or royal blue.

They seemed more favoured by Bengali women: brighter colours made the skin look fairer, they would say.

I shrouded my wafer-thin corpse in a black suit, rolling up the trousers at the waist and folding up the tunic sleeves. It was harder to see my protruding bones through the soft satin silk. It was even harder to see my ribcage, like a corrugated roof along my back. I brushed my netted web of hair free of the dust and cleared my eyes of the blackened eyeliner that looked like soot forming around my eyelids. I laid the scarf over my head like a headband, nestled over the wound, soft against my face, hiding the graze on my cheek and my forehead.

Shame overcame me. Or was it humiliation I was feeling? Something about being beaten left only distaste for myself. Disappointment that I somehow was in the wrong, and in the face of adversity, Syed's actions might be justified. I recalled that time when Babajee had beaten me, and I'd felt it then. I had done something wrong; something had been violated and subjected him to feel angry enough to want to attack. I was ashamed of what they would think if I had to go to that dinner party tonight, looking like this. His cousins, aunts, uncles, sisters, brothers, wives, husbands of the extended in-law population. I knew they would think it was something I'd done. I wanted to cover it up, pretend it had never happened. I was dreading the conversation later. How could I have caused someone to need to resort to that? I shouldn't have pushed it. I felt like a child again, the times I'd seen children being hit for not getting the verses in the Quran right, or when Mamajee had beaten us with a stick or slipper for doing something wrong.

"Doing something wrong," I repeated. Because I had done something, something wrong here. I was ashamed because here I was, a grown woman of twenty-six years, educated, graduated, free-willed, paying for things with her own hard-earned money. Wearing what I wanted, seeing who I wanted, being who I wanted. Here I was now, a grown woman being beaten up for being wrong. I faced this reality now with despair. Had I changed some aspect of me? Would it have made a difference?

I convinced myself again. "I have to accept this," I said to myself in the mirror.

I thought about Mamajee, all those years of beatings from Babajee, how she had accepted, persevered for us, and here I was, complaining. How I was to blame for her perseverance. My selfish needs for a mother had kept her there. How could I complain about being beaten up when I was being loved by this person? Mamajee had never got an ounce of affection from Babajee. He would never apologise. At least Syed did try to resolve things; at least he seemed to regret what he would do at the time. At least, after our big fights, it always ended with a round of reconciliation. He would beg for forgiveness from me and cry. There would always be hugs, grabbing onto my body and holding me tight while I tried to push him away. Mamajee had never received that from Babajee, so what was I complaining about? As long as he tried to be a better person, wasn't that all that mattered? "I shouldn't have pushed it," I told myself. I was ungrateful, of course I was. Here I have everything, and yet I am complaining.

I looked out of the bedroom window, the reflection of my closely shrouded face fading out to the autumn garden. To my surprise, the magnolia tree had sprouted pale pink flowers again, and a slight breeze made its branches dance to the whistles of the wind. The sun shone; a film of silver lined each leaf. Something about seeing that tree felt bitter and sweet all at the same time. It unsettled me. Something hurt now, watching it as I looked out.

I couldn't gaze at these things in the same light anymore. It was as though I had entered a different world and was looking at the outside world through a lens. Even that tree seemed free. It may have been fixed to the ground, unable to move, to speak or hear, but its natural state of being was free. It was fully immersed in being itself. Come rain or shine, nothing had to change. It could still be; it could still flourish; it could radiate of its own free will; it could blossom. If it were uprooted, placed somewhere obscured from light, perhaps then, its state of being wouldn't be the same. No longer in its natural elements, it wouldn't flourish even in the grandest of gardens. I could almost envy it.

It hurt now more because it sparked in me the real reason I was unsettled. I no longer knew who I was. I reconciled my own truth from looking at that tree. "I am nothing but a pleaser," I concluded, tangled in a web of guilt and betrayal. I had been badly bitten and betrayed by those around me. In choosing this path to please, for face and to honour their word, I had reached the soul-destroying conclusion that honouring them was not a bargaining chip for their love, and I realised then, in the coldness of those words, "dead than divorced".

It no longer mattered to my family about my well-being; it only mattered that I kept their honour. I had subscribed my thinking to such falsities and pretences, that the idea of marrying someone of their liking would in turn allow me to receive their love, sympathy and support. None of this had materialised. I had been handed over. The deal made, sale agreed, the transaction complete. There was no mention in the fine print, such clauses of after-sales support services. It was not in their remit. I could have rotted here, and it wouldn't have mattered. They could mourn a dead woman, but they couldn't mourn a divorced one. What had I entered?

Mrs Abbots was right. Was that what she had meant on the wedding day? Was that what she had been alluding to? I couldn't even think of her anymore. Who was she? Had she really had an affair with my father? All those years that I had known her, what had been her motive for supporting me? Was it because of her that Mamajee suffered such a disastrous marriage, which in turn caused us all to suffer? In some ways, I blamed Mrs Abbots for all of this. Maybe she had corrupted me spitefully, to turn me against my family. The coaching, priming, secret meetups, the notes. How farcical it all seemed. She had just wanted a piece of what she couldn't have. I felt betrayed by the very people I loved. How crude, how toxic, corrosive, hurtful people who you loved could be. It was dawning on me: I could not be loved, not in the real sense of the word. There were always conditions I couldn't adhere to.

My shoulders hunched, and I curled into a ball on the satin bed cover draped on the bed by the window. So small, deniable, nothing. That was who I was. The seven-year-old me appeared in my thoughts, as God was not even there for me anymore. *So, this is what is written for me?* I said to her.

The seven-year-old me replied, *You should have left your soul to the mercy of your parents' wishes, so they could laugh and joke, brag about how beautiful your wedding was, how proud they are that you are married.*

What? I argued with myself. *So that they could coat my bruised arms in golden bangles and drape a saree over my grazed ribs, crown my red, bloodied forehead with an embroidered veil and take me out for the final show?*

Restless, I got up and walked over to the mirror.

There, came the voice again as I stared at my reflection. That seven-year-old me smiled. *There is nothing you can do, Eleanor: this is your life now. Forget what happened before. You still have everything. A house, a home, a family, a future and, most important of all, a husband. That was what you wanted, wasn't it? You wanted to be married, have children, have a home. So why would you want to lose all of that now? Forget the pain. It didn't hurt, anyway. He was mad, but he loves you. So what he gets angry sometimes? You know you can still have it all. Just hold on, Eleanor. Forget who you are. There is nothing in the outside world, anyway. There is more to lose out there than in here. So what you get beaten? So what your family doesn't care? Be grateful: you have a family here; you are married. People accept you; people will love you and respect you here. They won't question you if you just do the right thing. Be the wife. Be the perfect wife and focus on everything you have to be. And once you have mastered that, you will have everything, and you will be happy.*

I gazed into the mirror. I pulled a tissue from the box on the table and wiped the teary eyeliner, the streaks like track marks along a torn road. I looked down at my hands, the grazed skin on my left finger sore, throbbing. I turned my hands and looked at my palms, and I remembered what Mamajee had once said. "You might get hurt, you might get bitten, but all you will learn is all this was written," she'd said.

Maybe this is just hardship; maybe I can get through this, I thought.

*

When I came downstairs, I found Sufyan sitting at the breakfast table with a mug of tea, deeply engrossed in a book. Seeing him suddenly made me feel calm about where I was. Sufyan was a great brother-in-law: he was kind, softly spoken and peaceful, quite the contrary to his brother. How the two ever came from the same mother was unbeknown to me.

"Assalamualaikum, Bhabhi," he said with a smile.

I suddenly felt a sense of normality flow through my mind, and I took in a deep breath and smiled to embrace it. "Waalaikumsalam," I responded back. I paced slowly over the cold tiles.

"What are you having for breakfast?" I asked him, trying to shape up a normal conversation.

He looked at me, then paused to look down at his bowl. "Cereal," he said, mocking me with an obvious grin.

I pulled my veil over my head to prevent him from seeing the wound. I was embarrassed and awkward about the fights Syed and I had. I didn't want him to know, and it wouldn't have made pleasant conversation if he had seen it.

"Have you had breakfast, Bhabhi?"

"No, not yet," I said, folding my arms to close myself in more.

"You should eat something, Bhabhi. I can make you some toast," he said, rising up from his chair.

"No, you sit and eat your cereal," I said. "How about I make you something, since I am going to the kitchen?"

"I will join you, then," he said, rising from his seat. I made the toast and coffee, my back to him as he made small talk about his studies. I brought the food back to the table and was seating myself near him when my veil slid down, the wound in full view.

"Bhabhi, what happened to your head?"

I covered my head quickly. He looked full of concern. I looked down at the toast. I looked at him. There were no words. What do you say to your brother-in-law who lives in the same house?

"Let's just eat our toast. You know it tastes stale when it goes cold." The air seemed to have frozen with silence. I could hear the buzzing sound from the kitchen light.

He took a piece of toast from the plate. "Yes, I agree, it's not good when it's stale, and it's a sin to throw it all away, even when it's tasteless." He paused to look at me when he said this. Was he trying to tell me something here? I couldn't tell.

"You can't throw it away?" I said, chewing on the toast. "Is that what is written for me?" I pressed, staring at my cup. "Is that the truth?"

He looked at me with a longer stare, his concern displayed only through silence. It troubled me more when he looked at me. What was he thinking? My saliva glands wouldn't kick in, and I forced the dry bread with one painful swallow.

"Is it painful? More coffee?" he said, raising one eyebrow up at me as he poured a cup for me. The small tokens of kindness salvaged me from the depths of despair. It felt good to have some open dialogue. I was mindful, though, of what I could divulge: there could be consequences in even the briefest exchange. And what might come of this small exchange?

"Bhabhi?"

I turned to look at him.

"You didn't answer my question."

I turned to meet his eyes. "Yes," I said with a half-smile.

"Well, I can't promise this is the cure, but it can certainly help," he said, pouring the milk.

"Help?" I said, looking at him.

"With waking up," he said, smiling and shaking his head.

My heart sank. I wanted him to say something. I wanted him to tell me it was going to be okay because he was my witness, my support, my encouragement.

"Bhabhi," he said, buttering some more toast, "do you like reading books?"

I nodded while taking a sip of my coffee. "Yes, very much so."

"I just want you to read something and tell me what you think." He reached over to his university bag and pulled out a book. He passed it to me, both hands holding it sacredly. "It might help you find your answer to what is written," he said, looking at me. "Are you ready to find the truth?"

CHAPTER THIRTY-SIX

– *Purification* –

I looked down at the cover; the book was titled *Purification* by H. A. Yasin.

I looked at him, perplexed, confused. "How can this help me?"

"When you get closer to your heart, you will get closer to your answer, and that's what this book will teach you to do. Only you can choose the right path, Bhabhi."

"How did you come across this?" I said.

He contemplated his response calmly. "Have you heard of Sufism?"

"Sort of. I don't really know much about it," I said, gazing at the book.

It was as if he could see through me.

"Sufism is an ancient, mystical Islamic practice. It seeks enlightenment and closeness to God by restoring purity and calmness to the heart. Often, we seek happiness through worldly things, and yet these are the same things that bring us anxiety and other such diseases of the heart. The book will help you find yourself. It all starts, though, with you, Bhabhi. That journey to the truth is within you. To find your truth, you have to search within. When you take back those veils of life that you have hidden behind, you will find your true light. The answers that you seek are all there within you. If you are willing to seek introspectively, within you, then the truth will reveal itself. Have a read. It may guide you. Remember though, the truth can only be found within you."

It was overwhelming, I couldn't understand all of what he was saying, but it couldn't hurt to read the book and understand it. I was intrigued. I could only conclude that he was perceptive to the turmoil I was facing. He could see that I was lost and I needed to find myself again. I didn't know who I was anymore; I didn't know what was true, what was right or wrong. I was alone now, and there was no one I could depend on for such guidance.

"Thank you, Sufyan. I will have a read and let you know."

I took the book away and placed it by my bedside. I decided to read it. It talked about the human heart, how we are clouded by our material needs, and once we can isolate our thinking, we can learn to be independent of worldly things. It talked about how we can never satisfy our needs through worldly desires, why we are not happy, and why prayer, meditation, solitude can help pave a better solution for happiness in our life.

The book captured my spirit and allowed me to resolve myself. I suddenly changed my way of thinking about my situation. I may be unhappily married right now, but I could conscientiously choose to do something about my inner state of being. I could choose a better place in my mind. Even in incarceration, one can find sanity in that single truth: don't let the outside destroy the inside. Nobody could get inside me. I knew now why Mamajee reflected on Allah: it allowed her to keep going even though she was deeply unhappy. It gave her life a purpose, a deeper meaning. It took her away from her wants and desires, because Allah was listening, and he had a better place for her. *Maybe this will work for me too*, I thought. It may also give Syed no reason to hurt me anymore. If I was completely isolated, if all I did was sit and pray, wear a scarf or a hijab, cover myself from top to toe and stay in prayer, then I could live out this life and be happy.

I read the book cover to cover. It gave me a sense of inner peace, a shift in my perspective, self-realisation of the inner self, the truest form of oneself and the realisation that the soul itself is not bound to worldly conditions. I learned how I could choose to be the happiest person in the world with just the basic things, a small hunk of bread, a humble shelter, and be just as content as the wealthiest person in the world. Happiness, I learned through this book, was a state of being. When we choose worldly things in the pursuit of happiness, we become more delusional. We promise ourselves that achieving the next great thing will make us happier, that this will bring us more contentment, more happiness, but it never does, because the soul does not need these things. Our state of being happy does not depend on them, but our minds perceive that our state of being is dependent on them. I learned from the book that the mind deceives us because we are connected to the world through it. I felt my breath become smooth and silky knowing this, as if my mind was clear of obstacles and my soul felt more alive. I was safe in the knowledge that I was free to explore the depth of this inner revelation, and I didn't need to depend on the world around me to make me feel happy. I could find it inside me. In solitude, away from all the distractions, away from all the things my ego had led me to believe. I learned from Sufyan the practice of deep meditation, that one strives for purity, cleansing of the mind and oneness with God.

But as I delved deeper, I also became inward. I started praying, taking time to reflect on Allah, meditating, carrying out affirmations. I felt clear-headed, calmer-spirited in this state, but also felt removed from the earth. All the things that I had attached importance to were dissolving here. Mamajee became a distant memory that I didn't have to fight anymore. I didn't call after that day she'd cut me off, and I no longer desired the validation from her. I took up my time in prayer in the evenings, apart from mealtimes with the family, where we all sat together. Syed didn't comment much on my new pastime: the days were getting darker, and the winter months brought with them the fasting month of Ramadan, where the nights were spent in prayer or reading the Quran, and the days were spent in frequent intervals of prayer. And while I became locked into this world of prayer and meditation, Syed only became distracted by worldly things. Dinners were a time with the family and offered no intimacy between us for conversation, and to the bemusement of Ammujee, the rest of Syed's evening would be spent on the games console, playing action-packed violent games with disturbing scenes of killing people with machine guns and other such artillery. I felt disagreeable to being entertained by it and often withdrew myself to the bedroom, where I continued to read and meditate. Ammujee and Abbujee could only admire my new-found devotion to Allah.

"Mashallah, praise be to Allah that you have found such enlightenment. Very good," Ammujee and Abbujee commended me one evening over dinner. I remained indifferent to their opinion. There was strength in knowing it no longer served any purpose; their opinion, good or bad, formed no superior validation for me. Internal bliss came from within me; it was untouchable.

They turned to Syed, who seemed displeased by the praise. "What about you? Are you going to join us at the mosque for evening prayers? You spend the whole evening on that game during the month of Ramadan."

I could sense their nagging in my presence irritated him.

"All right, Mum," he said. "I am not a kid anymore. I will work it out for myself, okay?" He rolled his eyes at her, and then he turned to glare at me as though I was to blame for his reaction.

Ammujee raised herself calmly from the table. "Would anyone like some mango?" she asked.

"Only if there's ice cream, Ammujee," Sufyan responded a little jovially, as if to make light of the tension forming at the dining table.

"Oh, yeah, that's not a problem. The youngest always gets what he wants," Syed sneered. I could see he was seething. It had been a couple of weeks, and he seemed venomous, hungry for a reaction.

"Bhabhi, did you want ice cream with your mango? I will get you some."

"Let her get it if she wants it. Why the fuck do you need to serve her?" Syed retorted.

"Yes, your brother is quite right. Let me get it. I will get some plates too." I dashed off to the kitchen without making eye contact.

Syed's eyes burned a hole through my back from the dining table while Abbujee sat neutral to the discord, arms resting on the table, swirling a glass of water, while the three of us busied ourselves in the kitchen. Ammujee peeled the mangoes carefully with a knife, the juice oozing from her hands. Sufyan immersed himself in the freezer, selecting a tub of ice cream, while I placed dessert bowls out onto a tray, but no sooner had our preparation commenced than Syed burst through the door.

"I am going to bed. Don't bother making any for me," he said, grimacing at me.

"Have a little bit," Ammujee said.

"No. I didn't ask for it, did I? So why are you forcing it?" Syed's voice rose with insistence, bashing the door as he stormed upstairs.

He needed to calm down. Maybe the sleep would calm him down, prevent things escalating. It was only 8 p.m., so after cleaning up, I joined Ammujee and Abbujee for a while in the living room. Sufyan had already made his way to his room to finish some university preparation. They were watching a Bengali news channel, and I had tuned out. The newsreader was speaking in another dialect, and I couldn't understand it. I was simply biding some time: I didn't want to arouse Syed, especially in his mood.

By 9 p.m. I decided it would be appropriate. He would be in a deep sleep by now. I crept into the dark room, Syed's snoring loud and grizzly. I quietly changed and slipped into bed.

*

That night I woke suddenly to the grasp of a hand across my waist. Syed had grabbed me tightly into him and was feeling me up, smothering his hand all over my breast as if it were to help fast-track me into the mood. I pulled his grip away, but he firmed up his hand so that I couldn't move. Still smothering me, he held me up tightly against him.

"Does it say anywhere in your book about how you should be pleasing your husband? It's been a while, and you don't even behave like a wife."

I felt like a lamb to the slaughter, held against my will. He undressed me, pulling down my panties with rough tugs. I didn't move, my body loose and resigned to the idea. Was this what he really wanted? It had been a few weeks or more, and his previous attempts had failed with me. As he motioned his way inside, it felt like somebody coming into your home without an open invitation. I wasn't petrified; I wasn't hurt, but silenced and shocked by his behaviour.

Slowly his throbbing stopped, and he let go of me, breaking away from me as I lay curled up on the side of my bed.

Then he shot up. "Oh, what's the fucking point, anyway?" he said, shoving me off the bed. I fell down, landing on the carpet suddenly. He stormed off to the bathroom. There was no getting away from the cold, ugly side of our marriage. This was the darkest, even with spiritual enlightenment. Surely this was not what we were designed to endure?

I lay in bed with my face towards the door. Syed came back into the room, slumped into bed and tugged the blanket over him, his breathing heavy. Within a minute he was fast asleep.

I lay shrouded under the blanket, nothing but my head giving away presence. I started to think about Mamajee, and what it must have been like for her to be married to Babajee, what it must have been like to sleep next to someone who you didn't love, have anything in common with and, most of all, who you were not physically attracted to. Mamajee never really spoke about it, but she did once tell me something that harrowed my thoughts.

After Mamajee had been carried out of her village in the bridal carriage, bound to her new home, there was more to come of the unknown. She told me how, on the night of the wedding, Babajee had tried to touch her. "I was a frightened child," she'd said. "Barely aware of what happens in a marriage. He wanted to touch me on our wedding night. I screamed, 'Why is this man touching me?'" Such innocence, such lack of awareness of marriage. "I had to quietly accept, of course," she'd said. "That was a man's right in marriage, and that was my duty."

How life was unfolding for me now in the same sickening circumstance. I was falling into the same trap, as if I was cast from the same mould as my mother, and her mother. Syed was raising the stakes; it was an expectation now. "Making love" was to be a service to my husband.

I lay there like an empty shell, hollow and dark as a cave. Now I knew what Mamajee felt all those years. "There are consequences," she had said once. "Every action has a price."

I was paying the price now, her perseverance for marriage now breathing into mine. *I have to keep this going,* I thought. *But how?* I had promised, for Mamajee's sake. There was still hope that we could make this work. After all, we had only just got married, and people had told me how hard it was in the first year.

If I do everything right, then maybe he won't have a reason to hurt me. Better still, what if I teach him? He just needed more explaining, understanding of how it affected me and how it affected our marriage. Maybe then we could avoid the heated clashes, the violence and the controlling behaviour. He could be a good person. Maybe I was just the wrong person for him.

*

In the weeks following that soul-destroying night, I started researching about violence, about domestic abuse against women. I read journals, publications on research into domestic violence and whether the attacker changes over time. I wanted to find out whether Syed could ever change or whether there was anything I could do to change or whether there was a way we could both change and make this marriage work.

One afternoon I took my research further. I nervously picked up the phone and called the police. I used their local number. The phone rang, and an officer answered.

"Hello?" came the voice.

"Hi," I said. "I wanted to speak to somebody about domestic violence. Can somebody help me?"

"Yes, certainly. First of all, can I ask, are you somewhere safe?"

"Yes," I said.

"Okay. I am going to put you through to one of our officers, so stay on the line."

I waited.

"Hello. This is the Metropolitan Police. How can I help?"

"Yes, hello there. I wanted to speak to somebody about domestic abuse. I need some help understanding what to do about my husband."

"Sure. Is your husband there where you are now?"

"No," I said.

"Are you safe?" he said.

"Yes," I said hesitantly.

"Do you need help with accommodation?"

"Accommodation? No. I just need some advice on what to do. He keeps hurting me, and I want to find a way of making things better."

"I understand your concern. However, there is nothing we can do other than to ask you to leave and find somewhere safe."

"Okay," I said, baffled by this response. *Why can't they tell me something, other than to leave him? Do they not understand that leaving is not an option for me? What will my whole family, life, existence become?* I thought.

"If you are in any danger and you need us to help, then please call us. We are here to assist. Or if you would like to file a report or if you need help getting the right support once you have made that decision, we will be here."

"Thank you," I said. I put the phone down. I was angry. I needed help, and the police were not able to help me. I wasn't even sure what I was expecting them to do, but I needed some reassurance of where I was. I was looking for someone to protect me while I stayed in this marriage.

I then called up a domestic abuse line for women.

"Hi. I would like to speak to someone about domestic abuse."

"Sure. How may I help you?" came a response from a woman on the line.

"It's my husband. I want to find a way to avoid being abused."

"Okay," she said. "The first thing I want to know is, are you safe?"

"Yes, I am safe."

"Do you need somewhere to stay?" she continued.

"No. I just want some help with what I am going through."

"I understand; however, we can only support and help you when you have made a decision to leave."

"I can't leave; it's not an option," I said, disappointed. "I just want someone to tell me how I can avoid being hurt."

"There is nothing we can suggest here other than you leave. Statistically, most abusers do not change, and we would advise that for your safety, you find somewhere safe to live. I do hope that you can stay safe."

"Well, thank you for listening," I said, but in the back of my head, I was dissatisfied. I just wanted someone to help me, someone to listen and make my marriage work, and all I was hearing was the opposite.

"You are welcome. Is there anything else I can help you with?" she asked.

"Just one thing: is there anyone else I could speak to about counselling?"

"Yes, sure. Let me email you a list of numbers."

That afternoon, I looked through the list of numbers and support groups that were sent to me over email. There were marriage counsellors, domestic abuse groups, family helplines, but the one that stuck out the most was a free introductory anger management class. Maybe I could entice Syed into this. If we were going to make our marriage work, perhaps he could find ways to control his anger.

*

Syed came home that evening. "Hi, janu," he bellowed from the doorway.

I joined him in the hallway before following him up the stairs.

"How was your day?" I asked, my arms folded awkwardly. I expected a mundane response.

"Good, good. How was yours?" he responded, loosening his tie.

"Yes, it was busy," I said, smiling.

He hung up his suit jacket against the cupboard door to air. I sat on the bed, watching him pull off his socks, undo his trouser button.

"I was just thinking," I said hesitantly, "maybe we should spend more time working things out between us."

"What do you mean?" He looked serious, glancing back at me as he sat on the bed, unbuckling his trousers.

"It was just, what you said last night made me think."

He looked blankly back. "Which bit?"

"Well, you know, about your expectations of me. You know, I want things to work between us. I don't want you to be angry all the time. I don't want us to fight. I want you to feel that you have a wife who you can be with and enjoy everything with. Right now, we are a little like isolated islands: you come back, and you are just playing games the whole evening, and I don't think we really talk unless we are arguing about something. I want us to start speaking to someone and working through our problems together so that we can make this work." I looked at him and held his hand. "I don't want us to be divided in our minds; I want us to be as one, you know, how you said – a 'cocoon'. We should do everything we can to make things work." I looked him straight in the eyes. He looked at me calmly in agreement.

"I love you, janu, you know that? I'll do whatever it takes to improve and make things better." His words were soothing as he wrapped his hands over mine, drawing them into his chest.

I smiled a half smile of appreciation. "So, I had a quick look, and I thought we could maybe try anger management counselling. It might help you understand what makes you angry." I could feel him freeze as he held me, my head resting on his chest.

"I already know what makes me angry; it's you, of course."

I shot him a look.

"But okay, okay," he said. "Why not?" He let go of my hands unexpectedly, turning his back to place his suit jacket on a hanger.

I needed to stay calm: I could tell he disagreed with going and, of course, that from his point of view, there was nothing that he had to change. "We have to start somewhere, Syed. I know there are bad things about us, but there are also good things too."

He smiled and flung his arms over me, edging me over to the bed, then pressing me down onto the bed oppressively and overbearingly.

"I will do anything for my janu, you know that?" His face close to mine as he smiled, pressing the words into me.

I ignored how it felt: there were bigger battles to fight yet, so let's just get past this one.

I rolled to my side. "The next session is on Tuesday evening. Do you think you can make it straight there from the office?"

"It shouldn't be a problem," he said blankly.

"Okay, I will call them and book it in."

*

The following week, we found our way to the community hall where the session was taking place. Syed greeted the other attendees with a firm handshake. A circle of chairs was arranged by all the participants. A grey-haired, academic-looking Englishman stood in the centre to start the session.

"Thank you, everyone, for joining this introductory session. As we all know, anger is present in our lives, and most of us here may have experienced it in some form or another with perhaps someone they know, a loved one or a colleague. And for most of us, anger is both good and bad. It helps us resolve difficulties and can often motivate us to take positive action. I am sure some of us may recall a time when we took positive steps because we were angry about something.

"Unfortunately, this is not true for everyone. A third of people polled say they have a close friend or family member who has trouble controlling their anger, and more than twelve per cent admit they have trouble controlling their own anger.

"Our goal is to lead an anger-free life. Anger is an emotion that the person feeling it can respond to. Often people lose control because they don't know enough to keep their cool. However, they can learn to respond to their anger as unwanted, rather than react to its cause. Forgiveness, for example, is a tool to turn anger off. Getting enough sleep is a tool for preventing anger.

"So, this session is designed to introduce you to anger management. It aims to help you identify your anger and seeks to provide guidance on ways you can control it. Now, as already mentioned, this is an introductory session. When you join the full course, you will learn ways you can achieve an anger-free life and we'll detail these techniques more.

"So, what I want you to do now is join up in pairs if you are not so already, and I want you to pass round a set of cards that helps you identify the main reasons for your anger."

The chairs shuffled as the group passed out the cards.

Syed gave me a dismissive look. "We all know what causes my anger, don't we?" He nodded suggestively at me.

The instructor handed round the cards; on each card was a cause for anger.

"Now, I am going to call out these cards, one by one, and I want you to raise your hand if you feel angry when you are put in these situations. Raise your hand if 'facing a threat to ourselves or our loved ones' would be a situation that makes you angry."

Syed raised his hand.

"How many of you respond angrily if you are verbally or physically assaulted?"

Syed raised his hand again; a few others also raised their hands.

The instructor continued on down the list, and fewer and fewer people raised their hands, until Syed was the only one with his hand up.

The instructor turned to look at Syed with acknowledgement. "Thank you," he said.

"So, we can see there are lots of causes for anger, and you can all relate to anger for some reason or another. So, the first and foremost step was identifying your causes for anger. The next step now is to look at scenarios where you have been angry and what you do in those situations."

The instructor went around the room, asking various participants what they do when they are angry, until it came to Syed's turn.

"So, Syed, yes, give me an example of when you were angry and what you did in that situation."

"Well, I get angry if someone isn't listening, and I normally just shout and tell them I am annoyed."

"I am glad you can identify the anger now. Is there anything you can do to improve the situation?"

"Not really," Syed said. "If there is a reason to be angry, then I feel that if I explain myself, then it should be enough."

I looked at him and thought that it was such an inaccurate view of where I saw his anger. The things he had done, the hurtful and physical pain he had inflicted, and yet even here he was not willing to acknowledge or accept that he had to make any adjustments. *This is going to be hard*, I thought.

The discussion went around the room before the introductory session came to a close.

"Well, that does bring us onto our last stage. When we are angry, there are things we can do to prevent our anger from getting out of control, and while this session is an introductory one, subsequent sessions will help find ways you can take control of your emotions. I will be handing out further leaflets and information if you wish to sign up. Thank you very much for joining us, and I look forward to seeing you on the course."

And with that, Syed headed for the door. "You see," he said, "you are the cause of all these arguments: if you didn't argue with me, if you just listened, then we wouldn't have these problems."

I felt like he had come out of there more empowered, more reinforced, that he had reasons to be angry. More reasons to justify why he behaved the way he did. I sat in the car silently. I didn't see the point: he had made his mind up. He didn't need to fix anything. I was the reason for his bad behaviour, and in his head, I deserved everything I got.

*

The following day I called the Anger Management Association. I wanted to speak to the instructor to see whether there was any advice he could offer.

I dialled the number; a man answered the phone.

"Hi. I was wondering if I could speak to Charles Camden."

"Yes, speaking. Who am I speaking with?"

"Yes, my name is Eleanor. I attended the anger management introductory session yesterday with my husband, Syed."

"Ah, yes, I recall. How can I help?"

"So, I was wondering if there is anything you can do to encourage him, that the sessions and booking the course will help his anger management." Now that I had said it out loud, it sounded all wrong.

"Unfortunately, that is not how it works. Clients have to make the first step with taking control of their anger and wanting to do something about it."

I sighed, coming to terms with his response. There was an awkward silence on the phone as I struggled to work out what to say, and then I blurted it all out.

"You see, my husband gets really angry and violent, and I am not sure what to do or say to improve our marriage and relationship."

"I'm sorry to hear that, and I also have some further bad news on this front: anger management is very different from violent behaviour and requires specialised skills to treat this type of behaviour. If it were to just assist with his anger, there are methods and practices that can help him. However, physical violence is a whole different matter, and a lengthy process of correcting. The person also has to actively want to change. Most people wanting to change go through a full eighteen-month to two-year programme, and even then, the outcome is not guaranteed."

My heart sank. How could people not correct their behaviour? Was this so deeply ingrained into a person's psyche?

"You see, it's hard work, and, er, it would take a lot of commitment from the client. I can give you a number for the association that deals with this programme, if this helps."

I was too overwhelmed to answer the question properly.

"No, er, I doubt that will be an option," I said vaguely.

"The only thing I would suggest to you is to remain safe. Your safety and welfare are important."

Haven't I heard that before? I thought.

"Well, thank you for your help, and thank you for the introductory session yesterday."

"You are welcome, and thank you for calling."

I put the receiver down and rested back into the chair. What was I going to do now? I had thought we could work things out, that somehow the violence would end and that this would offer hope, that things would change. Was this going to be the rest of my life? How was I going to live like this? I just had to accept his flaws and continue being beaten up. I nearly cried, but my tears just stopped midway.

There had to be some way to keep this marriage going without all the atrocities, and why did everyone keeping asking whether I was safe? Did they not understand this was not helping me? I was trapped. I was trapped in this horrible situation with nothing but the feeling of danger with every step I took and every tiny drop of wrong that was encountered in our relationship.

I felt sick. A wave of nausea erupted inside me. It felt like a surge of heat rising up inside, and I vomited into the office bin. My stomach churned. I felt tired. *What a horrible idea*, I thought, *to think this is the rest of my life and there are no solutions to fix Syed.* I couldn't understand why they couldn't help him and me.

I walked up to my room and lay on the bed. I lay there wondering what I could do to improve things, and each time, a wave of nausea rose up from my belly and into my throat. I felt a sudden, sharp pain in my abdomen and then moved swiftly to the bathroom, where I threw up once again. *I must be getting my period*, I thought. It felt like a brooding period pain.

Wait a minute, I thought. My head suddenly raced through today's date. I ran back downstairs to my computer and looked at my email calendar. *When was the last time I had my period?* I thought. *When, when, when?* I looked through, trying to trace back the days. *It was a week before the horrible sex*, I thought. A sudden panic awakened my body. It had been five weeks. *Oh my gosh, I am late!*

CHAPTER THIRTY-SEVEN
– Letting Go–

I *have never been late, I said to myself. I normally get my period every three weeks, so this can't be it, I thought. No, it can't, it can't.*

I grabbed my coat from the hallway and rummaged through my bag for my purse. It was 3 p.m., so I just hoped Syed wouldn't call, as he would spot-check to see whether I was at home every couple of hours. I took a quick and steady pace to the pharmacy, trying to calm myself. *I really hope this is nothing; this might be nothing. It could just be a miscalculation. I have been really stressed. People miss their periods all the time, don't they?*

I arrived at the pharmacy, and an Indian lady stood behind the counter.

"Hello. How can I help you?" she said, raising her head.

"Oh, just looking at the moment," I said, flustered. My eyes scoured the shop, looking for a pregnancy test. I paced the floor down the length of the aisle. It was a small shop, and I felt relieved I was the only one in it.

The lady looked at me again. "Anything in particular I can help you with, dear?"

I didn't want her to ask; I just wanted to be left alone, and now I would have to ask her. "Er, do you know where I can get a pregnancy test?"

She looked at me. "Yes, dear, just over on the aisle with the vitamins to your left."

"Okay, sure, thank you," I said, trying not to look at her. I walked over to the aisle, and much to my frustration, she followed me over. *Oh God, just leave me alone,* I thought.

"It's just here, dear. There are two types: one contains two tests, and the other just the one."

"Okay, thank you. I will take the one."

"That will be eight ninety-nine," she said. "Would you like a bag?"

"No. I mean, yes, please." These were questions that I couldn't process, but I didn't want anyone to see the test.

She thrust open a carrier bag. "Is it for yourself?" she asked.

Hmm, now, she is nosy, I thought. "Yes," I said.

"You know, if you go to the doctor, they can give you a free test; it won't cost you anything."

"I will keep that in mind," I said. "Thank you." I covered my head and raced back.

It was 3.15 p.m. now, and there were children with their mothers racing home. I thought to myself that they seemed happy and perfectly normal; perhaps that could also be me soon. I walked into the house and closed the door.

"Hello-o-o-o," came a faint voice.

Oh no, Sufyan is home, I thought. "Salam, Sufyan," I said, racing into the ground-floor toilet.

"Waalaikumsalam, Bhabhi." I could hear him making his way down the stairs.

Oh gosh, I thought. *I really don't want him to know I have a pregnancy test.*

I quickly walked in, locking the door behind me. I opened the box hastily, peeling off the film. I read the instructions, although my franticness meant not reading it properly. I just had to pee on a stick and wait a few minutes.

Many thoughts raced through my head as I waited. *It can't be. Where and how? We have only been married a few months, and people wait years before something like this happens. Come on, come on*, I thought.

A line came up, and I was relieved: one line meant negative; two lines meant positive. I waited, the wet trace slowly moved over the line, and then the unthinkable happened. The wet patch slowly emerged with two red lines. "Oh no, this can't be. I have read it wrong. Maybe I have it mixed up. How could I be pregnant? No, it can't be!" I cried.

I looked at the box, reread the instructions. I was pregnant. The instructions matched positively. "Oh no." My heart raced and panicked. "Oh, this can't be possible. How? When? Why?" I felt like crying.

Just then I heard Sufyan.

"Bhabhi!" he yelled. "Would you like a cup of tea? I am making one," he called out from the living room up the stairs.

"Er, yes," I called back. "Oh gosh, oh gosh," I whispered. "What do I do? What do I do? How do I make this not obvious? I need to hide the packaging." I ripped up the box and rolled it into a round toilet roll. I then wrapped it up in toilet roll. I pushed it down into the bin and covered it up with more toilet roll. *Oh gosh, what if Ammujee empties the bins?* I thought. I took the bin bag out of the bin and then emptied it into the main bin out on the driveway. I tied the ends tightly and looked at myself in the mirror, calming myself down. I smiled as I walked through the hallway.

"Salam, Sufyan. How are you?" I said, slightly pale and tired.

"Waalaikumsalam, Bhabhi. Yeah, good thanks, Bhabhi. Your tea is just here."

"Oh, thanks, Sufyan." I sat down, slouching into the living-room sofa, seated opposite him, still slightly in a daze.

"How was your day, Bhabhi?"

A whole myriad of thoughts ignited in my head, and my heart throbbed, pulsating down every limb. I could hear the sound of fear in my temples and through my sinuses.

"Oh, you know, I don't think I am feeling too well; I must be coming down with something," I said, shaking my head. I wished I could tell him. I wished I could tell somebody what was going on. The temptation was rife to let it all out, and if he had pressed me enough, I might just have done.

He looked at me, a little concerned. "I must say, you look a little pale, to be honest, Bhabhi. Did you have anything to eat? Ammujee's always telling me you don't eat enough."

"Eat?" I thought for a second. "No, actually, I haven't yet."

"No wonder, then, Bhabhi," he laughed. "It's nearly four o'clock."

"That's true." I laughed in disbelief that I had completely forgotten all about lunch. "Oh, well, I will wait now until dinner. There is no point in cooking something up now." I just needed time to think. I didn't want to be there sitting with him, and at the same time, I longed for some normality and comfort.

"So, what do you think of that book I gave you to read?" he asked.

"Oh, yes, it's been spiritually enlightening. It has helped me bring a lot of calmness to my soul," I said, nodding nervously.

He looked at me, smiling. "You could have fooled me with that frown across your eyebrows," he said, looking at me.

"Sorry," I said, looking down. "Not feeling the best today. I think I might go up and read namaz [prayers]."

"Yes, I best too. It's getting very close to maghrib [evening prayer]."

I washed in readiness for prayer and sat on the prayer mat. I thought about what all this meant. *Why now? We have only been married five months. What are people going to think? They will laugh at us, most likely, at the idea that we are having a baby so soon.* I thought about how he would react. He would probably be happy, considering that this would lock me down further. Then I thought about how quickly my life was becoming more and more like Mamajee's life. She was stuck in a loveless marriage with kids. *Maybe this will improve things, though, with Syed,* I contemplated. His parents would be thrilled, of course. It might make our relationship more stable, having a new person in our life. I thought about what it would be like to have a baby with him, in this house, around his family, how much care and attention he or she would have. Ammujee would make a great grandmother, I could imagine.

But then a horrible grey cloud cast over these thoughts. *What if he continues to beat me? What if next time it goes too far, and I hit my head? Who would look after me? Who would look after my child? Could I rely on Syed? And the worst of this, what if I end up in divorce? Would I be able to raise this child alone?* I felt nausea. *I can't have this child. I just can't see how we could make this work!*

It was now 4.30 p.m., and I needed to get my head together on this. But I had no time to think. My in-laws would be home soon.

*

I stood leaning over a chair at the dining-room table. I smiled at Ammujee, who had just made her way past me into the kitchen with a handful of bags. They had all come home from work, and I had set the table already for dinner. I followed her into the kitchen, trying to see whether I could help her.

"Anything I can help with?" I asked.

"No, no, Eleanor. You have done enough, poor thing. You set the table all by yourself? I hope Sufyan helped." She had a way of praising me as if I were a little child.

I turned to look at him, and he replied honestly.

"Sorry, Ammu, Bhabhi did everything. I came down from prayer, and she had set everything up."

"Oh, you silly boy. You know I ask you to look after your bhabhi when you are at home."

"Sorry, Ammujee. You do know Bhabhi said she isn't feeling well, and she hasn't eaten."

"No! What do you mean you haven't you eaten?" she said, horrified. "The whole day? My goodness, how do you survive on such little food, dear? Come, come and sit. I bought some fresh parathas from Manju's on the way home. That should put some meat on you."

"Yeah, Bhabhi will blow up in no time on those," Sufyan said mockingly.

"Stop," I said. I nudged him gently.

"Bhabhi, I think you best start eating!"

"I will if you all join. I won't eat on my own."

"Where's Syed?" Ammujee asked, looking towards the door. "I didn't hear from him today. It's almost six thirty," she said.

"I am not sure," I said. Secretly, though, I hadn't even thought that far. Engrossed in the events happening inside me, I hadn't even stopped to think. She took a plate and placed it over the serving of food she'd set aside for him.

"Well, I guess we can warm it up for him when he gets in."

Abbujee joined the table, having finished his prayers upstairs.

"Assalamualaikum, everyone," he said with a stern voice.

"Waalaikumsalam, Abbujee," I said, covering my head.

"Did you have a good day?" he asked.

I could have cried, but I looked down at the table and nodded. "Jee, Abbujee, yes, I had a good day. How was your day, Abbujee?" I replied calmly.

"Yes, it was good. Things are busy at the charity: we are meeting with some new heads who may have some improvements for how we run the community groups."

The conversation flow was relaxed and normal, and I started to ease a little more.

"Did you hear? Eleanor didn't eat," Ammujee declared to Abbujee.

"Oh dear, you can't do that. You must be eating. It's bad for your health. It can lead to many gastric problems, diabetes and all sorts." It startled me to think this had become a concern, a topic of conversation, when my physical form was subjected to much more severe forms of abuse and punishment.

"That's because she doesn't eat ice cream all day like you do, Mamajee," Sufyan said, teasing Ammujee from the kitchen as he entered with some dessert plates to place on the dining table.

"Oh, I eat ice cream all day, is that right?" she said mockingly at the exaggeration.

I looked at her bright smile as she laughed out loud and as they continued to make fun at Ammujee's love of ice cream.

Abbujee chimed in. "You do know this about your mother-in-law, don't you? After work," he said between mouthfuls, "she can't resist stopping by the ice-cream van just outside her office."

Ammujee laughed a hearty laugh, which felt immediately uplifting and distracting from the brooding nausea circling my stomach. One would have only seen a charming lady. A positive, witty, flawless conversationalist. You would never see her angry and upset at anything, even when you thought she should be rightfully disappointed. It was Ammujee who always took the high road. I felt very much at ease around her. It filled me with warmth.

This will be okay, I thought, coaching myself. *Ammujee will be here, and so will Abbujee, so what should I really worry about? Ammujee will support me through this; she would make a great grandma. And Abbujee, he is just as strong and supportive, and Sufyan, well, for someone so young, I am amazed at the moral support he has provided me with without realising. Maybe I can do this. Maybe I can do this! Maybe I don't need to worry about anything. It will be okay. Everything will be okay.*

It suddenly appealed to me; I felt warm and fuzzy. My belly soft and brooding with slight pulling tensions every so often. *I am going to have a baby!* I thought excitedly. *Oh, this will be such a great life for this baby; such great grandparents and an uncle you will have. And your abbujee, well, you will love him too, as he will be great for you.* I felt this warm glow from the centre of my belly. It rippled all the way out from my abdomen like a warm ball of love.

Then it all dissipated. The door slammed hard, shuddering the windowpanes, and we all jumped a little with the sudden noise.

"Where were you?"

I turned my back from the seat, and there stood Syed, his face confrontational and disappointed. I knew that look; it meant, "I am not going to hear what you say, so you better just accept what I am about to do to you."

Everybody around the table sat silently.

"Where were you?" he asked again.

I pretended I didn't know what he was talking about. It was embarrassing in front of Sufyan and his parents. "I don't know. When? Which bit are you talking about?" I said, puzzled.

"I called Sufyan this afternoon, and he said you weren't home." His face was full of anger. I should have realised every move I made would be scrutinised.

"I went for a walk," I said, looking puzzled.

"Where?" he demanded.

I should have known better, but I told him the truth. "I just went across the road to the pharmacy." *Oh God! Quick, tell me what to say*, I thought.

"Oh! What for?" he demanded as everyone sat around the table, listening to the exchange.

I took a deep breath to look at Ammujee. I didn't want to explain any more than I had.

Luckily, she interjected. "Syed, I am sure you can talk about this later; you haven't even taken your coat off, and dinner is going cold. Go, go on, go and get freshened up."

He glared at Ammujee, resenting the condescension, and breathed in, tutting. "Yeah, okay, Ammujee. I wasn't talking to you. I was talking to my wife, wasn't I?" he shouted at her, glaring at me one last time before walking upstairs.

Ammujee didn't like that one bit and gave a look of disapproval at his tone and disrespect. I just hoped it was enough of a diversion on the inquisition I would face later. Syed turned to look at me and paced a few steps backwards, still glaring at me before heading upstairs.

I started helping with the tidying and clearing and tried to keep my calm. The tone and atmosphere suddenly felt awkward for everyone. I hoped he didn't want to see a receipt or the item. Ammujee continued to make small talk, almost taking no notice of Syed's behaviour.

"What did you think of those parathas? Manju always makes the best." She smiled.

"Yes, Ammujee. They were very nice," I said. "I ate well."

"Ate well? Hmm, I can't see that. I still see everything on your plate." She smiled.

"I ate as much as I could," I said with a half-smile. It was the best I could do amongst the fear and commotion. I could sense a fight coming on, and I was feeling nervous. And she knew it. It was another one of those moments that she didn't want to acknowledge, because bringing it up would break up this wonderful portrait she had painstakingly crafted.

Ammujee and Abbujee were flawless in that respect. They never gave anything away for free. When it came to reputation, prestige, the face of the community, they took centre stage in Bengali high society. In the eyes of the people around them, they never had arguments, they never had conflicts, they never had a bad word to say about anyone. Ammujee would have impeccable clothes. She always wore conservative silk sarees that were simple and elegant. They were always neatly hemmed so that the folds of the saree were always even and fell into place. Ammujee always had neatly combed hair that was parted to the side and tied into a round bun. She was very fair, again quite rare for Bengali women.

The only time you wouldn't see her smile was when there was a need to show compassion and concern. She indeed was a compassionate lady. She was always two steps ahead of the planning, or priming herself for anything. If we had a dinner invite, Ammujee would have worked out exactly what she wanted me to wear, everything from my shoes, bag, earrings, bangles, rings, saree, petticoats, scarfs. I felt like I was part of the Ammujee, Abbujee Corporation brand. Turning up to any dinner invites was not just a social occasion, it was hours of public relations that led to their impeccable reputation. She would dress me in conservative sarees, which were normally similar to her mature, plain silk sarees. Then she would rummage through my large cupboard full of red velvet boxes that contained auspicious and generously gifted gold jewellery from the many guests at our wedding. For every dinner invite, she would carefully select the pieces of jewellery I should wear. It would normally be the ones given by the inviter. The bangles then had to match the saree. The rings for my fingers were then placed on my hands, mostly again gifted from those who were hosting the dinner party. My shoes had to match as best as they could with the rest of the outfit, but the main item was that they were tall, to make me look more elegant. She would then select a scarf that would be equally fitting with the rest of the outfit but would give an air of grace to my position as a new bride. I was a new bride, and people would always be judging every move I made.

In Ammujee's eyes, a woman's reputation could be so easily tarnished by one false move, and without spelling it out, this was embodied by outward appearance, by the things she laid out for me to wear and every move or whisper I made. After she had dressed me in all the finery, she would then begin the preparation work on who I would be meeting and what I would be doing or saying. She would explain who the gifts were from and who I would need to thank for the gifts. It was customary to bow at the feet of seniors who were present at the dinner party. It was important that I kept my saree veil pulled over my head, and to prevent it from falling, it should be pinned into my bun. She would normally help me with this just before leaving the house. I would have to be mindful of who I talked to, and what I talked about. Any affairs of the house were out of the question, of course, but there were also things that became engulfed into this boundary, such as where I worked, what I worked as, whether I had lived at home or lived outside. The fact that I travelled with work, the fact that I drove a car by myself. These were items I was not allowed to make mention of. Anything, to be honest, would be under scrutiny around these people. And in their opinion, if it were under scrutiny, then it would be hazardous to their reputation.

That night, after dinner and after washing and tidying up, I made my way upstairs to our room. I had felt the warmth of my growing embryo, and for a brief moment, folding away my laundry, it made me smile.

"What are you smiling about?" came Syed's stern voice from behind. He was looking at me through the reflection of the wardrobe mirror. His arm firmly gripped around my shoulder and wrapped around my neck into a soft locked position. In his mind, he was being affectionate. But it felt controlling, the headlock. His grip was firm, and it made my face rise up to the ceiling. "Hmm?" He kissed my ear. "What are you smiling about, janu?" he insisted again. He rocked me from behind, squeezing his groin into my lower back while the crook of his arm locked around my neck.

I tried not to make anything of this. I tried to convince myself that he was being playful, that his assertion was affection. I leaned into him more to show my mutual desire. No sooner had I melted into this embrace than I felt my head hit the bed, my neck jolting back from the force of the impact. I turned to face him on the bed. He was standing there, towering over me from the side of the bed. His face was fierce, but there was a sick smile to it. For my own sanity, I continued to deny it, as if it would ward off danger and appease the situation. I looked at him. "Are you coming to bed?" I tried to smile. Showing fear would only be treated as bait.

He shook his head. He wasn't buying it; it wasn't enticing enough. "You are a silly girl, do you know that?"

I sat awkwardly, edging to the other side of the bed to avoid his imposing and overbearing body language.

"Tell me where the FUCK you went this afternoon!" he yelled into my face, pushing me into the bed.

"Nowhere. I just went to the pharmacy," I said, trying to stay calm.

"You are a fucking liar!" he shouted into my face, and then he grabbed a wire coat hanger and reached it high into the air above my face. It came pounding down.

I closed my eyes. "No!" I screamed. It whacked my face, but I moved quickly, turning my side. He continued to beat the hanger on the bed, throwing it against the wall, then kicking me with full force off the bed. I lay there on the floor.

"Don't you dare fucking leave the house without my prior knowledge," he said, leaning over the bed and towering over me. My heart was pounding, my head in disarray, and my face stinging from the thrash of the wire hanger. I fell silent. He turned and walked out of the room, slamming the door behind.

I cried, looking at myself in the mirror, picking up my brittle back from the floor. I was gutted, not from the pain, not from the words, not from the mistreatment and the false accusations, but from what this all meant.

It meant I couldn't keep this baby; I had to leave this idea behind that I could bring a baby up in this world and give it the future it deserved. No matter how much I loved being around his family at times, they would never see this grandchild. The idea that I had to let this go was a devastating blow. If I were to be responsible for this child, I would have to give it everything I had to also be secure. I had to be safe. Here I was, standing, looking at a woman who, on the face of it all, had everything one person could have in Bengali society – reputation, a seemingly charming husband, a wonderful brother-in-law – and yet underneath the guise had nothing. I could be likened to a statue of perfection made of rubble. On the surface, it was beautiful, but only with one touch would it crumble to dust. How could I bring this child into a world like this? And would I really want to raise a child with these values and ideas? I would be perpetuating circumstances, what Mamajee faced and what her mother faced. As a woman in this generation, with the opportunities available, should I need to relent to such a life? Or was it fear that led even the strongest of us to follow and please, and be cut out from a template that our parents' culture had crafted and used generation after generation? The truth was that I was living Mamajee's life, not mine. Unlike Mamajee though, I wasn't proud of it. Mamajee had the war medals and wore them with pride. She had the battle scars; she had the birth marks mounted on her belly for every child born to her. She resisted all temptations to leave, and I owed her my life for that. I thought about whether I would do that to my own daughter, whether I could in time inflict such guilt, and shame her into the life I once had. Would that be me in the future? Were these the values I wanted to stand by for the rest of my life? I had to make a decision about my life and where I wanted to go. Was I going to choose a life here, persecuted by Syed and raising a child, or did I rise above my fears and give this false, delusional reality up for the authentic and real version of me?

*

I woke up in the morning, staring emptily at the ceiling. Syed had already left for work. *I could just walk out and leave, couldn't I?* I thought as I looked at the door. How many mornings had I let that thought run through my mind, only to unconvince myself? "But then what?" I would say. "I would be homeless then. No, I can't do that!" And my mind only resonated that I could no longer leave, because now I had no choice because I was pregnant.

I argued with myself for a while, then rose up and suddenly felt nausea. I raced quickly to the toilet. A large dose of vomit dropped straight into the toilet bowl, and my stomach churned as it compiled more. The mirror reflected a pale and undesirable version of me. I could feel some relief that there were no marks on my face from the night before, but the muscles around my neck felt sore. I wanted to go back and lie down. There was a low, brooding pain again, like a period pain, which made me feel hopeful that I might still get a period and this would all be over. It was a constant wave, which had the same low intensity.

I brushed my teeth and freshened my mouth, trying to clear it of the sour taste, and went back to lie on the bed. I thought about what I was going to do about this situation. Part of me wanted to pretend it hadn't happened, that the pregnancy test was wrong and that my period would come at any moment. I could just go on existing here in this house, with everyone acting picture-perfect. But then … then there was a side of me that just couldn't leave it like this. This would have devastating consequences for my baby and me. What if I died? What would happen to my child? How would I raise this child if I was living on my own?

Confounded by thoughts, I put it to rest and signed in to the office laptop to check my emails. I noticed Andrea was online, so I gave her a call through the office phone. The phone rang, and I eagerly awaited her to pick up.

"Hi, Andrea."

"Hi, hon!" she said with a shrill and excited voice.

"How are you?" I said, trying to get the conversation going.

"Ye-e-e-eah! Good," she said. "Enjoying Farmouth, loving it down here! How are you? How are things with you and Syed?" Her tone lowered towards the end of the question.

"Well," I said hesitantly.

"Eleanor! Come on! You are not pregnant, are you?"

It was like she had read my mind and taken the words out of my mouth. I couldn't deny it.

"Oh my gosh, Andrea, please don't tell anyone," I begged her. The secret was out, and now I worried about what she was going to say.

"Eleanor ... you are not keeping it, are you?"

"Well, I don't know," I said.

"Eleanor, no-o-o!" she said, horrified. "You can't; you can't do this. No, absolutely not, Eleanor. Not with this guy. Eleanor, he beats you up. What kind of life are you going to lead?"

I sat and listened, silenced by her question. I knew there was nothing I could disagree with.

"Andrea, I am really scared."

"Who wouldn't be? Of course, it's scary, Eleanor. This is not just about you anymore, is it? What happens that one day he beats you up so badly you can't even look after your child? How would you live with that?"

"I know, Andrea, I know."

"Eleanor, please, do you want me to come up? I can help you sort this out. Please, I don't think you should have this baby. This is not the right thing to do."

I paused, thinking. "I know, Andrea. I just don't know how I can bring myself to do this."

"Just call the doctor and make an appointment. Tell them this is urgent," she instructed with a shrill voice. I could see this frustrated her.

"And then do what, Andrea?" I asked.

She sighed impatiently. "Oh, Eleanor, you need to get a check-up and a referral from a doctor to an abortion clinic. Look, just get the appointment sorted, and then call me back when it's safe. Can you do that?"

I had frozen from fear, and it was almost like she knew it. Sometimes my friends were the only ones who knew me well enough. They knew I was in a vulnerable place, and they knew they had to make the decisions for me. I had full trust in Andrea, that she was saying the right things.

"Okay, Andrea, I will. I will call the doctor and book an appointment."

"Oh, Eleanor, I am really sorry you are going through all this. I know it is really tough. I just can't let you do this to yourself, not yet. It will be for the best, you know that, right? It is just so hard to make that call. I know because I have been through it myself, remember? It was hard; it was emotionally tough, but sometimes this is the right decision to make."

"Thank you, Andrea, and yes, I know you know. Let me call you back once I have called the doctor."

"Okay, hon. Speak to you soon."

I put the phone down and started to cry. I felt so bad about what was going on. I felt like the world had closed in on me. There was a terrible, emotional wanting for this baby, and a feeling this baby would make everything right. And on the other side, how irresponsible it would be if I left this to chance, that it would all work out. I felt selfish, as if I should persevere and make the most out of this situation, and not just bail out. I was angry with Syed: the bastard wouldn't let me take contraceptive pills. A couple of months after a row, he had wanted to know why I was taking the pill when we were married now, anyway. My hormones were now sending me into a rage over this thought. It felt wrong whichever way I turned, but the most significant question that put it all to rest was this: what if I had this baby, and then he hurt me so badly that I wouldn't be able to look after my baby? Then what would I do? The conclusion was that I couldn't predictably and stably look after myself and keep myself safe, so how would I be able to protect someone else? He was not the right person, and perhaps the option of having a child is only available to those who can answer these questions: can we protect ourselves? Are we safe? Because if we are not, then how can we protect those dependent on us?

I stopped staring at the wall and then looked over at my phone. It felt clear now. I called the doctor and booked an appointment.

*

The appointment wasn't for a couple of days, which meant I had to find ways of disguising the reason for the sudden check-up. After all, anything I did around Syed and his family seemed to arouse suspicion.

Since I had only joined the clinic, I gave Syed the reason for needing to attend the clinic for registration purposes and that they normally carried out a routine health check at the same time. He seemed okay with that.

"Do you want me to drop you off?" he asked, concerned.

The irony of his concern, I thought. *After he has just beaten me only a couple of days ago*. But this was the recovery period now in our relationship. The part where he felt bad for his knee-jerk reaction. It was the part his love and affection for me came out in barrels of sweetened honey, enough to intoxicate and lure me back into his offer of a relationship.

"No, don't worry," I said. "You will be late for work. It is just a check-up, anyway," I said, nodding at him.

His hands were fixed onto my shoulders, and a calm and concerned look graced his face. I only wished that I saw this side of him all the time. *Why is he so inconsistent?* I thought. He looked at me, trying to read anything else that I might be hiding, and what could possibly be maliciously intended. However, his look of concern was calming. I almost wanted to give in to him and tell him. That way, I'd have a clear conscience, but my mind came back to the reality. *This can't happen*, I said to myself.

"Okay," he said finally, after pausing a while.

"I will call you when I am back," I said, relieved that it hadn't gone any further.

I drove to see the doctor that morning, the throbbing, dull waves of pain swarming my navel intermittently. I thought about whether this was the right thing to do, to keep it a secret. I worried about what would happen if they were to ever find out. I would be beaten up by Syed for sure; inch by inch, he would make sure there was nothing left of me. The rest of them would judge me for being callous, inhumane, selfish. Ammujee would silently disown me. She would probably pretend like nothing had happened but make it known through her calm expression and tone that there was something she was not happy with. The silent treatment, like entering an invisible torture chamber. You were in the wrong, and they weren't ever going to give anything away about how they felt about your offence. Instead, they would take you prisoner in your head and feed you with guilt. "More tea, my lovely daughter-in-law?" You were always at their disposal this way. They could hold you accountable without trial. I knew all this; I knew I was in for hard times if they found out. I was shackled either way, and there would always be a price to pay, whichever choice I made.

I walked into the waiting room nervously. It was a tired-looking room with worn-out brown polypropylene carpet, the kind that curls up around the edges. Dotted along the weary walls were faded-out posters of various NHS services. A few patients were waiting in the room. They had all taken a quick glance at me and gone back to their world of waiting-room boredom. I edged nearer to the reception desk.

"Hi. How can I help you?" came a voice from behind the reception counter. She was a chubby lady about Mrs Abbots's age, with a comforting face.

I wish she were Mrs Abbots now, I thought for a split second. *Maybe she could sit me down and comfort me and tell me that everything will be okay.*

"Hi," I said, my voice coming out small and weak. I desperately tried to make it sound normal. "I have an appointment with Dr Ingram."

"Yes, we have you down for nine-fifteen. Take a seat; he will be with you shortly."

He? I thought. *Oh God, what if he wants to check inside me? I would rather it was a woman.* That was the least of my problems, I continued in my head. *What am I going to say or do about this situation?* My soul felt like a little ball, beating around, trying to find a way out of the trapped carcass. A pulse pounded in my head, my chest, down to my tingling feet and into my nauseous throat. I would tell the doctor everything, so if I died from Syed finding out and killing me, then they would at least have it on record.

My heart sank as I remembered Mamajee's famous words, *dead than divorced.* They echoed again through my hollow existence, down to the well of pain slowly rising up to my throat. I could feel the tears welling up at the back of my eyes. *They don't care. They wouldn't care. They would probably think it would be justifiable if they found out I had had an abortion,* I thought to myself. Then I continued playing out their words. *Why, of course he should want to beat you up. You had an abortion. You betrayed him.*

They weren't going to support me either way. I was as good as dead being married. They had given me away, and their duties were done. My fate now rested with my new family. I hadn't spoken to Mamajee in weeks. I had made every excuse not to. I didn't hate her; I wasn't angry with her comment, but there was a realisation of my fate that I couldn't bring myself to deal with. I was dead either way I looked at my life. I was dead if I was divorced, and I was dead living in this soulless existence. I cowered into the cave of my existence and surrendered to it with a deep breath. The sound of my breath, the only sound that offered any physical respite.

"Eleanor Hamid," echoed a voice in the waiting room. It was strange being called out by my marital name. Syed had insisted on it being changed on the medical forms, of course.

I rose from my seat and followed the doctor to his surgery room.

"Take a seat," he said, taking a quick glance at my records. He looked like he was in his late thirties.

I sat down.

"Now, how can I help you?" he said tersely.

"I think I am pregnant," I said, haunted by the idea that I was going to deliver more bad news.

"Okay, and how do you know?" he said, taking notes.

"I am late, and I took a pregnancy test, which came out positive."

"Okay, and when was the date of your last period?"

"I think it was the ninth of October."

He looked at his calendar and counted down the weeks. "So, you must be about four or five weeks pregnant. Okay, so very early days. Any nausea, vomiting?"

"Yes, a little."

He checked my blood pressure. "Your blood pressure seems a little low. Do you feel light-headed?"

"Yes, a little," I said.

"Are you eating well? Sleeping well?"

I paused. It was just so comforting to feel some genuine concern. "No, not really."

"Any reason for that?" he asked, making notes.

And then I broke down in front of him, feeling suddenly stupid at how vulnerable I felt.

"Let me get you a tissue," he said procedurally.

He handed me a tissue from a box and waited for me to get my breath. "It's okay; take your time."

I took a deep breath and sighed. "I can't have this baby."

He nodded with clinical acceptance. "And have you thought about what you wish to do in that case? Are you looking for adoption, abortion?"

I nodded. "Abortion."

"Okay," he said softly, as though he already knew the underlying reasons.

"And is there any reason for looking at terminating the pregnancy?"

"My husband is very violent, and I can't see how I could proceed."

He wrote it down and then looked up at me. I was hoping for something at this point, some comment or reaction, but he carried on with the next steps as if it had just been standard questioning. I felt like I was running out of time with him.

"Okay, very well. I will have to refer you to an abortion clinic, where they will carry out the procedure. I will fill out this form, and I will need to get a signature from another doctor before I can refer you."

"Okay," I said.

"If you bear with me one moment, I will check the other doctor is available." He then walked out of the surgery room to find the other doctor. I stared blankly at the floor, waiting and hoping that he could get this signed off. He came back with another middle-aged doctor, with dark hair and dark-rimmed glasses, who promptly sat down.

"I hear you are looking to seek a termination?"

I nodded.

"Can I ask your reason for the termination?"

"I can't support this baby in my current relationship."

"I see." He turned to the other doctor while signing the forms. "You have taken the other notes?" he asked Dr Ingram.

"Yes, I have them all here," he responded.

"Yes, then, I have no further questions and can leave the rest to you, Dr Ingram."

"Thank you, Doctor," he responded as the other doctor left the room.

"Okay," he said, turning his chair to face me. "You need to contact this clinic and take the forms with you on the day of your appointment."

Oh gosh, I really hope nobody sees these at home, I thought.

*

When I arrived home, I called the clinic. I hid the notes in amongst a folder full of my old statements. I arranged an appointment date for a weekday; the earliest was in a couple of weeks. I could only hope that I could hold out until then.

I then called Andrea to tell her about my visit.

The phone rang, and she answered immediately. "Did you do it?" she asked cautiously.

"Yes," I said. "I have an appointment in a couple of weeks."

"Okay, good," she said, emptying a bellyful of air down the phone.

"How am I going to get to this clinic, Andrea? It's in central London. What am I going to say about where I am? I am going to need a few hours."

"Hmm, good question." She thought. "Could you pretend to be away?"

"No. Where would I go for half a day?"

"Why don't you say you are going to your gran's house? She lives not too far, right? We can go to the clinic first, then I will drop you there."

"What if my gran asks why you are there?" I said.

"Well, we will just tell them I have come to see a client and was in the area."

"Okay. Hmm, it might work."

"You seem worried, Eleanor," she said.

"I am. I don't think anyone understands what I am dealing with here. If he gets an inkling of suspicion, then he will hurt me."

"We have to get to that clinic, Eleanor. Just drive to your gran's. I will meet you there. We will then drive to the clinic in my car. I will drop you back there when we are done, and you can stay with your family for a little while. How does that sound?"

"Thanks, Andrea. I hope he will let me go. Thank you for helping me sort this out; I just feel a lot better having some support."

"I know. I know how difficult this is, but we will get through it, okay?"

I just had to figure out a way that I could broach the subject of going to see my gran. This wasn't going to go down well with him, I was sure. I sat and worried, preparing all the words, calculating all his responses and conjuring up my responses. I was so tired I felt like my eyes were not peeling open.

I sat and pondered how this would come together, until I couldn't work it out anymore. I decided to think about something else for a while. It was almost midday, and it already felt dark outside. I thought about what Ammujee and Abbujee would like for dinner. I went downstairs to the kitchen cupboard and saw a large bag of rice flour. Mamajee used to always make rice flour chapattis for Babajee, and they were one of the most delicious dishes that she would make for him. It was rare for her to make them, as they took quite some time and preparation to put together. I thought it might be a nice treat for Ammujee and Abbujee after their long day at work.

I began preparing the dough and spent the whole afternoon rolling out endless balls of dough into rice chapattis. It gave me a sense of relief from everything that was playing on my mind. This was going to be difficult and risky, I thought. I just hoped I could pull it off.

CHAPTER THIRTY-EIGHT
– *The Innocent Departed*–

The door slammed, causing the mirror on the kitchen wall to sway. Syed had arrived home.

I kept myself busy, flouring out rice chapattis in the kitchen. Being busy kept some distance between us. I heard the pounding of his feet up the stairs; it sounded angry. I wanted to broach my visit to see my gran and knew it would warm up his mood if I cooked. Such pleasures men took in seeing a woman behave subserviently. The power and control one gains from having someone at one's disposal. If that was all it needed though, then I wanted him to relish in it. No sooner had I finished baking the crispy rice pancakes than I served it up to the lord above me.

I came into the darkened bedroom, a plate of curry and chapattis in one hand and a glass of water in the other. There were clothes thrown on the bed, and beneath the mountain of covers lay the grizzling beast. I could not see his face and had no idea what would erupt from below the surface.

"Are you okay, darling?" I asked endearingly.

"I am tired," came the response from under the duvet.

"Oh? I thought so. It's very unlike you, poor darling. You mustn't be feeling well."

My insides resisted lulling him in this way, but I was desperate. I needed to get to this clinic without him knowing.

"I, er, have something here for you," I said, inviting him to look.

He lifted the covers now, looking a little bleary-eyed at me. "What is it?" he said, raising himself a little from the bed.

I lifted the cover from the plate of warm curry and rice flour chapattis. "They are fresh baked, crispy rice flour chapattis, with beef and potato curry. Here, this will warm you up a little. Just take it easy and sit and eat here."

If only I had laced it with a laxative or something, I thought. I was seething internally, watching him take pleasure; he must have been getting high on this.

"Thank you, janu. Oh, you are so beautiful, do you know that?" he croaked with a pained expression. "Hmm, come, come sit next to me."

I did as requested and perched on the bed with the plate of food on the bedside table. I broke the chapattis, folding up the pieces with curried meat and potatoes, and fed him. I would have liked to have stuffed it down his throat so that he choked. If only he knew how weak he was.

"Mmm, delicious. I can't believe you did all of this by yourself," he said, rolling the chapatti in his mouth and licking his lips.

I sat silently, feeding his hungry, fat face as he scoffed it up like some greedy, hungry pig, leaning into the plate. I didn't hesitate to offer him more. *Eat, oh lovely, hungry pig*, I thought. You could hear the Bengali man's grunt, chewing the gristle from the meat in his mouth. This was still not the right time to talk about this. I would broach it later. He might still get confrontational if I made such demands about visiting my gran.

*

That night I climbed into bed, Syed under the covers, as I had left him earlier. I heaved a great big sigh. A long afternoon of cooking, tidying, cleaning and, of course, my growing embryo had taken a toll.

"What is wrong, janu?" Syed asked sleepily, turning to look at me as he caressed my arm. I felt the revolt of knowing where his intentions really were with his kind words.

"Oh, nothing," I said, almost knowingly, that it enticed him more.

"Tell me," he insisted, turning over to hug me.

I felt my core freezing up with his touch. I wasn't interested in his concern anymore, but I had to play the game.

"Oh, it's just …" I said, staring at the ceiling. I started to contemplate whether to say anything or not.

"Janu, I know you are hiding something. What's the matter with you?" He leaned up from the bed, turned on the bedside lamp and looked at me, concerned.

"My gran's not well, and I just wanted to go see her. It's been a while."

"Why? It's a bit random. How did you hear about it?" He was always suspicious, of course; it was a gamble if I said I had spoken to someone. I wasn't allowed to call, or if anyone called, it was monitored.

"I don't know, she hasn't been feeling well for a long time, you know; she is in and out of hospital a lot, and she isn't getting any younger. I miss her," I said, worrying that this wouldn't be a good enough explanation.

"Okay, I will take you there," he said.

I paused, wondering how that would work, given my plan to meet Andrea.

"It's okay. You are not well, and I just want to spend some time with her. I will make my way there myself."

"Why?" he demanded, annoyed and suspicious.

"Because she is not well, and I would like to spend some time with her," I insisted. I rose up from the bed, the heat inside me rising with it. His control made me uncontrollable. "It's not like I am going to a frickin' nightclub. I just want to see my gran. Does everything need a reason?" I said, annoyed and desperate. I couldn't stand that it needed justifying and that he needed the last say on something like this. This was the bitter source of all our conflicts. He always had to have control, because that was what Bangladeshi culture had empowered men with.

"You are not going to your gran's."

"What?" I barked, livid.

"I don't have to explain my reasons. You fucking do what I tell you to do," he yelled into my face, leaning over with his knees on the bed.

"Don't talk to me that way!" I shouted.

"You better fucking listen to me," he shouted, moving off the bed towards where I stood. Then he pushed me with some force. I lost my balance. I fell to the ground, my body tumbled to the floor. I landed with some impact as my bony carcass of a body hit ground on four or five points along my back.

"Syed, open the door." Ammujee banged and knocked on the door, the door handle turning viciously.

I then heard Abbujee shouting from behind the door. "Hey, Syed, what's going on in there? Open up."

I crawled up off the carpet. He walked past me, opening the door a little.

"What was that noise?" Ammujee asked, concerned.

"Nothing. Why don't you all just go to sleep?" he said.

I wasn't going to let him get away with that. I was fully charged with adrenalin now.

"Nothing?" I said. "Nothing? Is that right?" I approached the door.

He closed the door on them while pushing me with one hand back to the wall.

They continued to shout. "Hey, Syed, you better open the door and explain." I heard Ammujee's voice again.

"Just go away and mind your own fucking business," he shouted at them, and he rolled back into bed.

They stood outside for a few minutes and, after not getting any response from us, proceeded back to their rooms to sleep. Syed turned off the lights, and I stood silently in the dark room. I didn't want to sleep in that bed. Instead, I walked downstairs and quietly cried in the dark of the living room. I felt so angry, so disgusted by the lack of reaction from his family. They knew something was wrong; they could tell this was not normal.

I couldn't see how I could continue like this. It only confirmed my dilemma on the abortion. I wasn't going to let my child go through this. I didn't want it to be witness to this. I could leave now, I thought. But how? Where could I go at this hour?

*

I woke to a sudden shuffling of sandals on the tiled floor in the hall-way. I rose from the sofa, covering my arms and head. Ammujee paused as she caught sight of me down the hallway.

"What are you doing down here?" she asked, concerned.

Does she need to ask? I thought. *But okay, I get that she needs a starting line.*

"I was just making my way upstairs."

"Get some rest," she said. "It's only five."

"It isn't rest I need, Ammujee, but thank you anyway."

She looked at me curiously and proceeded down the hallway to the kitchen to carry on with her daily routine.

Still livid, I went back to the room, where Syed slept, deeply snoring. It was Saturday morning, and the rest of the household were silently in slumber. I got dressed. I packed ten sets of clothes. I put my make-up and shoes into another bag. I went into the bathroom, brushed my teeth, washed my face, put my make-up on. I then went back to the room I shared with Syed and grabbed my handbag. I paused and realised that my wallet and phone were downstairs in the office room. I took my belongings and left them by the front door and then raced down the hallway to the office to get my wallet and phone.

"Are you still awake, Eleanor?" It was Ammujee's voice from the kitchen. She came out. "Oh, you are all dressed," she said, con-fused, as I brushed past her and went to pick up my things.

"Where are you going?" she asked.

"I am leaving," I said, then paused. "I am not staying here any longer," I added.

"What are you talking about, Eleanor?" Ammujee was horrified.

I started walking away from her.

"Eleanor, come back." She raced down the hallway, following me.

Then the worst thing that could have happened happened. She started shouting, in a panic, as though I was some kind of thief attempting to run away with something.

"Syed, oh, Syed! Come downstairs."

I hastily grabbed my bags and opened the door.

Syed came racing down the stairs, followed by Sufyan and Abbujee.

He grabbed me by the arm. I wrestled out of his grasp, trying to keep hold of the bags.

"What are you doing?" he said, pulling me towards him.

I drew myself nearer to the door, the full restraint of Syed's grip holding me back.

The others stood behind him, watching the scuffle.

"Let me go," I screamed.

"Syed, let her go," said Abbujee calmly. Sufyan stood there looking blank. I didn't really know what they were trying to do, but I knew it wasn't because any of them cared about me, it was because they cared about themselves, how this would look and how soon before the cracks on this facade would appear.

Abbujee and Ammujee waited for me to say something. I stood and looked down at my bags.

"Beti, tell me, why are you leaving us?" Abbujee begged. His voice trembled. "We can sort this out. Do you want the whole world to know and hear about everything? Everybody has problems in marriage. Come and sit down, and we can talk about this."

My head was shaking from side to side. "Your son beats me, and you both think that's okay. Well, I can't be here for that."

"It's not just my son at fault, is it?" Abbujee retorted. "You provoke him, and that's why he gets upset at you."

I was speechless and livid at his conclusion.

Ammujee looked intently at me. "Please, Eleanor, please don't go." She begged and cried. I couldn't bear the tears. No, I didn't want to disappoint them; none of this was meant to be directed at them, but they wouldn't be able to save me, not if they continued living this fallacy.

"I can't be here. I can't carry on like this, Ammujee," I cried. "I am going to go to my nanni's house, and I am going to stay there for a while."

I picked up my bags and walked along the driveway to the car. They all stood and watched except Syed, who was no longer at the door. Ammujee stood crying, and Abbujee walked out onto the driveway to see my car out. Sufyan stood and watched closely behind Ammujee. I reversed out and made my way onto the main road. I drove away. I wasn't sure what I was going to do, but there was a release, the cold air seeping in through the air vents. I felt alive again. Driving on that motorway and getting to Nanni's was thrilling, until the reality sank in. They weren't the only ones who didn't want me to leave.

*

When I arrived in Luton, where Nanni now lived, Nanni didn't want to hear anything. She sat me down and brought me some food, and when I had calmed down, she let me talk out my problems. It didn't seem to faze her, as though it had been expected. She accepted how I felt and agreed that it was wrong and Syed shouldn't have done what he did. But at the same time, she seemed to accept that men can get angry if you don't do as you are told, and that can lead to violence. It was as if the words were polluted, like taking a dip in clear water with crap floating everywhere. All she was doing was moving it aside, as though you could make do; it was still drinkable. It left me in utter disgust. The older one got, it seemed, the more resolute one was about life.

It was clear to my friends Syed was in the wrong, but my family were persistent that he had every right to be angry, upset and get violent. After all, I should listen to him and not challenge him. In fact, resorting to this behaviour was a natural reaction for men in Bengali families. It was so common in families that it was almost normal.

I sat on the sofa in Nanni's living room, looking dismally at myself in the reflection of the TV. I was brought back to life with a sudden pulsing pain in my lower navel, and then I remembered that I was pregnant, and I still had to work something out. At least now I no longer needed an alibi to visit the clinic. I called Andrea to let her know that I had made it safely and arranged to get the train down to London and meet her at the clinic instead. She was relieved that I was okay and somewhere safe.

I was in safe hands now; a plan was in place, and I could bide some time here, at least for a little while. I lay on the sofa, thinking. Nanni was busy fussing in the kitchen. She had already started making some of my favourite dishes and insisted I didn't need to help her and that I should go and relax. I couldn't help for once but indulge in this very idea. I listened to the faint clanging and chopping from the kitchen. I enjoyed the sound of an aeroplane flying over while a soft breeze gently made its way through the patio window. I breathed in the aromatic smells of sautéed onions, bay leaves and cinnamon that came in waves through the kitchen. For once I could let go, and hear and feel the world around me. For once, in a long time, I did not feel incarcerated in my own head, full of fear and tensions about what might happen next. My body, intoxicated by the sounds, felt increasingly heavy as I sank into a deep sleep.

*

The phone rang, and Nanni made her way slowly to it. My heart quickened with an adrenalin surge. I kept my eyes closed.

"Hello," she said, following a long pause.

"Yes, she is here," she continued. "Did you want to speak to her?" She looked at me as if to ask me the same question.

I shook my head, signalling a no.

She continued the conversation awkwardly. "Okay, let me have a word with her, and then let's work something out. These things happen, and I am sure it will all get sorted."

The idea that she was giving them some promise repulsed me. I wished someone would stand up to them and take me away from this hell. She put the phone down.

"That was your mother-in-law, dear." She sat down, easing herself gently onto the sofa beside me with a big, tired sigh.

"So, what are you thinking? What do you want to do?" she asked me.

"I don't want to go back," I said, fearing that I was about to get another round of persuading.

"You can't do this forever; we need to sort something out. They want you to talk to them, find a way forward. How about you call your ammujee and come to some arrangement?" She said it softly, but it was enough to antagonise me.

"No! I don't want to talk to anyone. I just want to be left alone, and I don't want to go back there."

Nanni sighed; she didn't want to say too much lest it upset me further. "Take some time, then, dear, and let's talk about it again some other time."

I suddenly felt at ease: she had finally relented.

*

That afternoon Mamajee and Babajee called; they had been given the version of events from Ammujee and Abbujee, that I had walked out following an argument with Syed. I hadn't spoken to Mamajee since the last incident a couple of months ago.

"Where are you?" she shouted down the phone. I could hear and feel the disappointment in Mamajee's voice. She was in despair about the fact that Ammujee and Abbujee had called them, reporting what sounded like me literally walking out on them without any real cause. "How dare you leave that house without consulting with your in-laws?"

I could hear Babajee chiming in in the background.

Again, this was more important. The dishonour *they* faced.

"How could you do this? I can't show my face to anyone in the community because of the way you behave. Where are you, and what are we going to do with you? You have little awareness of anyone's respect, not to mention your own self-respect. Why didn't you just call us before you left that house? We could have done something," Mamajee barked.

I wanted to launch into a full-scale attack on this remark but almost felt she didn't deserve any explanation. Neither of them were people I had much time for anymore. I didn't respond to any of the questions. Yes, they wanted me dead. Here I was, dead.

Babajee kept repeating the same question. "What are we going to do? How despicable. Look at all the people getting married. Are they behaving this way?"

I had a rifle ready with that rhetoric: *How about you tell me about honour, marriage, when you have been having an affair?* But I wasn't going to stoop so low. He wasn't winning me over. I chose to disengage.

"So, what are we going to do now? They will be wanting to know, wanting to know why our daughter has walked out," Mamajee added as though she was responding to a client.

"Just tell them I am not coming back," I said calmly, clinically, unemotionally. I was fuming at her impudence, that she even had the nerve to ask, that she even had the right to even ask now, given the apathy demonstrated before.

"You are not going back? You wanted this marriage. You made this decision, and now you are going to ruin us? What do we say to people? Life is not easy, Eleanor, when you make decisions about someone. You don't just walk out! In marriage you have to work at it. Yes, sometimes it is hard, but you can't just throw it away."

"I am going to go now," I said in a flat tone. I cut the receiver and put the phone down.

I went and lay in the spare room Nanni had put aside. A cold draught seeped through the windows. I looked down at my feet and pressed them up against the radiator beside the window. I couldn't see out: the condensation had steamed the glass pane. I saw a heart-shaped imprint on it that someone must have drawn. *Love is everywhere*, I thought. I recalled a time when Mrs Abbots said those things to me. Where was she now? Love wasn't everywhere; it was nowhere. I couldn't feel it in any of these surroundings.

*

Andrea and I met at the clinic. She hugged me. It was as though years had slipped by in the space of a few months. Seeing her felt like I had walked back into my old life but with battle scars. There was a shadow looming over us as if it were a point where two worlds met, like the grey matter between black and white spheres. She belonged to the whiteness, and I to the blackness, and we were joined by one sad grey occasion. Abortion. And all that had happened, and all that had brought us here, was hanging amid it.

The waiting room was empty, and Andrea sat quietly next to me.

"I brought some things for you," she said, pulling items out of a large handbag. "There's a pack of mints to calm you, some water in case you get sick, some tissues, and, oh, I left some sick bags in my car too for the ride home."

"Oh, Andrea. You are so thoughtful," I gasped, feeling blessed and teary.

I still couldn't work out how to thank her. *Why are words lost in moments like this?* I thought.

"Gosh, all this way from Farmouth too. Did it take you long to get here?" I asked her, concerned about the length of time she must have travelled that morning.

"No, not long, don't worry." She smiled. "This is more important," she insisted, holding onto my hands.

I took a deep breath and tried to relax. *It is the right thing to do, it is*, I chanted to myself. *Will I regret it though? What if things work out with Syed?* I thought.

Then, I said to my inner self, *you will be thankful that you didn't let this happen now and you waited until things improved.*

Yes, I said to my inner self. *You are right. When things are better between us, then I can look at this again, can't I?*

Of course, came the inner voice again. *There will be plenty of opportunities. You have your whole life ahead of you, if you choose so, if you choose so.* It echoed. It was the voice of Mrs Abbots. Oh, how I missed her and hated her all at the same time. How she infiltrated my thoughts without being present.

As I sat in that waiting room, my moral compass swayed between the various fragments of my shattered life. It pointed to the east, and I saw my seven-year-old self lying next to my beaten-up mother, who had blamed me for locking her into her marriage. It then turned to the west, my future, and I saw the debris of my own marriage, with a child, and a broken home. It swayed to the north, and I saw a blissful picture of my parents and in-laws and the entire family rejoicing at the baby being born. Everyone seemed happy and pleased for me in that world. It was tempting to join it. Mamajee looked so pleased; it was as though she had waited and dreamed for this, the day her daughter was married into a respectable home, with respectable in-laws, and now a family. But it was south … it was south where I was headed on that day. It was somewhere dark, somewhere I never thought I would have to go.

I will be going to hell, I thought. For making this selfish decision, I knew I would be hated. *This was not the plan; this was not written anywhere in God's plan. I am heading somewhere dark and unknown. I don't belong anywhere, so what hope can I bring for this child? Perhaps I can just run away somewhere far and just have this baby in hiding. Perhaps then I wouldn't—*

"Miss Rabbani," came the voice from a large Nigerian lady.

She has my old name, I thought with a welcome relief.

Andrea and I rose up from our chairs. The lady had a warm face and looked very calm as she approached me.

"Come with me," she said.

I looked over at Andrea.

"It's best if I speak with you alone," said the nurse.

"I will wait here," Andrea whispered reassuringly.

I took another deep breath as if air was hard to come by.

I followed the nurse to a large, dark room with an assortment of hospital apparatus dotted around the room. It had a clinical appearance but felt warm. A calming sound of something bleeping in the background kept my attention for a few seconds.

"Take a seat," she said, seating herself into an office chair. She rustled through the medical papers and went through my details, my address, my reasons for killing – I mean, abortion – and whether I had any previous medical conditions. She checked my blood pressure, my heart rate and finally the procedure for the medication. The first pill I had to take at the clinic; the second one I had to take twenty-four hours later.

"Now we are to carry out a quick scan," she said. "You won't feel any pain, but I will apply some pressure on your abdominal area, which might be a little uncomfortable, okay?"

I nodded with agreement to whatever she had to do.

"I need you to come and lie on this bed and lower your skirt down for me so that it is beneath your belly." She looked at me and smiled.

"Will this have any effect on having babies in the future?" I asked her.

"No, you will be fine," she said, reassuring me. "Just think of it as a miscarriage," she said. "It is a little like that. The baby is still an embryo; it's smaller than a pea right now, so don't be afraid. This won't prevent you from having children in the future."

It didn't completely settle me, but it gave me a better reason for it to happen now than later.

She placed a cold gel onto my stomach. "Now I am going to check to see where the baby is and how far along you are."

I sat looking at the screen. There on the screen was a small dot.

"You see?" she said. "Right now, you can't even tell it is a baby; it is a tiny small dot. You are about seven weeks pregnant," she said.

Seven weeks, I thought. *Right now, if this was a normal world, I should be an excited mother at the prospect of bringing a child into the world. Instead, I face the flaming fires of hell for what I am about to do.*

"Okay, Miss Rabbani," she said. "You look fine; everything is healthy. I need you to sign this document that you have been examined and that you are happy to proceed with a medical abortion."

I rose up from the examination bed and signed the paper on the clipboard. I tried to detach myself from what I was about to do, concentrating on the noise and beeps coming from the medical equipment while she busily typed away on her screen.

She came back to me. "Now, I have a pack. There are two tablets: one you have to take here, and the other I want you to take twenty-four hours later. The first one will make you feel nauseated, and you may have some cramping; the second will cause you to bleed, and you may experience heavy cramping. Just take your normal painkiller if you feel any pain, but if you have any other symptoms, just call me on this number. I will also be in touch with a follow-up appointment. Okay?" She gave me another reassuring smile.

"Okay," I said. Then she handed me a cup of water, and I took the first pill. I tried not to think of anything other than what I had to do.

"Can I offer you any further protection for the interim period? Condoms, the pill?"

"No, I think I will be fine."

"Very well. Please do keep it in mind: during the next weeks, you will still need some protection during intercourse."

"I will, thank you."

"Now," she said, "I will take you back downstairs, and I will speak to you in a few weeks to see how you are getting on."

I followed her downstairs, where Andrea sat waiting for me.

She immediately rose from her seat. "Are you okay?" she said, miming the words.

I nodded and smiled at her.

*

We walked out into the cold, bitter wind to where Andrea's car was parked, and I suddenly felt nausea, only this time, I threw up, uncontrollably, without any warning, from my gut.

"I am sorry," I said to Andrea, holding my stomach, embarrassed at myself.

"Don't worry," she said. "I came prepared." She pulled out a bag of wipes and mints. "Here, the mints will help calm it down a bit. Hopefully, you can rest in the car." She helped me in as I cradled my tummy, easing myself into her car.

"I will drop you back up to your gran's," she said.

"No, Andrea, don't worry. I will take the train," I said, squirming.

"Eleanor, just relax. You are with me, remember. You'd do the same, wouldn't you? There are some bags there if you need to be sick again."

"You brought bags?"

She smiled, smug with her preparation skills.

"Like I said, it is all taken care of," she said, shifting the car into gear.

There are no words to describe how thankful I was to her.

"It will be okay," she said. "Things will get better, and you will be happy that this has happened."

*

The following day I took the second pill, and within an hour or two, I felt some excruciatingly heavy cramping. I clutched hold of my belly and walked to the bathroom at Nanni's house. It was only at this point that it hit me again that I was killing a life inside me.

"I am so sorry!" I cried in the toilet, howling at my selfish being. "I am so sorry for what I have done to you. I am so sorry," I gasped, breaking down on the bathroom floor. I was letting go of life, something that Mamajee would never have done. *I am the selfish one*, I thought. I had let go of a child. I saw my inner seven-year-old look at me with disappointment. The tears resonating down her face at the thought of Mamajee leaving her.

I felt a heavy blood clot make its way downwards, fleshy and thick on the tissue.

I cried, "Goodbye, my child. Goodbye. I am really sorry. I hope one day I will see you and that you will forgive me for letting you go."

CHAPTER THIRTY-NINE
- *The Return* -

I stayed at Nanni's house for two weeks or more, sitting out the Christmas period. I spent time catching up with my aunts Nashira Khala and Naheeda Khala, both of whom now had their own children. I managed to work remotely from Nanni's spare room. It was pleasant to be with them, occasionally distracted by their hospitality of tea and snacks and desserts, and in return feeding them with atrocities that, oddly, only affirmed to them that I was still in a better place than them.

Nashira Khala shook her head as if competing in a game of one-upmanship. "At least you knew who you were marrying. I didn't. I didn't even meet him, remember? And you do know that he is a her-oin addict, don't you? I tried to save the child benefits when I was eight months pregnant. Do you know what he did? He tried to stab me, threatened to kill me if I didn't hand it over. I forgave him though. You have to."

Then Naheeda Khala chimed in. "You know I was only sixteen? I didn't even know who I was getting married to. He wouldn't even let me leave Bangladesh unless I was pregnant. We had to accept it, because this is what you have to do. That's what Allah has written for us, hasn't he?"

There were countless horror stories, similar to, if not worse than, mine, and around these women – my aunts, Nanni, Mamajee and

Ammujee – I felt like another statistic. It didn't faze them, hearing my stories; it was almost a way of life. They were immune to it. It gave them more reason to explain that I had to endure, persevere, tolerate and take the good with the bad.

"Here, have another samosa and eat. You are withering away with worry," they would say, as if eating solved all of life's problems.

I could see why it was a necessary distraction. What else do you have to do in a day if not devote it to the household? One had to find purpose. I could see how they directed their energy, just as Mamajee did, to the kitchen. Baking, frying, preparing, kneading out pastries, rolling out savoury treats, such as pakoras, rice cakes, onion bhajis. Or they would bicker endlessly about the right approach to make the finest curries with carefully roasted spices, or the right ingredients for tantalising chutneys.

Before I knew it, the whole day had gone, in amongst making various snacks and devouring them. The day passed swiftly, cooking breakfast, lunch and dinner, preparing for breakfast, lunch and dinner, and cleaning up after all of the above. All of which seemed sickening, and formed for me a hollow opinion on the whims of men and servitude of women.

I also felt empty after making that terrible life-destroying decision. *It's done now though.* I consoled with the spirit of that unborn baby. *What I had for you wasn't safe. What if I died? Who would protect you? Forgive me. I did it for love, knowing that it wasn't safe for you or me.* I grieved over my loss, thought about what it would be like if I'd had that child, how much I would have adored it if things were different.

In years to come, I would have many dreams of that child. They were blurred out, but it was a girl who came in those dreams.

*

Christmas was drawing nearer, and tensions were flaring about my plans. Mamajee and Babajee had called several times that week. They wanted me to work things out with Syed, despite all my efforts to explain what I had been subjected to. They weren't listening, and despite what I had been through, it wasn't justifiable grounds for separation or divorce.

Their words tore me open even more. "You have to go back and apologise to your new parents about your despicable behaviour. We are not your parents anymore, they are, and you must adhere to their every word. The fact that they still want you back in their lives is a godsend after what you have done to disgrace them." It felt as though she was slicing me with her words. I was being ordered to go back and serve my husband and his family. I was still raw from Mamajee's last cut-throat exchange during my hour of need those months ago. The words *dead than divorced* echoed bitterly every time I spoke to Mamajee, and yet she continued on inconsequentially.

It was as if everyone resounded the same sentiments. My aunts, sister, brothers, Mamajee and Babajee were anxious only to get me back there.

"Isn't that what happens in marriage?" Suraya said.

"Well, yes, but that's marriage," explained my younger brother.

They didn't want the gossip spreading like wildfire and spoke jovially to people that my extended visit to Nanni's house was a holiday, dispelling rumours that the dreaded D-word was on the horizon.

They directed their pressure on me to try harder. And each time I declined, refused, became uncooperative, my aunts' and grandma's approval of me staying with them slowly diminished. I could feel their enthusiasm depleting, the novelty of the drama running low. I realised that I was being a burden and had outstayed my welcome and being so disagreeable to their advice only compounded it further.

I started to feel the pressure, the emphasis on me to salvage their honour, spare them any indignity. They moved me into the kitchen when visiting wives came over for tea, or when relatives asked what I was doing there. Meanwhile, my in-laws were in the same quandary as my family. How would they keep a lid on what was going on? They had told the family that I had gone to see my family for the Christmas break, and made excuses for the disruption that I had caused to the invites and dinner parties they had arranged for me to go to with them, introducing me as the new bride to their extended family.

They had frequently been calling to see how I felt and whether there had been any changes to the circumstances. Syed had also been calling my phone, sending long-winded text messages and apologies for his behaviour or about how much it meant that I came back. There were promises of a new start and changes to the way he behaved. All of which sounded great on paper but offered little insurance to what should, could, would happen in reality.

*

One afternoon Nanni came over and sat next to me with a plate of sliced mangoes. "Here, have some of these, my dear," she said, looking at me. "You know your mother-in-law called again today. She rang the last few days too, but I said you were busy. You should at least ring her. She was very upset. You know you have become very dear to her, almost a daughter that she never had. It must be very hard for her, you must understand."

I looked at Nanni and sighed. "Do you know how hard it was for me, living there, Nanni?"

"Yes, of course I do. We have all been there, haven't we, with men like this? Look around you. Your aunts, your mum, me, we have all been there," she trivialised. "You have to look at things differently. There are no perfect situations anywhere, and running away won't change anything. What's to say you are not faced with this again if you married again? It has been only a few months. It takes years of perseverance to make a marriage work. And of course, Syed," she added. "He has been trying to call you, you know. He has called numerous times, but you don't wish to speak and discuss and talk things through?" She seemed baffled and confused by this. "Marriage, my dear, is about two people, not one. It is about working together to create harmony. You can't clap with one hand, but joy can be heard when you clap with both hands. Isn't that the truth? And the same is said about marriage. You both have to work this out together. Just give this one more try. I pray it is the last time, but heavens, you cannot give up just yet."

I could only half agree. "Why do you want me to go back to this, Nanni? Do you not see that he is a danger to me?"

She shook her head in disagreement. "You can't just look at his flaws; you also have to look at yours. You have to be understanding of his needs. Men are different; they get angry and upset, and you have to find ways to support each other. What guarantee would you have that this wouldn't happen with someone else, anyway? He loves you; he praises you. Look at all the flowers and the numerous calls, trying to make amends with you. Have you tried once? You haven't once tried to call them and work things out."

I silently thought about what she was saying. How twisted this situation had become; how little sympathy they had for my safety.

"Listen, Eleanor, this is not a situation you can be so dismissive about. The minute something goes wrong is not a reason to cry for a divorce. You have to think about everyone, everything. I will tell you one thing: if he does this again, you come back, and we will be there for you, but you can't give up; you must try to work things out."

I thought it was a dumb thing to say. It was like being told to go back into the lion's den because my head wasn't bitten off enough. *If he hasn't finished you off at breakfast, go back and see whether he will have you for lunch.*

I stared at Nanni blankly, washed of any want or desire for anything. "Okay," I said, staring blankly at the ground. "Tell them I will be coming back."

Nanni smiled and immediately started to cry with tears, raising her hands in the air with relief. "I pray to Allah that you remain happy. I pray every night that you are all happy. Only Allah knows whether this is in your fate to remain happy always. Just stay healthy, eat well, stay well."

Somehow it came across as fickle. *How could she really be praying for my happiness if they are leading me back to the beast?*

*

When I arrived at the front door, I was greeted with an emotionally smiling Ammujee. She hugged me, holding onto my face, and nuzzled my cheek. Then she greeted Nanni, kneeling down as expected in the traditional way, bowing and touching her feet. Syed stood closely behind, pressing his lips in a half smile, and Abbujee looked calmly back as he welcomed us in.

We all sat down in the living room, and I suddenly felt like a guest in a place far too familiar. It was smiles and pleasantries as Ammujee served tea. I tried to help, but she insisted that I stayed sitting. Mamajee and Babajee had also travelled down from Manchester, and the parents mingled in small talk. Nanni then broached the subject to my in-laws, how she had explained things to me, that I had to work on my marriage. I sat there quietly looking down.

"These things happen. Sometimes there are fights, even between your abbujee and me. Especially in our early years, he was very angry about everything," explained Ammujee.

"Oh, yes," Abbujee added. "That was me all right. I had quite a temper in my early years," he chuckled, and the fat on his cheeks wobbled with it. "But it all calms down eventually. Every marriage has its problems, and you both need to communicate and talk to one another."

I felt the problems were deeper than just minor problems with Syed. I continued to listen to the conversation, the incessant, trivialised nature in which both males and females in this community discussed domestic violence, as if it were a part of life. How unperturbed it was, or that it was not seen as an act of injustice on one another. I almost questioned my own beliefs, whether they were right, and I was wrong. I started to feel there was something wrong with me. How could I be the only one not prepared to live like this?

"Now," said Nanni. "You two, go upstairs and have a talk," she said, looking at Syed.

I looked at him, glum, and he looked back passively at me.

"Go on," she nudged insistently, lifting up my elbow.

I rose from my seat awkwardly, and Syed mirrored me. I walked slowly upstairs with him following behind. We both felt awkward as our parents looked on at us going up. When I approached our room, everything was laid out nicely, flowers on the dressing table. The room was scented with Arabic perfume oil, and the bed neatly made. It was his way of welcoming me back, I guessed. I stood a few feet away from him, and he stood silently looking down at the floor in thought.

"I am sorry," he said. "I am sorry for what I did; it was wrong of me. It's all going to change now, I promise." He edged forward towards me and tried to touch my shoulder.

I stepped back. "How are things going to change?" I said.

"Janu," he said, staring into my eyes, "you being away has made me realise what a horrible person I have been to you. I had time to think about what kind of life I would have without you. I want us to work out. I don't want to be without you, not only me but Ammujee and Abbujee. It was deeply upsetting for them to see you leave. They made me realise how much of the core you are to our family. I can't treat you like this. I should never have got so angry. This was all my fault that you ended up leaving."

I couldn't believe what I was hearing. *Is it genuine this time? Or just another game?* He seemed softer, passive, gentle; he made me look hard, stubborn and cruel in the calmness of his voice. At the same time, I had my suspicions.

"Janu, just give me a chance, okay? I know it's hard, but I promise I will do everything I can to make you happy here."

I started to melt. It was just a chance I was giving him, after all.

I started to forget what had happened. It was almost becoming a blur because his words were full of love. I couldn't be mean; it was only right to forgive, especially when someone was doing everything they could. I looked at him, and then he hugged me. It was nice to see this side of Syed. It felt warm; it felt right still.

As we headed back downstairs, we met Nanni making her way slowly up the stairs. We waited for her to pass at the top.

"Have you two had a good talk?" she said, holding onto both of our hands, joining them together with hers, her skin like marble and cold to touch. "I want you both to work at this. Allah will make things better. You have to pray to Allah and keep him in your hearts. That is all I pray for these days, that you can find peace in your hearts."

"Nanni, of course we will work things out," Syed said, smiling at me.

Was that another victorious smile? I thought.

＊

For a while things calmed down between Syed and me, by avoiding conflict with him. Losing the baby had become my torment. It was the unspoken truth spreading through my conscience over and over. I spent most of my time in meditation, shutting myself off from the world, and in deep prayer. I would spend hours in prayer, meditating, each time getting deeper and deeper into this world with Allah, and then, from out of nowhere, she would appear like a flash. The seven-year-old me and that fear on my face that Mamajee was going to leave me and abandon me because of Babajee's mistreatment of her. *Because of you, I am going to die here,* she would say. It happened every time I meditated. It came back in floods of guilt now, though it was laced with the guilt of abandoning my own child.

I tried to keep my mind away from this by looking forward to things. I kept myself busy by helping Sufyan with his aquarium. He only had a few fish in there, so I cleaned out the tank and introduced new fish. One by one the tank became lively with different types of fish. It was a wondrous sight to see life in all those colours thriving. I could relate to it: wasn't I in the same circumstance as them, surviving a volatile man-made ecosystem? I gave the fish names, and I bought them furniture for their tank. Syed would happily take me to the garden centre, which had an aquarium, so that I could buy more fish. It made him happy that I bonded with his brother over something as simple as fish. Each week, we would go to the garden centre and have the water tested for ammonia levels. The specialist would check that it was safe to introduce more fish. Each week, we would introduce new ones, being careful to introduce the right type that would not be a threat to the other fish. I had angelfish, neon tetras, small red goldfish, bluegrass guppies and a handful of catfish that would sweep the floor, cleaning out the tank. Sufyan was thrilled to see how the tank was thriving, and the care and attention to detail I would give it at home meant that everyone coming through the door would always marvel at it.

I felt settled somehow. I had found a way forward; anchoring my anxiety to the seabed of a fish tank seemed to work. I continued with my meditation and found that my sleep patterns and dreams were now becoming obsessed with the fish. One night I went to sleep after my prayers and had a vivid dream. There, in the dream, I was attending to my fish. I looked into the tank and found the angelfish dead, floating at the surface of the water. Each morning, I awoke from this same dream, and I would find, to my horror, an angelfish dead. I was having premonitions and then finding the angelfish dead in the tank, floating in the water, and it was terrifying.

It made me depressed, and I felt that it was my fault.

I also related to their life: an instrument of vanity, cooped up in an artificial tank and on show for everyone's pleasure. And now they, too, had given up on survival. I broke down in tears, feeling that my dreams were becoming a reality. I felt demoralised that I couldn't look after the fish, and now I was affirming my existence through theirs. I cried at my loss, like a mother crying for her baby. Syed would comfort me the best way he could. I was becoming dependent on these fish for my sanity. I realised it was all I looked forward to; it was a pleasant distraction from the trauma I felt in that house. Slowly, however, one by one, the fish died, and the tank became an empty vessel, a lifeless world of water.

I would look at that empty tank, now empty of life, and I, too, became empty with it. In my dreams, I saw the tank like a womb, the fish swimming in and around my belly. I longed for them, because I longed to love something unconditionally, I longed to have kept that baby, and I longed, more than anything, for life. But these were all things I couldn't find here, not in the confines of these walls.

I returned to my life of prayer and meditation, and denied myself the right for any other feelings to come into play, such as what if I had married Rohit? What if I hadn't married Syed? What if I hadn't returned? And what if, just what if, I had had that baby?

The images were always there when I prayed. The seven-year-old me holding onto a baby next to a beaten-up Mamajee. There she was, nurturing a baby, scorning me. I realised why this picture kept coming into my head: I was also angry at Mamajee, angry at her for manipulating me.

All those feelings I harboured, that guilt that I had obliged her to persevere with my father, and what joy or pleasure did it really serve her, in seeing me married like this? I couldn't accept the things Mamajee wanted for me, and I still couldn't accept that I could have a child with Syed.

When I realised this guilt I had for making Mamajee stay, I realised a lot of justifications in my life were deeply flawed. I had covered up the consequences of my actions and lost track of my identity. I had lost track of why I was here, what I was doing in this life. I had let that baby go because I didn't want to be Mamajee lying on that floor with a child scorning her leaving. I had married Syed because I owed it to Mamajee for the price she had to pay for suffering with Babajee. It was giving her a gift, the gift of honour. I was written in her plan, an object of her vanity, from which she took pleasure in showcasing to her community.

I looked at all I was now, a tiny fragment of a vision she had of her future, something to keep her going through it all. I was just a bottle dream for her, thrown into a vast ocean and waiting for the tide to cast me ashore. There was no grand plan, or at least, if there was, it seemed to end here for me, deserted, isolated, stranded and counting my days with the hope that I would be saved.

They never called after that; they had dumped me there once again. I became unresponsive, numb of life. Fatigued by the fallacy my entire being had now become, I resented presenting this farcical persona they had contrived for me. I could see that they all knew this: the way both sides of the family danced around me, how the superficial conversations became more impersonal, short, sweet and lacked any depth.

I became inward from that point and went to bed early after dinner and prayers, prayers that often took me an hour to complete. It meant less interaction, avoided unnecessary disputes or corrosive conversations. This didn't seem to affect Syed; it meant more time on the games console or watching films downstairs. There were more hours spent sleeping; at least that was one way to forget about it all. And I had little need anymore for making myself up: I was covered in black most of the time. I stopped brushing my hair, because it was always covered in a scarf anyhow, and only came downstairs in the morning when the rest of the household had left for work or university, at 8 a.m. I didn't want to be around anyone, avoided contact with Sufyan during the day, although he seemed pre-occupied with his own life now, anyhow. Often, I was woken by the door bolting shut downstairs, and I would stare blankly at my bed-room and think about my day ahead. I tried to stop myself from thinking I was locked in a prison or some mental asylum. "This is my home," I said. "You work from home; you live in a home; and you are not alone in this home. Look at the positives. You are lucky you can even work from home," I agreed with myself. "Yes, I am grateful for that." Then I would rise up from the bed and stare out at the magnolia tree. At first, in the winter months, it was as lifeless as I felt, but I noticed the buds forming now, and it gave me some-thing to look forward to. Soon it would be spring, and the blossoms would be out. Each day, I would watch it for a few moments as I drew open the curtains. Now the tree outside was budding again; the pink petals were creeping out of the bud like a butterfly flourishing. It danced and waved at me. It was uplifting to watch, to think it would be in blossom soon. I fought back the thoughts that often crippled me with the despair of ever having any freedom to flourish and blossom again.

I walked past the empty fish tank, resisting the urge to liken it to my own empty existence and the life I now had, on my way to the kitchen. "There," I would say, "I can get through this every day." I would listen to the kettle boil and imagined it like the sick and angry man I had married. I would watch the steam pour from its spout, reconciling that it would switch off after a minute.

Then I would start up my PC, check my emails and begin my day at work. I used to work long hours before I met Syed, and would always be able to complete everything thoroughly, but since the wed-ding and living with my in-laws, it became restricted somewhat. It didn't meet their approval if there were conference calls in the morn-ings or late in the evenings. "It doesn't seem appropriate," Syed would say. I had no social conversations with colleagues over the company's online messaging, in case any remarks were seen by Syed, and most interactions with my global team were carried out over conference calls or emails. I got through my reports and documentation in isolation from the team, remotely, with hardly any contact but by email or conference call.

Going into the office was kept to a minimum and fortunately unnecessary, being part of a global team, and that by nature meant interacting over conference calls on various matters with colleagues in Australia, the US and Asia. However, there were quarterly meetings where the team would meet in various cities around the world, such as San Jose, London and Sydney.

One morning my manager emailed proposing that the team meet in Australia this quarter, as that was where he and a few other team members were located. I took a deep breath and gasped for air. How was I going to tell Syed that I was going to have to go to Australia? I could feel myself curling up into a shell. Although my family and his family had agreed before the engagement that I would be allowed to travel for work, and they were happy to accept this occasionally, it still worried me. *What might come of this? What will he say? How would his family respond?* I made myself a coffee and paced the floor, thinking of my next move. *How can I approach this subject without it turning into another raging dispute?*

"Oh God, oh God!" I exclaimed as my heart beat faster with every possible sentence. I formulated my words, pre-positioning every adjective, verb and syllable in an order that could satisfy the ears of such a wily character.

I need some air, I thought. I had spent months cooped up indoors, so I decided to get out. It was a warm, sunny afternoon, and I had finished my work early, around 4 p.m. It had also been a few months since I had even driven my car. *A short drive won't hurt*, I thought. *Just ten minutes to clear the anxiety, and respite from suffocation.* It was March, and the spring blossoms were in full bloom along the roadside. I rolled down the window and felt the wind stream across my face. The mixture of sounds, cars passing, people talking, engines roaring had become alien to my ears. But I relished it all the same. I drove through the outskirts of London, a few more miles from home. I sank into oblivion as I passed the world I had once known.

Then the phone rang. It was Syed and I started to panic. I hadn't thought this through, of course. I hadn't prepared my response for if he did. At first, I tried to ignore the phone call and get back to the house, but traffic was bad, and children were coming out from a nearby school. I wanted to jump ahead of the queue to avoid the rush and Syed's interrogation. He would probably get really annoyed at my being out for any reason. He called again, only this time I couldn't ignore it.

"Salam, hon," I said in a calm voice.

"Janu, where are you? I called the landline, and you didn't answer," he said with a concerned voice.

"Yes, it's been a long day. I just felt like I needed some fresh air. It's nice outside, isn't it?" I said, smiling and setting a more positive tone.

"Okay, well, I am on my way home too, so I will see you soon," he said rather calmly.

"See you soon," I said, relieved it hadn't spiralled out of control. *Panic over*, I thought. *Now I can relax a little.*

The traffic had barely moved since Syed called, so I turned the music up. I could listen to something as I sieved through at snail's pace. The music brought back memories that I melted into. When it faded out, I heard the phone ringing again. In the time I had listened to two songs, I had four missed calls from Syed, and when I called back, it went straight to voicemail. He must be on the train, I thought. I had now been stuck in traffic for over an hour, and it was getting closer and closer to 6 p.m., when everyone got home.

When I finally arrived home, it was 6.15 p.m. I got out of the car, taking my handbag with me, and opened the front door. There, standing at the staircase, was Syed. His arm was crossed over the other but with one hand resting on his face. It was as though he was deliberating the punishment, the way he twiddled his fingers over his mouth and nose.

"Hi," I said, following a long pause as I closed the door slowly.

"Where have you been?" he said, looking very stressed.

"Like I said to you on the phone, I went for a drive and then got stuck in traffic."

"For two hours?" he said, rising to his feet.

I just knew where this was heading.

"Yes, the traffic was really bad, and hence why it took so long."

"I called you several times, and you didn't answer," he said, edging towards me.

"Yes, I know. I saw your missed calls. I tried to call you back, but it went to voicemail."

"Well, why didn't you answer when I first called you?" He stared at me suspiciously.

"I didn't hear it. I had the radio on," I said, confused and stressed.

"Well, that explains a lot about who you are, doesn't it?" he said, standing close to me.

I stood calmly, hoping this might appease the situation. But it did nothing but aggravate him more.

He pushed me into the wall and shouted into my face, "Where were you?"

"Look, I told you where I was. What do you want? Blood?"

"Oh, you fucking need to do better than that."

He gripped his hands around my shoulders and got up closer to my face. I could hear his breathing angrily blowing air onto my cheeks. I struggled to get away from his intense grip.

"Let go of me!" I said angrily.

Just then the front door unlocked, and Ammujee and Abbujee walked in with bags of groceries.

He loosened his grip. Ammujee noticed him straight away and that something was wrong.

"What's going on, Syed?" she shouted.

"You ask this bitch," he said, walking away.

She looked at me, confused. "Eleanor, what is wrong?"

I remained silent. Anything could fuel the fire.

Syed then charged down the hall, calling out from the office room. "She has been driving around aimlessly like a stray dog."

"Syed, that's enough. Stop this at once," Ammujee retorted angrily.

"I'm sorry. I just went for a drive, Ammujee, and got caught in traffic."

"Eleanor, you need to be careful. No wonder he's angry," Abbujee remarked. "Something could have happened outside."

I bit my tongue and tried to stay quiet.

That evening I kept some distance with Syed. The last thing I wanted was to antagonise him further. *I wish I hadn't gone out at all*, I thought. *Perhaps it's better that way. Things only worked when I just didn't move.* How fragile my existence had become in this house. I had already spent months alone, weeks being depressed. The hours I had spent avoiding clashes, the intimidation and threatening behaviour if I took one step out of line. Was this normal? Was it ever avoidable? And most of all, was it realistic to be living like this? Why did things end so catastrophically?

I decided it wasn't worth talking about the Australia meeting. That night, when we had all finished dinner, I went upstairs to carry out evening prayers in my room. It was already quite late, and everyone had gone to sleep. I came into the room to find Syed sat on the bed with his legs crossed over.

"Janu, come sit down," he said.

I hesitated. I sensed trouble.

"Come here," he said, calmly patting the bed. I could tell that while he seemed calm, there was a tone of anger brooding in him.

"One moment," I said. "I just need to get changed." I was trying to stall it, get my thoughts together.

"Just come and sit down, please."

This time his tone was firm.

So, I paused. Lowering my gaze, I sat calmly down.

"I didn't like what happened today, especially in front of my parents. Are you going to tell me where you have been?" His arms folded, cross-legged, perched on the bed and demanding an answer.

I paused, looking at him with disbelief. I couldn't understand this level of doubt.

"Look, I have explained this already. I went for a drive."

"For two hours?" he said. "You are making a mockery out of my family and me," he added.

"What? How do you suggest that? I do nothing but right by you guys. I never step out of the house, and the one time I do, everything is falling apart?"

His folded his arms, with a livid glare from his eyes. "Don't you dare give me any bullshit," he shouted. "You do not leave this house without my permission."

"What? Are you totally out of your mind?" I looked in horror. "You really think that's going to work, do you?" I regretted the words coming out of my mouth.

"What did you just say?" He looked at me as if my words had cut through him. He raised his hands in the air, his eyes bulging out of his sockets, ready to hit me.

I jerked away suddenly.

"You better take note of what I just said." He walked out of the room, slamming the door behind him.

My body trembled for a moment. I could hear his steps downstairs to the hallway.

Oh God, oh God! Is there a god? I drew out my prayer mat. I needed to calm down: I felt jittery. Things were going to end badly over this. I crouched into a ball onto my mat. I cried helplessly now. "Oh God, why am I here? Tell me why, why am I here? I thought you wanted me to shine. There is nothing left of me here. I am lost, and I need help. God, please, I beg you, tell me what I should do. Just give me a sign," I cried, my face resting on the soft velvet mat.

Just then, as if by some miracle, God heard my prayers. The phone rang.

It was Sonia.

CHAPTER FORTY

– The Sign –

"Oh my God, is this true?" I whispered and sniffled. "I can't believe this. I am so happy you called, hon." I choked up, and my voice cracked with the words.

"Hi, hon," Sonia said softly. "I couldn't bear it anymore and was checking to see how you were."

I cried a silent cry. She could tell I could barely get my words out. "I can't speak for long," I whispered. "He's downstairs."

"Eleanor, I just can't bear this anymore. You are crying. Look at you. We have to get you out of there. Are you ready to do it? Are you ready to get out of there now?"

"Well … yes, but how, Sonia? How?" I said, weeping into the phone.

"Is there a way you can get out to see me? Maybe even stay over at mine?"

"No, he will not entertain that. He won't, he won't." I panicked as if it was happening to me right now.

"Hmm, okay," she said. "I guess, yes, he would hate that. There must be some way to get you out for a bit."

I thought about it.

"I am going to Australia for a week in a couple of weeks for work," I said. "But that's hardly plausible. I mean, you couldn't get out there easily."

"Eleanor? Are you kidding me? You are going all the way out to Australia?"

"Yes, for work, for a meeting."

"What? How is that possible? You aren't even allowed out from your doorstep. What the fuck is wrong with these people?"

I giggled quietly. "I don't know, status, I guess. They think I am doing something important."

She laughed. "Okay, look, let's just count our blessings here. I am coming with you, then," she said adamantly. "I'll book my flights."

I was shocked. "Oh my gosh! What? Really?"

"Yes, Eleanor, for fuck's sake, really," she said. "Absolutely without a doubt, I will literally go to the ends of the world for you, to get you out of this fucking shithole."

I could hear and feel the smile rising from the words. "I love you, hon. Thank you."

"I can't watch you go through this anymore. I need to get you back from the dead."

"Oh my gosh, this is amazing. I can't believe it. I can't believe that you called." I breathed. "Okay, let's do this." My voice screeched with excitement. I tried to keep myself together. I held my breath and could feel the tears reaching the surface.

"Just tell me your flight details, and I will book the same flight. I will meet you inside the departure lounge and hope to God he doesn't see us together."

"Okay. I need to get sign-off, but okay, that's a good plan."

"Fuck the sign-off. Just fucking tell them. That's it."

"I will work it out, don't worry, hon. Thank you for this. Can't wait!"

"I know!" she said excitedly.

"I will email you the details," I whispered.

"Okay, speak and see you soon. Take care now, won't you?"

"I will."

*

I felt nervous about bringing this up with my in-laws. I decided to wait a day, let things settle down a little with Syed. I would bring the topic up at dinner in front of his parents. That way he couldn't argue too much with me. Safety in numbers was often better. I knew I could mention it, as they had agreed that I had the right to travel with work occasionally. I drafted up my responses to all the questions in my head before the family arrived home.

At dinner the following night. Syed seemed in a spritely and effervescent mood. "How was your day?" he asked as he strolled slowly over to the dinner table. I had kept myself busy, laying out the table with plates, cups and serving mats.

"Good, thank you for asking," I said politely. "It is really getting quite busy at work."

"Hmm," he said, half-interested and picking at the food on the table.

I decided not to say anything more until Ammujee and Abbujee were settled and seated at the table. The typical banter adjourned at dinner with the usual questions, "How was your day?" and "What did you eat?" It was funny how things only touched the surface in that house; the conversation never really came close to personal or intimate, and now I would see whether sparks flew, whether what I would say endangered civility or became unsettling to hear.

"It is getting really busy with work," I said to everyone at the table when Abbujee asked. "They are setting up the budgets for next quarter, and my manager wants to have a team meeting to work this all out."

"Oh, okay," Ammujee said blankly, serving up some more food. Abbujee continued wolfing down another fistful of rice and meat curry. "What is the meeting about?" he said, clearing his throat.

"Well," I said, enthused at his interest, "where I work, the company develops new technologies that are trialled out in our offices globally. So the team and I work to develop these products to be used in-house, and of course, this part requires a lot of planning, especially when we are split across multiple geographical locations. So they want the whole team together to discuss it."

Abbujee listened intently, nodding as he ate another mouthful. "And where will this meeting be held?" he asked.

"Australia," I said calmly. I could feel myself getting nervous, but I kept calm.

"Australia?" Syed raised his head up from his food, looking at me square in the eye to see whether I was telling the truth.

I looked back coolly, refraining from showing any fear in my response. "Yes," I said matter-of-factly, as this, to me, was a normal part of my role. I travelled all over the world in my line of work. "My manager wants us all to meet in Australia this time, as it is the country he is based out of."

A long silence followed, and Abbujee carried on eating his rice. Ammujee looked calmly back at Abbujee, pausing from her food. Abbujee looked down, continuing his food. I could sense this was not going down very well. Either that, or the food had become indigestible.

"I see," said Abbujee. He was assessing and considering it. "So when do you have to go?" he asked.

"In about two weeks," I said flatly.

Syed looked back at me from across the table with a look of horror and interjected, "Two weeks? That's not much notice!"

Oh no, here we go, I thought. *Syed is probably going to say no.*

"Won't the flights be expensive?"

I breathed a sigh of relief: so, it was just a cost issue for him. "Well," I said calmly, "it's all expenses paid – they normally book all my flights and hotels, anyhow."

"Huh, you are lucky, then," said Ammujee, smiling.

"It won't be for long, just a week," I added. Now I felt reassured they would be okay. I was relieved Syed hadn't launched into an attack. I suddenly felt my heart stop racing, my pulse in my throat stop throbbing so fast.

Nothing further was said that night, and Syed was nice for once. All of the clamour and pain that was caused from the week before seemed a thing of the past. He was making it up to me. I could tell.

This was surely a breakthrough. My rite of passage. A small victory, but I still remained sceptical, that his behaviour might change any minute, any day. I could never be sure when my luck would run out. I had a couple of weeks before the trip. *I just have to make it through, that's all*, I thought. *I just have to survive by not rocking the boat, making all the right moves, saying all the right things.*

*

"Here, let me hold onto your bags," Syed insisted as we headed through the airport terminal.

"It's okay, I can wheel it. It isn't a problem," I said.

"Look, just give it here. There is no need to get all Miss Independent on me," he said jokingly.

I wasn't going to push it, but I was anxious: anytime now, Sonia might appear at the check-in desk, and crossing her path would immediately arouse suspicions.

We got to the check-in desk and slowly stacked the bag onto the conveyor belt.

"Which row would you like to be seated in?" asked the ground staff.

Oh, shit, I thought. *I hadn't thought about this. Sonia and I might not be able to sit together.*

"Ah, okay," she said, scanning the computer screen. "I have you down here on row sixteen."

I hoped she wouldn't say any more about the details of the seating arrangements, and luckily, she didn't.

"Are you okay, janu?" Syed said, pulling my shawl around my neck. "You will call me, won't you, when you get there?"

"Yes, of course. I will call when I get there." I was relieved he was playing his soft side.

He hugged me. "I am going to miss you," he said affectionately.

I let him draw me closer. I wanted the sweet game to be done with so that I could get through to security, but I told myself to be calm and patient.

"Well, it's only a week; it will take two days to fly there and two days to fly back."

He smiled. "You are going to spend most of your time sleeping too, in the middle, I would imagine."

He finally walked me hand in hand to the security gates. I waved back at him, a bag of nerves and tension in my stomach as he watched me walk away.

A rush of excitement went through me again. Oh, what a world away I was now. I wanted to take it all in, but I was anxious; I needed to call Sonia.

I called her, and she picked up immediately.

"Hey, girrrl," she said with a cheesy fake American accent.

"Aargh!" I screamed, leaping with excitement. "Where are you?"

"I am in the cafe, first floor."

"Okay, I am coming now."

I ran through the terminal atrium, climbed two steps at a time up the escalator, making sure my long bohemian skirt didn't catch on the escalator steps. I was wearing the closest I could get to Western clothing that was permitted Islamically: a long brown bohemian skirt, a loose, long-sleeved turquoise crew-neck top, with a long-sleeved black cardigan to go on top to hide my thin waist, and a cream scarf that had been wrapped over my chest and neck area to hide my very flat bosoms.

I found Sonia seated at a small table with two glasses of white wine. There was an air of confidence about her, one that questioned how many glasses she had already had. Her hair, beautifully layered, and her eyes, like two sparkling emeralds. She had a smirk on her face as though she had finally won this battle, but with some reservation. She rose from her seat and gave me a long squeeze.

"Ohhh, I am so glad you made it." She kissed me on both cheeks. Then she quietly sat down, shaking her head with disbelief. "Jesus, Eleanor, what the fuck are we doing?"

It thrilled me, her saying the very words; it had me on edge, like jumping off a bridge, the adrenalin tingling in my feet all bolting with the thought that maybe, somehow, I could be free again.

I shook my head with dismay. "I have been so tense, hon. Thank you so much for coming to Australia with me."

"Eleanor, like I said, if it means I have to fly halfway round the world to see you, then that's what I have to do. But what the fuck are we doing this for? I mean, does this not tell you how nuts this is? Does this not give you a hint of worry about what is going on? I mean, look at what the fuck you are wearing, anyhow." She pointed down at my shawl covering my neckline. "You look like a refugee."

I nodded. "I agree."

"Okay, come on, knock that back in one, will you? Let's get you some clothes from that shop over there. How did you even pass security looking like that? Drink up," she said, knocking down the remaining white wine. "We haven't got much time."

We linked arms as we walked around the shops. She picked out things and I just let her decide. I could only be glad to be out, to be here, free. To be able to think without being questioned. To be able to move without scrutiny, and to be able to breathe without pain.

Sonia spotted a red fitted dress. "Here, this one," she said. "You love red. I want you to wear this."

I hesitated. "I am not sure. What if someone sees me?"

"Darling," she said, looking down at me. "Number one, nobody is going to see you, and number two, if they do, it's because they have the hots for you, and all the better, I say."

"Here." She pointed me to the fitting room. "Go get changed."

I went into the changing room. I undressed, taking off the long skirt, untangling myself from the scarf wreathed around my neck. I unlaced my skinny arms from the long-sleeved top to see my bony, useless, corpse-like body. I put on the dress. It clung to my frame, and I suddenly felt shameful, as though walking out in this would be wrong.

"I can't wear this," I said to her, peering out from the curtains in the fitting room.

"Eleanor, you look gorgeous; it fits you perfectly."

The assistant came over to have a look. "Madam, that does look gorgeous on you. We have some shoes that would go with the dress too. Would you like to have a look?"

"Yes, please," Sonia interjected on my behalf.

I let her continue fussing over me. The assistant brought the shoes, and I put them on.

"Okay, she is all good to me," Sonia said, looking over at the assistant. She picked up my old outfit and handed it to the assistant. "Would you mind putting this in the bin for me?"

"Sure, madam," she said, surprised. "What about the shoes?" she said, pointing to a scruffy pair of brown plastic platforms, the kind you wouldn't even see in a pound shop.

"Yes, those are hideous; they can go," Sonia said, looking at them with disgust.

The assistant didn't question any further and proceeded to cut the labels off the dress from behind me.

"Okay, I am getting these," Sonia declared, waving a credit card. She marched over to the till and proceeded to pay for the items.

"Sonia, no, please, let me pay."

"No, you have done enough damage to your credit card with that grand wedding of his. You won't be paying; this one is on me, okay?" She looked at me, raising her eyebrows insistently.

"Thanks, hon, really appreciate everything."

"Say no more. I am just glad you are here. Now," she said, "next stop, booze."

I smiled. It seemed quite simply that the order of events should be prioritised by Sonia in this way: look good; then feel good.

"We have to get champagne from duty-free." She picked out a couple of bottles of champagne.

It felt relatively relaxed and fuss-free. There were no issues getting through security with them, and they didn't seem to flag that we were bringing two bottles of champagne on board.

We seated ourselves, and Sonia asked the flight attendant for two cups. She hid the bottles down by the bottom of her seat.

She poured out glass after glass as I poured out the contents of my atrocities. I was tipsy from the first glass, and a few minutes into the flight, we were completely knocked out. I woke up from the announcement that we would be landing in Singapore, finishing the first leg of our journey.

Sonia woke up next to me, bleary-eyed. Her make-up had smeared around her eyes, and her hair had bunched up in a tangled mess at the back.

"Where are we?" I said, bleary-eyed.

"They are serving breakfast soon, and we will be landing in a couple of hours. Wow," she said. "What the hell? We really knocked ourselves out, didn't we?" She giggled. "Do you remember the flight attendant coming 'round to tell us off?" she said, laughing hysterically.

"No," I said, confused.

Sonia looked at me. "You mean you don't remember? She told us off and confiscated the remaining second bottle from us, at which point we were safely and securely bound for gaga land!"

I laughed. "No. I don't remember."

"Eleanor, you were so off your trolley, and you were saying some shit, like you wish you were still with Rohit."

I looked a little stunned by my admittance; maybe my subconscious still had feelings for him.

"No, it must have been the alcohol. I can't go there. I *won't* go there."

"Eleanor, we all know you love him. It's okay."

"I know, but we can't go there. I can't have their marriage destroyed."

Sonia looked disapproving. "You know they forced that situation on themselves. It's pretty much an arranged marriage, anyhow."

"They are happy though; that's all I wanted," I said, pointing my fingers up above my ears.

"Okay, let's not go there, then. Still, I am so glad to see the real you coming out again, hon; it has been shit hearing about your crap. Look at the state of you. You look like a corpse."

"So, what am I going to do? I can't leave."

"You can, Eleanor, you can. I don't know how else to convince you of that yet, but I am working on it."

*

We arrived, after the second leg of our flight, at the Shangri-La Hotel in Sydney. It was evening by then, and it was difficult to work out clearly the time difference. We both were hungry and tired.

Sonia asked for a smoking room, and we soon settled into the room, which we were to share.

She lit up a cigarette, blowing smoke at the window as she looked out through the curtains.

I called Syed. Which made her squirm.

"Salam, hon," I said in a quiet, timid voice.

"Janu," came a croaky voice.

"It must be early over there, sorry. I will let you get back to sleep; just wanted to let you know I landed safely."

I was relieved that he was too tired to ask any more questions.

"Okay, will speak to you later," he said, yawning before putting down the phone.

I put the phone down, relieved that it didn't cause arguments.

"Okay, I can rest easy now," I said to Sonia.

"I bet," said Sonia, taking another drag of her cigarette.

"Shall we just order some room service?" she said. "I am shattered from that second flight."

"Yes, let's do that."

We ordered food and, shortly after our showers, fell asleep in the bed.

I woke up disorientated from the change of location and time. Sonia stirred sleepily; it was 7 a.m., Sydney time.

I got up and sipped a bottle of water. Sonia pulled over to get her phone to check the time.

"What time is it?" she croaked with a husky voice.

"Seven. I need to get moving so that I can get to the office. What are you going to do today?" I asked.

"Probably have a look around Sydney, get a feel for this place."

"Okay. Are you sure you will be okay?"

"Eleanor, it's you we need to worry about, but thanks all the same."

"Okay, let's get some breakfast and then meet up tonight."

I departed for work shortly after, leaving Sonia to enjoy the city at her leisure.

After a long day trying to stay awake, I finally made it back to the hotel. Sonia was already back from her tour, lying on the bed, texting.

"Hi, hon," she said. "What do you want to do tonight?"

"Well, the guys mentioned they were going out for a team dinner and drinks. Did you wanna come?"

"Okay, if it's okay," Sonia said. "Let's do that."

We all met at a rather large steakhouse, where fifteen members of the team were seated.

They were quite surprised at seeing me, and now with the added bonus of Sonia there, they seemed even more pleased than ever.

Rohit said little to me despite us sitting directly opposite each other. I also felt awkward talking to him. It was the first time in over a year that we had been at any social function. He spent most of the time laughing loudly in conversation as the beers flowed in over the steak-and-chips meal hosted by the company.

Sonia sat next to me, sipping a glass of wine, half-interested and half zoning out of the conversation when it got too techie.

I could see she was tired. "Shall we go?" I said to her.

"If you want." She shrugged.

"Let's go after the mains," I whispered.

"Okay, we can go have drinks at the hotel bar."

"Sounds good," I said.

Soon the mains came, and the guests finished their food shortly after it had arrived.

"We are going to head back to the hotel," I said to Jay, who sat next to me.

"Ah, are you going already?" he said rather loudly, silencing half the table.

"Yeah, we are pretty jet-lagged. We might stop by at the bar for a quick drink though."

"We'll come by later, then," he said, looking at Rohit agreeably.

"Okay, see you over there."

Sonia and I left. We picked up a cab and headed to the hotel bar.

"That was so dull. You guys really talk shit, don't you?" Sonia droned.

I smiled at her. "I am so sorry; you are right. Anyway, what are you having to drink?"

"I am gonna have a white. What about you?" she asked, hollering at the barman.

"Yeah, I will have the same."

"That Rohit talks shit too, you know. It's plain obvious he still fancies you."

"Leave it, Sonia. Neither of us can do anything about that. We are both in marriages with other people. Let's not confuse anything. He is happy, and to be honest, I don't think I would want to be with him in that way. I think I would be happy if we are clear on that."

"Okay, okay, I won't bring it up anymore."

"Anyhow, we need to get you out of this fucking shit situation you are in first. Eleanor, you have to get out of this."

"Yeah, Sonia, I think I know that. I can't do it. I just can't."

"Why can't you?"

"I just don't know how."

"Just leave, damn it. Just get of there."

"Let's go back to the room. I don't want to talk about it here in case someone comes from work."

I settled the bill, and we went up to the room. Sonia lit up another cigarette and started pacing the room by the window.

"Okay, look, I just don't understand what the problem is here," she said. "He hurts you; he is physically violent; you don't want to be with him; and yet you insist that you can't leave him. Why?"

She pressed me again for an answer. "Why can't you leave him?"

"My parents, Sonia. They would be so disappointed with me, and not only that, I just won't get any support from anyone if I want a divorce. In my head it is just not so simple. I mean, where am I going to live? I need a plan or something that will help get me out of this."

"Okay, I get it now. Is that all you are afraid of? Is that what has been stopping you? So here's the plan," she said, pacing the room like a barrister in a courtroom. "Here's what you do. You—" She paused, pointing and looking at me. "One, get home; you play nice wife to him while I set things up for you, somewhere to live. Two, I want you to keep your handbag close by you, your car keys, driving licence and wallet with you at all times. Three, you are going to save some money, about three thousand pounds; keep it safe somewhere. Four, when the time comes, leave the house during the day when no one is at home. Five, once you do this, just call. Six, I will help you settle into our new place. Seven, once you have everything in place, I will move in with you."

"What about my belongings?" I said, trying to suss out every angle.

"Well, what's more important in a fire situation, you or your belongings?"

"Me," I said.

"So, fuck your belongings; you don't need them – we'll figure that bit out later. I just want you out of there as fast as possible without him catching on."

"You are right, I don't need them. The main thing is that I am out."

It felt good that Sonia was taking the lead for me on things. When you have been mentally beaten down like this, it is hard to make sense of anything, what is wrong, what is right. It is like being a mental cripple, and you need somebody who will act like a walking stick for you. You are leaning on them to help you get through the decision processes as to which way to go.

"Okay, I have a home; I have money; but what the hell am I going to do about my family? They will be devasted that I am putting them through this. My mother already said that she would rather see me dead than divorced."

"And you are more likely to be dead than divorced in this marriage, Eleanor. Do you not see? And if this is the case, which one of your parents will hold themselves accountable for it? Which one would you rather be? Dead or divorced? I think they would know the answer, and you know your options here. Your safety always comes first. You must trust that everything will work itself out with your decision to leave."

And with that, it was clear; the plan was made. It was clear now, I had given myself permission to move forward.

CHAPTER FORTY-ONE
– The Plan–

I arrived back in London. Syed was there to pick me up from the airport, and we drove home silently in the car. Things were different now. I felt less of a need to worry about his every move or motive. I could no longer entertain his every whim and teeter around him. I had a new perspective on things. Within a week, I had transformed my outlook and felt that I was now facing a new reality, one with a new plan. A plan that I still feared may not work.

Upon my arrival at the front door, Syed's family were beaming and happy to see me. I was overtaken by guilt at seeing their joy: here I was, planning to leave them, and they had no idea. I could only feel selfish then. But this I later felt foolish for thinking. One cannot make another happy if one loses one's sense of inner self, inner contentment and love for oneself. You cannot truly be giving lovingly if part of you is suffering in doing so. Being here for them in this way would not complete them, and neither would it complete me. I learned this because I could not complete my own mother by sacrificing what I loved. Real love could only come from giving it freely, without conditions. I realised that I was not giving my love to my mother and my family freely. I was asking for their love in return. My act of kindness was coming from a place where I felt that giving myself up, sacrificing myself, would make them love me back. I had, without realising, set conditions for myself, that to be loved, I had to give them a part of me. But that part of my being would leave a gaping hole and would leave me feeling discontent and unfulfilled for doing so. This was not real giving. One cannot succeed in giving if one has not built within oneself the capacity to give. It is like lending someone money when you are already in debt.

I couldn't sustain this way of thinking, and I knew it. I wasn't the truest version of myself, and I would only be servicing a deficit living this way. This would not benefit anyone. I spent some time analysing the grand plan, working out whether it was feasible. Did I have enough money and savings? The wedding costs had chewed up most of my savings, and I had credit card debts stacked up high against my monthly income, of which I gave some to my in-laws as rent. I looked at my accounts to see how much I had saved. I had about three thousand pounds. It wasn't great, but it was better than nothing.

I knew I had to keep things quiet though, for the time being. I disguised Sonia's number as a female manager at work, although it would still arouse suspicions. So I kept the calls short when I needed to speak with her.

The following week Sonia had organised a meeting with an estate agent to view a rental property. We arranged to meet during the workday. It was hard for me to justify going into the office, and I knew this could be a tipping point with Syed, as I barely went into the office anymore. The rental was in Hampton, a small town not too far from my place of work.

After the meeting, Sonia and I went off to a pub. I felt uncomfortable and nervous as Sonia lit up a cigarette and poured out a glass of wine for me.

"Drink up," she said. "You look like you need it." I took a few sips, but I was anxious they would smell it on my breath when I returned home. I didn't want to die just yet.

It was a sunny spring day, and the blossoms were gently falling off the trees behind her. The pub had hanging baskets brimming with spring flora, and I could only see everything around me overflowing with life. It was a feast in itself to enjoy snippets of this.

"I best get back. He will be home soon," I said anxiously.

Sonia nodded reluctantly as she took one last drag of the cigarette before stubbing it out in the ashtray.

It was 4.30 p.m., and there would be ample time for me to get back home before Syed arrived home. But the traffic was typically bad and was not moving. I arrived home at 6.30 p.m., relieved that I was more or less on time – in time enough to not arouse any suspicions, anyway. I breathed in a sigh of relief, only to find Syed sitting on the hallway stairs, his eyes narrow, hands together in prayer position, jutting them against his mouth as if to ponder the right words to throw at me.

His eyes were fixed on me as he rose silently from the staircase.

"Where have you been?" he asked as I slowly came in through the door.

I delayed my response by closing the door slowly to gain some composure on what was coming.

"You know, I have just come back from the office," I said, putting my laptop bag down.

"Don't lie to me. Where have you been?"

"That is the truth," I said.

"Okay," he said, edging nearer. He proceeded to grab me by the arm and drag me to the office room. "Do you want to explain what this is?" he said, swinging me in front of the office desk.

He pointed at the phone, where a red light indicated a voicemail message.

"Maybe let's listen to it, shall we?" he said, seething and pressing the button for the voicemail replay.

"Hi, Eleanor. This is John here from Maxwell Estate Agents. Thank you for visiting the property this afternoon. Just following up with you to find out what your thoughts were on the apartment you viewed earlier. Of course, do contact me if you are interested, and we can get the paperwork and contracts together. Look forward to hearing from you."

I wanted to fall apart hearing that message. I could sense where this was going.

"Well?" he said as he moved closer to me.

I crept backwards, away from him, nearer to the staircase.

"Do you care to give me an explanation?"

I stood silently for a second, but before I had time to offer any explanation, I felt his hand bash the side of my face. I screamed as I hit the wall.

Sufyan heard me from upstairs and came scrambling down the staircase.

"Bhabhi, are you okay?"

"You fucking bitch!" Syed screamed into my ear where I had fallen, cowering into a wall.

"You lied to me! You fucking lied to me!" He grabbed me up by the front part of my blouse and pushed me towards the stairs. I tried to climb up the stairs towards Sufyan as quickly as possible, hoping for some salvation from his brother.

"Bhabhi," Sufyan said, standing in front of me, horrified.

"You stay out of this," Syed said, pushing me from the last step onto the landing hallway. I crept up from my cowered state, crawling to the next step, where I managed to climb to standing position, but I felt a second blow to my head, knocking me sideways into the door frame and onto the bedroom floor.

"Let me go," I cried.

Sufyan tried to intervene, trying to pull Syed away from behind him. Syed pushed him away, knocking him into the newel post of the stair handrail and onto the steps.

Sufyan hit his back, his skinny, bony frame knocked against the post, and I caught a glimpse of him lying there on the floor in pain. I had picked myself up from the bedroom floor, in tears at the events unfolding.

Syed stood at the door to the bedroom, fuming, his breath heaving, the rage in his eyes as though he was possessed. I looked at him in fear of what that meant and what he was capable of doing next. He launched at me with his third attack, this time pushing me into the wall. I tried to run towards Sufyan, but Syed closed the bedroom door.

Sufyan banged on the bedroom door from the outside and called out to me, his voice quivering with shock. "Bhabhi, are you okay? Bhaiya, let her out. Please don't hurt her, Bhaiya."

Syed pressed the door shut with one hand on the door frame, his foot wedging it to prevent Sufyan from pushing it open. He pressed my neck with one hand against the wall.

"What the fuck do you think you were you doing?" he asked me, breathing the words into my face. I didn't want to answer his question, because it wouldn't have led to any good outcome. It was more to justify his reason to hurt me, pain that would only get more severe than the first time.

"Just let me go," I whispered, trying to stay calm. Fear seemed to fuel his rage. His fingers pressed into my neck, the sweat damp against my throat. I tried to push him, but the weight of his grip made the struggle harder. Sufyan continued to push and bang at the door.

"Let me go, Syed." I choked now as I tried to say it louder. The coughing intensified with his hands pressed against my neck. I managed to knee him in the pelvis, and it freed his hand from the door.

Sufyan managed to push the door open. I crawled underneath Sufyan's arm, arched against the door frame, and tried to find safety in the bathroom. Syed pushed his way through, grabbing me by the hair, drawing me back.

"Oh, you are going nowhere, janu dear. I don't think a shower is going to clean your filthy lies today, darling."

I cried a helpless cry, begging him to let me go. He pushed me back into the room, onto the floor towards the bed. I crawled up, bruised, jittery and in shock, and suddenly I couldn't put up a fight anymore, or whatever it was that I was doing. I sat numbly on the side of the bed. I couldn't care at this point whether I was going to get a further pounding, or whether there would be anything left to justify. I stopped listening to the physical pain my body was generating. I stopped listening to the noise of Syed's voice yelling. I silenced the need for protecting myself with Sufyan's help. It seemed that I was only creating more pain for him. I was either going to be damaged tonight, or survive being damaged, anyway.

Syed's voice came into present form. "What do you want?" he said sternly.

I looked at him, tears blurring my vision of him as he stood ready for another attack at my response. But I was no longer in fear. I had surpassed the fear of pain, the fear of death, the fear of losing respect, the fear of bringing shame, and I recalled that moment that I saw in Shelley's eyes in Bangladesh, after she had been subjected to Babajee's physical violence. That look of fearlessness in her that I couldn't comprehend, the one that releases you. "What is there to fear when you have nothing left to lose? That is when you are truly free." she had said all those years ago. All the fear had diminished now. What was there left to fear? What was there left to lose? And in that moment of revelation, I felt at one with myself. There were no tears, and I could no longer feel the pain. I looked at him calmly. I was facing a moment of complete inner bliss, and so I simply and calmly told him my golden truth.

"I want a divorce."

An inner smile glowed as if my soul rejoiced in the declaration. It was as if those words had released a thousand dreams, and a new world was presenting itself. It was as golden as the sun rising in the morning sky in forming it on my lips. The sweet words of golden truth were melting on my tongue like honey. I felt it now: all those years with Mrs Abbots and the wise words came before me like a platter of sweet delicacies. It was golden, and nothing else made sense when those words were released. I stood, calmly looking at him in the eye. He seemed still for ten seconds as he took in my words, and I knew that my truth was a powerful truth, one that nothing could change.

"Right," he said, looking down and nodding. He stepped back. "Go on, get the fuck out, then. Here, here is your bag. Go on." He was powerless with those words. When there is no value left in something, there is nothing, no punishment or force, that can change what is golden. I knew he didn't want me to go, but there was no power in anything he could say or do.

I grabbed my handbag from the chair, which, thanks to Sonia's plan, had my belongings. I walked down the stairs slowly, Syed and

Sufyan following behind. I stood at the front door. High on adrenalin, shaking as flashes of his violence came from my memory. Then I seemed to grow nerves of steel, surprising my own ability to say what I wanted. "And I want my laptop bag," I turned and demanded calmly.

I didn't think he would give it to me without a challenge, but for some reason, he seemed to have been silenced. He handed it to me from the hallway, where I had left it on entering the house. "Here," he said, dangling my car keys. "You might need these," he said calmly.

I tried to reach for them, but he grabbed my hand as he put the keys into it, and twisted it round into my back.

Sufyan stood at the front. "Bhaiya, no!" he shouted.

Syed let go of my hand from behind my back. I quickly opened the door. He moved towards me, pressing my head into the car like the police catching a criminal. I quickly closed the door and locked it. Something he used to make me do when I was in the car, in case anyone attacked me. I reversed the car out of the driveway. I glanced over to see Syed standing there by the door, waving emptily and victoriously, Sufyan stood behind, arms folded, shaking. I was shaking, my hands barely holding the steering wheel. I reversed onto the main road, and a car stopped to let me through. Syed continued to wave at me. His eyes were glazed over, from what I remember; it was as though he had turned into a zombie and was unable to think or action anything else.

When I finally pressed down on the accelerator, I felt my body wanting to collapse; there was a sense of release, of complete liberation and exhaustion all at once. As if completing a race, and your body gives way to the emotional upheaval. I was crying with joy and elation and laughed hysterically for a moment. It turned quickly into sweet and sour tears. In disbelief of the sheer weight of what had happened. My eyes were now swollen, my face a mess of tears, sweat, my nose so blocked that I could hardly breathe.

I drove a straight line on the road. I didn't know where I was going. It dawned on me that I didn't have anywhere to go either. I called Sonia, but her phone rang out and went to voicemail. I continued to drive. My head went into overdrive with thoughts. I took a left turn onto another main road. I could just about make out where I was, and then I did the unthinkable. I couldn't bring myself to do it at first, but I wasn't thinking anymore. I was in survival mode. I just wanted to feel safe; I wanted to be somewhere where I never had to worry; I wanted to be wrapped in a warm blanket. I called someone, someone who I knew would help. It was Rohit.

At first I hesitated. I let the phone ring but then cut the call. I couldn't do it, but then the phone rang back.

"Hi, Eleanor," came her voice. It was Nia.

"Hi, Nia." I tried to speak calmly, disguising the tears that were streaming down my face. "It's ... it's Eleanor."

"Hi, Eleanor. Are you okay? What's the matter? You don't sound good. What happened?" she said, concerned. And that was it. I couldn't hold the dam of pain. I had to tell her everything. How I had been kicked out, how Syed had figured out I wanted to leave.

"Don't worry, say no more. We are coming," she said calmly. "Just get yourself to the supermarket car park, and we'll come and pick you up, okay?"

I nodded in shock. "Okay," I said.

*

They brought me inside, and I stood looking numbly down at the floor of their airy, pine-floored apartment. Nia settled me down on the sofa. "Let me get you a drink, Eleanor," she said softly.

Rohit sat quietly on the sofa opposite. I wanted to cry, but I couldn't let him see me like this. He took a deep breath and locked his hands in front of him. We sat quietly until Nia came with three mugs of tea. I was grateful for their willingness to help and comfort me, such that it set off another flood of tears.

"Thank you," I croaked as I gulped down the tears.

They sat quietly, giving me some time to put my words together.

"He found out," I said. "He found out I was trying to leave, and then that's when it all got bad, and I had no choice but to leave with nothing but the clothes on my back."

Nia had an empathetic look on her face, and for once Rohit showed some emotion and looked angry.

"That's wrong," he said, looking down. "You won't go back, will you, Eleanor?"

Nia suggested I switch off my phone to prevent my parents from ringing, and Syed for that matter. "They will ring," she said. "They will guilt you back. Just be calm for now; don't think about anything."

There, in Nia and Rohit's world, I did feel I was doing the right thing, but we all knew what was right could easily be laced with guilt. To do right by your parents.

The phone rang, and it was my parents.

Nia reached out her hand to where the phone lay on the coffee table. "I know they are concerned, but don't answer that phone. You are feeling vulnerable, and they will just persuade you to go back to something you are not clear about." She insisted, "You need to get your head straight and get clear about things."

I looked at the phone. I wanted to answer it because I was worried about going against them, and at the same time, I couldn't bring myself to do it. I knew what the answer would be from them: "Come back; go back to him, and things will work themselves out." But there was not an ounce of my aching body that could be tempted to see it through again.

Nia and Rohit listened as I pulled out story after story. Rohit sat there bewildered. His eyes glazed in shock. I wondered what he was thinking in those moments. I had forgotten that only two years ago, we were together as a happy couple, but how we had both moved on from that time. How he had unquestionably accepted my proposition of him being with Nia, and how things had changed when he had been. I realised that what he had with Nia was something mutual and special, and while some of it was premeditated, and I had helped arrange, they had a bond and were mutual to one another. Out of respect, there was nothing I wanted more than to keep it that way for them. After all, I knew how destructive I had already been, entering his life, reminding him of me. I didn't want that. I didn't want to be in Nia's face despite how willing and supportive she had been.

They gave me a blanket. It was the blanket that I had given Rohit as a present one year for his birthday. They put on the TV to try to keep my mind off things while Nia arranged a room for me with some of her freshly laundered clothes. I had a shower, seeing all the scars on the back of my shoulder from where he had thrown me against the wall. The seven-year-old me came back to haunt me again. *You can't do this to Mamajee; she won't be happy.* I shunned her with the closed door of the bathroom. I put on the spare clothes Nia had given me, my eyes swollen, my hair wet from the shower.

Nia knocked on the door. "Stay with us for as long as you need, Eleanor. We are here for you, okay?"

It dawned on me that I had to figure out what I was going to do now. I didn't have a home, and I couldn't rely on Nia and Rohit for eternity.

"Thank you, Nia. I appreciate that."

She smiled. "Goodnight. Call me if you need anything, okay? Oh, and tomorrow," she said, peering through the door again, "I really think you ought to go to a police station and file a report about the violence you have experienced. It won't mean any harm to you, but at least it will be noted that you have gone through all of this."

"Okay," I said. "You are right, I should do that."

I lay on my back in the empty spare room. I felt calm and safe, and for once I could start thinking forward rather than about how to keep myself safe. I looked at the ceiling blankly, tired and sore as I sank into the sheets. My mind wondered in and out of thoughts. *Where do I go from here? How do I face my parents? What if Syed tries to attack me? How am I going to face the world?* I felt the sores from the bruising as I turned in my sleep, the tugging in my heart with each turn, how Syed had behaved. At times I wanted to feel sorry for him. After all, he had been betrayed. I was the one planning to leave. On the other hand, I knew I had little left in me to keep accommodating his behaviour.

There were times during the night when the seven-year-old me tugged on my hand too. *You better go back. You are going to ruin the family name. What about Mamajee? How disappointed she will be. What about your future? You promised, remember. You promised.*

Then I pictured a time with Mrs Abbots, sitting under a tree, her smile, that calmness, the confidence that everything would be okay. How she managed to fill me with peace and love after my parents' abusive fight. I missed her, and I was bitter from the betrayal. Whatever she had done had wrecked Mamajee's life, and now those very same people had wrecked mine. I pictured her stroking my head, though, now. I pictured, once upon a time, how she had helped me through the tough times, how she was the only one who had supported me, had my back. *You are going to be okay,* I pictured her saying to me calmly. *Eleanor, just rest now. Just rest.*

*

The following morning, I woke early, stiff, shaky, with hunger pangs, yet no appetite for food. I hadn't eaten the night before, despite Nia and Rohit's persuasion. I heard the bathroom door open, and much to my relief, Nia had already woken. I felt a little awkward being there like a stray cat roaming their home. I could only bring myself to use their bathroom once they were up and pottering around, in case I disturbed them.

Nia knocked on my door gently. "Are you awake?" she whispered.

"Yes," I whispered back. She peered in. I had already dressed in the fresh clothes she had given me and brushed my hair with my hands.

"Would you like a tea or coffee, some breakfast?"

"Sure, that would be really lovely, Nia."

I followed her out to the kitchen. She set about putting the kettle on, filling the toaster with sliced bread and rummaging through the cupboard and fridge.

"So, how are you feeling?" she asked, buttering the toast.

"A lot better." I nodded. "I am going to meet my friends today, maybe also do a bit of shopping, get myself some clothes and toiletries."

"Eleanor, can I ask you to do one small thing for me today?"

"Sure," I said.

"Can you get to the local police station and make a statement about what happened? You need to file this as a report. You don't have to press charges against Syed if you don't want to, but something of this magnitude will protect you should Syed try to pursue you, or even just so that they are aware. I know some cases where women fail to do this out of fear, but really, this will reduce your fear and will allow you to have some peace of mind for your safety and welfare. Make sense?"

Initially this made me squirm. I didn't want to get in any more trouble with Syed and his family than I had already. In their eyes, as a family, none of what had happened was a crime. In fact, going to the police, in their eyes, was the crime, and I knew to them, that would be the bigger betrayal.

But really and truly, no real family would endanger a member of their own family, and I could see the benefit of letting the police know for my defence rather than a form of prosecution.

*

Sitting at the police station, I felt like a castaway stranded by a giant cruise ship, and the rescue mission was coming to save me.

I sat holding myself together in the waiting area of the police station. An officer came out to greet me, where there were three other strangers seated. A guy with a grey hoody sat laid back across from me, shaking his left leg incessantly. He never made eye contact but seemed agitated. When the police officer came towards him, he shot up and walked ahead of him. Another man seemed drunk and was leaning against the door frame, mumbling, and another young kid, around sixteen, just sat with his eyes fixed to the floor. I wondered what these people were here for, what crimes they had or had not committed. I felt vulnerable, as if I were on the wrong side of town. The policeman came over to where I sat.

"So, how can I help you?" he said, bending a little to show some compassion.

"I would like to file a report," I said nervously, trying to push back the tears.

"Okay, sure," he said softly. "Would you like to come into this room, and we can talk about it further?"

I followed him into a small room with a table and two chairs.

"Take a seat for me," he said as he poured a cup of water for me from the dispenser. "And what is this regarding?" he said, sitting opposite me.

I paused, contemplating how to explain it.

"My husband," I said, looking down at the table. It didn't feel right calling him that anymore. "He has been violent towards me, and I just don't want him to come after me," I cried. I guess that was what it was that set off the tears: I just didn't want him trying to persuade me to go back.

"It's okay," he said, calming me down. He reached over for a box of tissues and presented a plastic cup of water in front of me.

He gave me a minute while he wrote things down. He asked a series of questions: my name, date of birth, the incident, my husband's name, where we lived, my address.

"Do you have any bruising anywhere?" he said, looking up at my forehead.

"Yes, there are a few," I said, closing in. It didn't feel right telling him. I didn't want to get anyone in any trouble; I just wanted some peace of mind and safety.

"I will get one of our female officers to come and take a look. Firstly, though, do you want to press charges?" He looked at me square in the eyes. I sensed that he knew my answer.

"No," I said, shrugging my shoulders.

"Very well," he said, taking further notes. "Are you safe? Do you need a place to stay?"

"Yes," I hesitated. I hadn't worked out where I was going to stay yet. "I am staying with a friend," I added. "I just want to feel safe; I just wanted a report to be filed, that was all."

He proceeded to write the report. A round of questions about where the incident had taken place, where it had happened, when it had happened then followed. A female officer then took me aside into another room and took pictures of my bruising and marks. They didn't press it any further when the report was filed.

Nia was right, it made me feel a little better to have it all recorded, an imprint of time. The police officer was very compassionate and supportive. He gave me some numbers for support groups, women's helplines and the police station's local number, and assured me that I should contact them if I needed anything.

I left the police station feeling secure and not in fear. It was as though I had put decisions in writing to the world of what had happened. I wasn't trying to blame anyone or finger-point. It was about choosing what was safe for me, that no matter what happened, I deserved protection. I stepped out through the door and could see the world better now.

Talking to the police had also made me realise that I didn't have to be afraid of speaking up. That seeking my own protection was my given right. I realised then that I had starved myself of that need to feel safe for a very long time. I no longer had to fear that I would suffer a blow over minor things with Syed. My mind had been racing all those years, such that I'd had time for little else. I could see things differently now. I could now enjoy the everyday things, the trees glistening, the sun shining, the calmness of life and, more than anything else, that I was a part of it. I could belong to it, not just see it from a window as if it were another world.

I drove to a shopping mall, picked up some cheap clothes, underwear, dresses, shoes to match a new jacket, a full set of make-up. I had nothing other than the clothes I had worn the night before. Starting over was thrilling. I was taking baby steps towards being myself again, and this time I was determined to not go back. The plan that Sonia had set out was working: the money that I had set aside helped me to start over again on things that I had never thought

I would have to buy again. I changed immediately into the clothes I had paid for. A green knee-length dress – yes, knee-length, not fully covering. It felt strange showing my legs at first; the paranoia set in that someone from my family might see me, but I shunned the thought. I wanted to feel the real me now.

I applied the make-up in the mall toilets, covering the bruises on my forehead, the dark, swollen eyes. I brushed my hair, cleaning away the knots that were tangled up. I walked out of the shop like a new woman. The cheap sunglasses that I bought sheltered my eyes from the piercing spring sun. My inner smile glowed with liberation as I strolled the mall, but by lunchtime my anxiety started kicking in. Where was I going to live or stay?

I calmed the panic with a coffee from the mall cafe and set myself at a table, and although the hunger pangs kicked in, I hadn't the appetite for food. I turned my phone on to try to call Sonia; a flood of voicemail messages bombarded my phone. It was as if I was being attacked emotionally by voicemail and text. I was tempted to hear out the messages from Mamajee and Babajee, but I couldn't bring myself to listen to the guilt and the manipulation. At the same time, I wanted to listen to them. The reality was that I would have to face them at some point. I told myself that I could listen to the messages, but I must not be drawn into the messages.

There were messages from Mamajee, disappointed. "Eleanor, where are you? Can you call back? We have been ringing you all night."

Another from Babajee. "Eleanor, is that you? Where are you? Is this how you should behave, disrespecting your parents like this? We called several times. You are destroying us. Eleanor, if there are problems, you should talk to us, and we can work this out, not walk out aimlessly."

There were countless more messages from my aunts. "Eleanor, where are you? Call us. We are all worried. We can help you. Call us back so that we can talk."

Much to my surprise, there were no messages from my in-laws, nor from Syed.

I ignored the messages; it was as if they were hitting a brick wall and dying out. I wasn't going to let them in this time. I didn't care about reputation, or face, or shame, or their opinions, their thoughts. What was most important now was me. The only person who mattered right now was me, my safety, how I chose to move forward. I told myself not to be lured back into that hole no matter how scary it was going to feel, and if I wasn't strong enough, I would build a dam in its place. I told myself, no one was allowed to enter into my world unless I chose them to. Their opinions were no longer credible.

I wasn't going to let their messages be translated into guilt. I knew there was nothing worse than going back to that life, even if it meant that I would be homeless or penniless, even if it meant that I would be seen as shameful in my parents' and family's eyes. I told the seven-year-old me that I had nothing to be ashamed of anymore: at rock bottom, you have nothing to lose. Then I remembered what Shelley had told me all those years ago in Bangladesh: "When you have nothing more to lose, that's when you are the freest."

*

Later I listened to a message from Sonia. "Hey, hon. Are you okay? Call me when you get this." The message was from last night. I called her back. There was a sigh of relief when I told her the good news.

I met her that afternoon at a bar in Putney. She grabbed me a white wine and immediately lit up a cigarette.

"Bloody hell, Eleanor," she said, taking another drag and shaking her head in disbelief. "I can't believe you got out. How horrific!"

I had moved on from the need for sympathy and emotional support. I was desperate to get my life back on track. "Sonia, what the hell am I going to do now? I need somewhere to stay."

"Ah, that whole thing, that's the easy stuff. Just stay with me," she said matter-of-factly, puffing on a cigarette. "Stay for as long as you need to while we work on something long-term."

I felt the weight being lifted. "Thank you for all of this," I said.

"For God's sake, Eleanor, as long as you are out of that hole, for goodness' sake, as if you even have to thank me."

That evening, after thanking Rohit and Nia and collecting my things from their place, I went over to Sonia's house.

Sonia opened the door immediately before I had a chance to knock. She flung the door open and dragged me in, her face full of relief as she leaned into a hug.

"Aargh!" she screamed. "So glad you are here. Fucking hell, Eleanor, you really scare the life out of us."

I continued to stay in her embrace. "Thanks, hon," I said with deep relief.

I let go, looking at her with a beaming smile.

"Come inside. Let's get you sorted with a drink. How are you feeling?" she said, pouring me a glass of white wine.

I sighed. "I am okay. I am still feeling anxious. I have nowhere to live," I said, exasperated.

"Eleanor, that's the easy part. Why are you so worried about that?"

"I don't think people really understand the turmoil you go through when you don't have anywhere to live," I said to her, tense and worried.

"Do you think I am going to let you hang about on the street? You can stay with me until something comes up, okay?"

I hesitated. I didn't feel totally comfortable. I didn't enjoy relying on anyone. That was the truth.

"Okay?" she asked again, nodding for me, insisting I respond.

"Okay," I said.

"Now, next steps," she continued. "We will look for somewhere, of course, and make sure you find somewhere to rent, but in the meantime, I need you to keep your head together.

"Number one, no alcohol after tonight – I don't want you going out and getting drunk. I think your head will be messed up enough as it is, so now you must keep your head clear. You will be an emotional wreck one minute, and you will be happy the next. One minute, you will love the freedom, and the next minute, you will be on a downward spiral of depression and anxiety. I want you to avoid alcohol so that we can avoid any addiction or going into a depressive mental state."

"Okay, no, I am with you on that," I said to her. Like she was my boss.

"Number two, no matter what advice I give you, it is not going to make you feel any better until you have worked it out and are able to process your feelings constructively. Anyone can dispense advice, but to stop you from going into a black hole with your life, I want you to go see a counsellor. They are going to help you process your feelings and put them into perspective. Can you do that? I am pretty sure your work will have some counselling service that they can offer, and if not, then we can look for somewhere else."

I nodded, listening. It was good advice.

"Number three, can you relocate your work for a while? Maybe ask your boss if you can go work at your US campus. I just think you will be constantly reminded here in London. To have a change of scenery might just help put things into perspective and stop you getting so anxious and paranoid."

"You are right, that will help. I will see if I can get my boss to help on that front," I said.

*

That night, as I lay in bed in Sonia's room, I felt like I had a plan. It wasn't a grand one, but it was small steps in the right direction. I thought about Mrs Abbots and how she had always taught me that.

"Sonia, can I ask you something?" I said.

"Sure, hon," she said, grumbling half-wearily.

"That day when you called me, what made you call me?"

She turned, thinking, facing me in the bed. "You know, after your wedding ceremony, after you left in the wedding car?"

"Yes," I said.

"I saw an English lady standing there. I don't know who she was, but she seemed in a bad state, very upset, in tears in fact. Lenna and I had been waiting outside the hall for a while, of course, and I had watched her. I couldn't fathom what she was upset about, so I asked her if she was okay. She replied, 'Yes,' but I could see she clearly wasn't. 'Are you a friend of the bride?' she asked me, trying to distract my attention a little.

"'Yes, I am,' I replied. 'How about you?' I asked.

"'You could say that.' She nodded. But she burst into tears again. 'I love her,' she continued. 'I just want the best for her.' That's what she kept saying.

"Eleanor, who was that woman?" Sonia asked rhetorically. She looked baffled as she stared up at the bedroom ceiling, shaking her head. Then she paused, thinking it over before continuing. "She was so devastated, Eleanor, I cried with her! I told her that I wanted the best for you too." Sonia looked up at the ceiling, her eyes glistening by the light for the lamp.

"She asked me ..." Sonia continued. "She said, 'If you are her friend,' and this lady was sobbing. She said, 'Will you promise to look out for her?' I saw how it was tearing her apart, as much as it did for us watching you go down the aisle, Eleanor.

"'Of course,' I said to her. 'I will look out for her.'

"Eleanor, that woman seemed like someone who really loved you, and if you ever wanted to know that you are truly loved, then know that she really did. That's the real reason why I couldn't give up on you."

I couldn't feel her words: I was blocking it all out. How could I even trust Mrs Abbots, or my family, in light of what happened on that wedding day? That day was like watching the death of my existence, and everything and everyone I knew. I had said goodbye to it all.

"That lady," I said. I paused, thinking about how to answer a question I had never had to answer before. My relationship with Mrs Abbots had never been defined, and nobody really knew about it. I guess she must have been upset about the horrible exchange with Mamajee at the wedding, and that she had betrayed my trust. I had blocked out the thought that she had fractured my parents' marriage. I couldn't bring myself to wonder about what had happened there. It was the only way of salvaging any respect for her, if I could block out what it might have meant for Mamajee. It was all so painful. I could only deal with one tragedy at a time.

"That lady," I said, "that was Mrs Abbots, my teacher."

CHAPTER FORTY-TWO
– *Breathing Light* –

The following day, I took the morning off work and headed to the park. I strolled through the entrance, the sun glistening through the arching trees that embraced each other from each side along the path. I could hear children playing in the distance, and watched toddlers straying from their parents, who then came running for them. I roamed around the old stately home within the park, which stood grandly before a still lake where swans and ducks glided through the water, causing long, sweeping ripples to glide across it. It was still and calm here. To feel like this was like being gifted a magical box of intense pleasure. I relished in it, immersing myself in the sounds, the softness of the cool morning breeze, the light between the trees. In survival mode, these are all things you lose the ability to enjoy, because your mind has urgent things to process. I listened to the murmurs of people passing by on bicycles, clinking their bike bells as they passed. It was peaceful for once in my mind, with no sense of danger.

I strolled farther and found a farm shop selling fresh organic vegetables. There were large, plump tomatoes and carrots, ripe and chubby. I wandered on, looking up at the trees, thanking God a million times. My inner smile radiated with these golden nuggets of priceless freedom. It was like a smile I could only feel from inside me.

I went to the tea house and rustled up some spare change for a hunk of bread, cheese and a black coffee. I had survived on so little that everything now became enriched with taste and abundant in pleasure. I was breathing in the light. The truth became clear that life is abundant regardless of your circumstance; it is only in the confines of our minds that we are poor or perceive happiness to be lacking. I had subscribed to many other ideals of life; to make others happy was what I had prescribed for my own happiness, to the point where I had lost sight of myself. I realised in that moment that I had to learn to love myself and feel joy in being, to be in a position to give or pass on love or happiness. If that beacon of light within one's soul is burning low, then how can anyone see its light?

I sat pondering this by an old redwood tree, its branches stretched out wide, and as I nuzzled myself comfortably between its roots, my mind drifted into those moments similar to this, those moments where Mrs Abbots and I would sit by the roots of those trees near the school playground, overlooking the glorious hills. I recalled that very first day, when I gave myself permission to eat the jelly. "You can choose it," she would say. "You can choose to smile; you can choose to not suffer; you can choose to be happy; and you can even choose to eat the jelly."

"Here I am now, Mrs Abbots. I finally chose it. I finally realised that happiness was always there; I just had to choose it."

*

When I came into the office that afternoon, I found three large bouquets of flowers sitting on my office desk.

Rohit looked at me, motioning to the desk. "That's the third one today from Syed." I looked at him, and he knew instantly where they belonged. "Here, let me help you," he said, smiling as he dumped them in the bin. I smiled, passing him the next one as he crushed them down with his feet. At his house, Rohit hadn't expressed much about his feelings, but men like Rohit show their truest opinions in their actions. I watched as he crushed the flowers into the base of the bin, one by one. His actions spoke volumes, and I could feel in him a sense of powerlessness in all that had happened.

The next few weeks were a whirlwind of emotions and stresses. My work was suffering: I couldn't give it the attention it deserved or required. I had spoken to my boss and explained that I was suffering from marital problems and needed some time to get back on track. When I suggested that I continue the project from the U.S., he was completely supportive of the idea. I moved to South Carolina for a month, working in the labs. Having time away created physical and mental distance from my family. Reality set in, though, upon my return. I still hadn't found anywhere to live.

Sonia and I visited a handful of rental properties, but they were all depressing. I couldn't bring myself to consider any. Some of them looked in dreadful condition. The plan that we would share a place had also gone to pot, and my rental costs would become more than I had anticipated. She was in the process of starting an assignment in the United States. I stayed with her for a week, sharing her double bed. Although we were like sisters and neither of us cared about sleeping in the same bed, I couldn't take liberties with it; I couldn't take it for granted.

I spent some time down in Farmouth, where Andrea and her new boyfriend lived. It bought me some extra time while something came up on the accommodation front. In the meantime, Lenna offered to have me at her place for almost two weeks. And while I took the generosity of my friend's goodwill and compassion for my situation, I felt anxious and exasperated about finding somewhere to live. Having my clothes in the boot of my car and bumming from lounge sofa to lounge sofa, or lounge sofa to double bed, gave me a feeling of disarray. I was also in danger of exhausting my options. I couldn't bear the idea of asking my friends whether I could stay for another week, and at the end of the week at Sonia's place, I decided I would definitely need to find somewhere else to stay.

I returned back to the office that week to more morbid, wilted flowers, a reminder of the sad state of affairs.

"They have been sitting there for more than two weeks now, I think," came a voice from behind. I turned and saw one of those infectiously beaming smiles, the ones that make you immediately smile back. It was Matthew, the colleague I worked with sometimes from a different team. He seemed to be chuckling silently now; we did this often when we saw each other. He would chuckle silently, and it became infectious, and for seconds we would giggle together. I couldn't have been more pleased to be in such positive company.

"Matthew!" I beamed back at him. "How wonderful to see you again. How are you?" I said. Seeing him was like that ray of sunshine you needed after the rain. I felt grateful just for that moment.

"Good!" He continued giggling silently as if it was the funniest thing.

"Oh, yes, we can bin those," I said, smiling at the flowers.

"Oh, do you not want to see who they are from?" he said, then rather seriously peered over the top of the bouquet.

"Well," I said, "honestly, not really."

"Oh?" he said, surprised.

"They are from Syed, and we split up."

"What?" Matthew said, horrified. "No. Really? I feel like I only just got back from your wedding." His face dropped a second time, and he shuffled himself over by the chair at my desk. "I am so sorry. I didn't realise," he said. "Are you okay, Eleanor?"

"Well, it just wasn't going to work. You know, it was just very difficult," I said with a smile, wanting to reduce the tension on the matter, but it was as if he could see right through me, and for once I saw his smile fade out. It made me sad to think that I could create such ill feeling around me. I wanted to switch to something more positive.

"Well, I am shocked and sad to hear that," he said grimly.

"Don't be sad. I am happier now, and it was the best decision I made for myself. So, how about you?" I said, smiling and teasing him with a nudge.

"Ohh, yes … well, no good news there, I'm afraid. Emma and I split last month."

"Oh no, so sorry to hear that," I said.

"No, don't be. It hadn't been working out for a long time; it was coming to an end."

Matthew changed the subject, as if moving on was as simple as just that. "So, what are you doing tonight? Andy and I were going to go for drinks near my place. Did you want to come?"

"Er." I hesitated. "I would love to, but I have to find somewhere to live, so I will be busy house-hunting."

"You mean, you don't – you don't have anywhere?"

"No. I have been away and need to find somewhere. I'm staying with a friend temporarily."

"Well, I have a spare room at mine. If you want to stay there," he said.

"That's very kind of you, Matthew, but I think I will continue to look first."

"Well, the offer is there, but you know, why don't you just come out tonight? I can help you find somewhere later. Go on. We haven't seen you in ages."

"Okay!" I said, as if seizing the opportunity. "I will come for one drink," I said, peering at him earnestly.

*

Soon Matthew and I were meeting up regularly. He heard my highs and lows, and listened to my horrific accounts, one by one, restoring the little broken parts and putting me back to a place where I felt safe and out of danger.

Through his support, he helped patch my life together in ways I wouldn't have managed by myself. At work, when my projects were falling behind, it was Matthew who helped me get things back on track. He could see it, more than anyone, that I had suffered a severe tragedy in all aspects of my life.

It was Matthew who helped me find a place to rent that summer. In my desperation for somewhere to live, I finally settled on a small room no bigger than a box room in a houseshare with three other professionals, and although we shared the same house, there were no communal spaces or living areas where people were able to so-cialise. In the evenings, you could hear the tenants blaring their TV or stereo from the adjoining rooms, the stale smell of cooked food lingering through the weary, dank hallways. And a respite from this would mean opening the windows to the noise of low-flying jets landing at Heathrow Airport. My nights were spent in the confines of a small room, nobody to talk to, no television, no entertainment or a view to look out at. It was difficult to see my friends. With Sonia away in the US on business and Andrea all the way down in Farmouth, it became an empty and isolating existence.

It was Matthew who pulled me out of the darkness in that room, illuminating it with his pleasant, cheery smile and softly spoken words. At night we would sit together, legs crossed or perched on the end of the bed, to watch TV from my work laptop. It was Matthew's ingenious idea to set up my laptop with a plugin aerial, as I didn't have a TV. Sometimes we'd have dinner together, on a narrow dining table that faced the wall. But with him present, it didn't seem to matter what the four walls surrounding me looked like.

He also helped me get organised, such as getting me to file my letters and statements. He helped me buy furniture I needed for my room, fixing up the cupboards and rickety drawers that needed repairing. He helped me get out of the financial rut I found myself in after my split. The money needed to fulfil my parents' wishes for me to be married had racked up thirty thousand pounds' worth of credit card debt, which I was paying back with interest. I was living on what I earned and barely making ends meet, with debts coming out of my ears. It was Matthew who helped me get back on track with clearing it. He helped me organise my credit cards, advising me to move to interest-free balance transfers and interest-free credit card periods. It was under his advice that I sold my company shares, something I was reluctant to do, given that I had been with the company and had saved them all these years. "It's the right thing to do now," he said, insistently. "There is no point in holding on to savings if you have debt. It's best to clear the debt and then start saving."

When Syed finally agreed to give back my personal belongings, it was Matthew who did the dirty work of confronting his family and collecting the items. My parents and family would have nothing to do with it. He hired a taxi, drove to the house, knocked on the door and kindly and patiently confronted Syed and his family about my belongings.

"Hi. I am one of Eleanor's colleagues from work," he said calmly to Syed at the door. "I am here to collect some of her belongings." He kept the conversation professional while Syed looked at him dubiously.

"Oh yes, I remember you. You were at the wedding, weren't you? Come in, come sit down," he said in a firm and commanding way.

Matthew described how Syed had tried to be difficult, of course, pacing around the room, ordering Matthew around with the belongings he was handing back.

"Here, take this," he said, taking the heat out on Matthew as he shoved or threw bags of my belongings from the garage door.

Then, strangely, as Matthew was leaving, Syed asked Matthew to pass a message on to me. "Tell Eleanor, if she comes back, that new Mercedes is hers." Pointing at a new Mercedes E-Class convertible on the driveway, as if it were a way to entice me back.

"It was uncomfortable and unpleasant," Matthew explained later. "You should have seen the way he threw things into the boot of the taxi, as if it were garbage going into a waste truck."

When he arrived back to my place, Matthew unloaded four bin bags full of clothes, boxes full of CDs, books, paperwork, which he later had me file away. He helped get rid of the letters I didn't need anymore. There were crockery boxes that had been left untouched from when I'd first moved in with Syed. Shoes that matched all the sarees that my mother-in-law had made me wear for dinner parties and special occasions. I had stacks of imitation jewellery and a large thirty-kilogram suitcase full of Indian sarees and suits. There were wedding gifts, unopened or in their packages. Mostly these were items that Syed would not have wanted, such as books, vases and picture frames. My already small room was turned into a scrapyard of items that I mostly didn't care for, want or need anymore. We spent that weekend sorting through all the items, Matthew being ruthless in helping me decide what to keep, given I only had a small space.

"Do you need this?" he would ask, looking at the boxes of books that I had read.

"Well, no, not really," I would say, hesitating. "I have read them."

"How about these?" he would say, looking at a whole suitcase of sarees. "No, I guess not." Some of them were expensive, glittering, bejewelled and embroidered pieces for special occasions, and while I wasn't attached to them, I couldn't bring myself to throw them away. So I gave them all to Mamajee and my sister on a later visit back home. By the time we had finished, we had sent some of the items to the tip or charity bin or thrown them away in the recycling.

Soon my room became clutter-free again, almost at least, with only a couple of large boxes remaining.

"What about this last box here?" Matthew asked, opening the lid of the box and lifting some of the contents out. It was filled with pictures and more unopened wedding presents. He pulled one out. "This sounds interesting," he said, pulling out a cardboard box and shaking it. "What do you think is in here?" he said, passing it to me.

I sighed, wondering whether this decluttering was ever going to end. I cut the taped box with scissors; it sounded like a rattle as I tore away the tape. And there it was. Inside was something familiar, something that I could only see flashes of in my mind's eye. There inside was a box wrapped in a pink floral cloth, the tiny flowers now faded with time. It had been neatly tied together with a silk ribbon. I recognised the handwriting: "For you, Eleanor. You will always be loved. Love is in everything. Just open your heart and keep creating the capacity to feel it."

I opened the tin box. It was filled with things, flattened, dried leaves, pressed petals, shards of glass, pebbles, all of which were shaped like hearts, and I recalled my childhood once again. How we had sat under the tree behind the school gates, and she had taught me to find it in everything. How I had spent hours scouring the earth on my way home from school, and the days when all I needed was a heart-shaped leaf or puddle to bring me joy. I had collected them and given them to Mrs Abbots. I recalled her tears when she opened the box, and now here it was again.

"What is it?" Matthew asked as he saw my tears.

"Love," I said. "That's what it is; it is a gift of love." It had been thrown into a box somewhere amongst my belongings, and Mamajee probably would not have wanted me to see it, and like everything important to me, it had been lost in the debris of life.

*

With my life now slowly being restored to some normality, with a comfortable place and manageable finances, I began to enjoy myself again. Matthew and I spent the summer on the beaches of Wales and Cornwall. Some nights we'd dine at restaurants, and other nights I would cook in the confines of my humble space, and sometimes at Matthew's. We took walks around the park near me and would sit in the hazy sunshine around the lake. There were days filled with laughter, and there were others filled with pain. But all the while, Matthew listened to all my stories, lovingly, compassionately and expecting nothing in return. It was great to spend time with him, platonically, as friends. With Matthew, I was happy in ways I had never felt before, free.

One night we went together to one of his friend's birthday parties. They hosted the party at their house in Putney. It was a balmy summer evening, and the party was in full swing by the time we arrived. The garden brimmed with twenty-somethings, drinks in hand and cocktails being served with ice in plastic cups. The sun was setting, and the evening grew darker as we mingled with cups of margaritas and crushed-ice cocktails.

My head felt heavy from the alcohol, having abstained from it for so long, I could no longer handle the effects. I propped myself against a wall, stirring my cup with the swaying motion. I could see Matthew a few feet away, laughing and chuckling with his friends. I loved his smile, his calmness, the way it felt around him. That feeling that I was completely safe, away from any harm. Around him, it didn't feel complicated. I didn't have to change anything. He accepted me as I was. He wasn't going to change me; I was enough. I finally experienced what trusting someone really felt like. For once I began to feel an inner state of calm. I closed my eyes and could hear the laughter, the clink of glasses, the taste of Pimm's and cucumber on my tongue.

When I finally opened them, Matthew was standing before me. The sky had darkened now, leaving crimson spots between the trees. I couldn't see his face clearly but could see that he was smiling in the way his eyes illuminated and the creases around them deepened.

"How are you doing there? Are you okay?" he asked, holding up a glass of water for me to drink. Matthew always had the right thought or phrase or gesture with him. There was never a moment that could be mistaken for anything but love. I felt mesmerised by his small acts of effortless kindness. I pressed the glass against my lips, swaying slightly.

His hand was light against my shoulder as he steadied me from the wall I had propped myself against. I held his arm, embracing him a little as I took a sip of the cold water, the ice melting in my mouth. He took the glass gently from my hand, placing it on the windowsill. His smile softened as our eyes locked and our arms drifted into a gentle embrace.

Nothing was holding me back at that moment, and as we kissed, it was as though a million years had made that moment. It wasn't just love I felt for Matthew; it was a feeling of deep-rooted connectedness.

"Shall we go home?" he said with a warm, calm and deep smile.

"Home." I nodded with a smile. I hadn't heard that word for a long time, but with him, I had found a place I could call home. "Yes," I said. "Let's go home."

*

Within a year, things were looking up. I had moved in with Matthew, changed jobs and cleared all my debts. I had finally received my divorce papers; it had taken almost a year for Syed to sign the papers and give back the Islamic divorce settlement of £2,500, an agreed amount that is obligatory for any Islamic marriage to settle a divorce. I asked for nothing from him, no house, no furniture, no jewellery, no gold or gifts, even though some of it rightly belonged to me. I didn't want the reminder of Syed, and any of these material things would have given space for more arguments and interactions, which I couldn't bear to go through. But even when I made things as easy as this, Syed still made it difficult. He wanted me to pay for all the court fees and dragged out responding to any letters until my solicitor sent reminders. I didn't contest any of this though, but my solicitor fought on my behalf, and the courts responded by asking him to pay the full fee, mine included. It was a small victory for my solicitor, as he did not understand why I wouldn't ask for my jewellery back at least, but the very sight of it would have been a dark reminder of all that was vain and bitter in our marriage.

I paid off half of my debt by selling my company shares, the other by changing jobs. I wasn't challenged anymore by my role and had been underpaid for years. I knew I could do more. I could earn more, and it was a necessary move to feel secure and safe again. I didn't want Syed or his and my family to know where I worked anymore. In December of that year, I was headhunted by a partner company that had seen a copy of my CV. They offered me a position. At first I declined. I couldn't see myself leaving my current job – it was too comfortable – but Matthew soon made me see sense.

"What do you mean you are not going to take it, Eleanor? You will double your salary. It will also help you get back on track with your finances and your life."

"I know. You are right, it will help me move on." It wasn't so hard in the end. Even Rohit was pleased for me.

*

We shared our time between Matthew's place and mine, and by spring we agreed it made sense that I moved in with him. Matthew and I were in a world of bliss together. Every month, we packed our bags and set off for a weekend away, like two souls floating around the world in a bubble together. There was an essence of spiritual calmness about him, the way he conducted his normal daily routine, in washing, cleaning, organising the house, work and social engagements. He didn't ever get angry or upset, for example, not in the way even I would sometimes. There was never a raised voice or frowning face, and if there were any conflict, he would always manage to explain it patiently and calmly. Such qualities are rare in people. He was someone whole, clear, calm, collected and content in being himself, and I only aspired to be like him. He wasn't complicated and didn't have hang-ups about things that normally came with relationships. I was thankful to have met him, and abundantly grateful to have had the honour of meeting him.

After we met, I distanced myself from my family. I never told them about Matthew: I didn't want to open myself to them. My family no longer knew where I lived, who I was with or where I worked. I would have preferred it if they didn't know I existed, so that they could go on pretending it was all perfect in their world. I also never revealed my issues, my problems and suffering or anything of that manner about myself. They would never hear about how I had moved from house to house with a suitcase in the boot of my car, or how penniless and broke I had become with debts from the wedding. Or the countless tears and torments from the challenges of divorce.

My phone calls to them revealed nothing about me, and I only visited them a handful of times, as if it were to make them know that I existed only in the fragments of their minds, in only the heartbeats that pulsated with blood. And in those brief encounters, I would make it all about them, deflecting the focus from my existence to theirs. It was different now, going up to see them. I was outside their world, the realms of their reality, their way of thinking. I could only be likened to a handicapped person, and meeting people who my family knew became awkward. Mamajee avoided people coming over when I visited, in case they asked about the shameful D-word, and often left people to assume that I was still married. She kept the wedding portraits on the mantelpiece, and although it stung seeing them, what hurt more was knowing they still talked to Syed and his family as if it were inconsequential. I knew I could not belong to a culture that cultivated men to behave like this, and women to be at their disposal. I could no longer support something that didn't support me. And while Mamajee spent her time avoiding the D-word, it only confirmed that I was indeed as good as dead to them.

I avoided weddings. Attending them only made my family cringe: the way people gasped upon hearing I was divorced, the brooding questions that lingered in the afterthoughts as they turned away, my family biting their lips or eating their words as they heard the comments, the looking me up and down.

"I told you there was something wrong with her."

"What do you expect? It's like that amongst those Western, educated ones."

Or secretly gloating with a thin veneer of shocked expressions. "Oh dear," they would say. "Sorry to hear about this."

The looks and stares were enough to mutilate you in society. The cold silences and awkwardness when I walked into the room. It was as if I had a disease or had become severely impaired. They tried to gloss over it, talk amongst themselves and pretend I didn't exist. There was some truth in Mamajee's words now. Dead than divorced now. I appeared merely as a ghost, the unwanted evil that was casting a shadow on their lives and haunting them from time to time.

I stopped going to the local shops with Mamajee on those weekends at home, and she silently no longer offered or objected. She wouldn't have to lie or mock up a shiny portrait of my marriage. It seemed reckless on their part and only filled me with undeserved guilt and a sense of failure.

*

I slowly crept away from their lives, and as another year went by, I became more immersed with my own new-found happiness in Matthew, travel and my job, until one day at our flat in Kensington, as I was fixing up a meal for both of us, the phone rang and went to voicemail. I received a message from Mamajee. "Eleanor, it's your mamajee. Please call; it is urgent. There is something I need to speak to you about."

CHAPTER FORTY-THREE
– *Perpetual*–

"Hello," I said bravely. Mamajee sounded calm and pleased to hear from me.

"What are you up to?" she said coolly. I felt reluctant to open up: her tone sounded too casual, upbeat and with no sign of conscience about the past.

"Nothing really," I said vaguely.

I waited for her next question; I knew there was one coming. She paused, and I wondered what her motives were for calling after so long.

"A couple of people have asked about you, hmm. What are you going to do with your life now, Eleanor? Are you going to live on carelessly, aimlessly? What are your plans? What are you going to do with your future? People are talking; you are ruining our name like this. I can't show my face to anyone."

I sighed, wishing I had not entertained the idea of calling her back. I remained quiet, unresponsive to the rhetoric.

"I have had a word with a few people here," she continued. "One of our family friends in Birmingham has a relative in Bangladesh. He married recently, but when he came over, he and the girl split up. The marriage only lasted a month, so you can hardly call it a marriage. The problem is he has to return back unless he can be married again, and when speaking with his family, he seemed willing and happy to consider you. Well, he knows you are spoiled goods and all, but you two would have a lot in common, being now recently divorced. Beggars can't be choosers, can they? Allah knows what is written for you, and you should be thankful to Allah that he has put this opportunity in front of you. Especially after you dragged our name in the mud with all this divorce business. Maybe you can restore what we have lost. I can't show my name in the community anymore, not like this. Come up to Manchester this weekend so we can talk about this further."

I said nothing. I was livid and speechless to the point where I muted myself, because her opinion had become of such little importance now that I didn't feel she deserved to know how it felt. I couldn't even begin to understand what stung the most: the idea that Mamajee still saw this as my fault, that giving me away again solved everyone's problems, or that I only deserved to be with divorcees or people seeking immigration.

"I have to go," I said to Mamajee. "I am not going to talk about this right now," I said, putting the phone down.

I sat numb with sadness, seething inside with a war of emotions, processing her words in silence. I was still seen as a reject by her. Something that could be tossed out. Self-doubt kicked in. I guessed I couldn't make them proud like this; that hurt. Why did I care what they thought? But it hurt.

The seven-year-old me kicked in with that chant again. *Remember, you still owe it to Mamajee; you owe it to her*, she said. *You broke the promise; you let them down.*

What? I said to myself. *And give up my life again? Everything I have painstakingly built?*

"*You owe it to her: she almost died for you. All that pain was all for you. Did you want it all to be in vain?*"

My head felt heavy and in disarray again. *Am I be prepared to let everything I have with Matthew go? Could I do this? On the other hand, what if it doesn't work out with him? What if we break up? Then what? What support network do I have then?*

Matthew came into the room. He looked at me, a little concerned, as I sat, head low, deep in thought. "Are you okay?" he asked gently as he came and knelt next to me. The soft, calm face made me instantly connect with that place that felt like home again, but I couldn't tear away the thoughts that I had displeased Mamajee. I paused, looking at him with a concerned look.

"That was my mother on the phone just now. She wants to get me married again."

"What? To who?" His expression was horrified and confused.

"She's found this guy. He is divorced and wants to marry me so that he can stay in this country."

"What?" he said, shaking his head. "Are you serious? This is insane? Why would she want this?"

"I don't know," I cried. "And it hurts. It hurts a lot that she has this hold over me." It was difficult for me to explain to Matthew the intricacies of it all.

"Eleanor ... you would be making a huge mistake. You know that, don't you? Please don't consider this." The tears streamed down my face. In my head my seven-year-old self was overpowering me with guilt; it was hard to break through and fight it. I saw Mamajee lying there, half-dead, her limbs loose, her saree all over the place, her hair a long, tangled stream of mess along the floor. I saw the look on her face, the horrible choice she had to make, the suffering and humiliation with Babajee's difficult and poor behaviour. I wanted to make this all good again, make up for her grief-stricken past.

"Eleanor ... what are you thinking?" he said, his arms gently on my shoulders.

I paused, fighting the war inside.

He pressed my arms gently. "Eleanor, Eleanor, talk to me."

"I can't do this anymore," I said, looking at him with fear. I couldn't bear the thought that this would lead to failure, that I would then be on my own.

He shook his head calmly, unable to fathom me. "You can't do what?" he asked, pressing on my arms.

"I can't be with you," I cried. "It will just be too hard to make it work with my family. They will probably hang me."

"Eleanor, please don't let them do this to you. They are manipulating you. I am not asking you to stay with me, but please do this for you. Don't just get sucked into this guilt they are feeding you."

I shook my head, refusing to see his point of view. He'd never met them; he didn't know what they had put me through.

"I can't just ruin my family's name. I can't let that happen to them. I have created a lot of dents in their lives, and this would ruin them." I looked down at the ground, as I couldn't bear to look at him without a smile and happiness. Wasn't I stealing happiness from people again? Maybe this was what I was born for. My attempts to please had left me void of pleasing anyone, and now I was hurting the one person who had brought me back to the world of the living.

"I am going to go back to Manchester and honour my parents' request to meet this guy on the weekend," I said, looking vacantly down at the floor.

I walked out of the room before he could say anything more. Although he tried to reason with me, I knew I was hurting him just as much. He stayed quiet that night. I could sense in Matthew that while he could not fully understand what was going on with me, he knew some things couldn't always be explained. And once again I faced a dilemma I knew very well. This was nothing short of what I had been through before with Rohit.

*

In the morning, Matthew saw me out of the flat, his face no longer the cheery soul I knew, his eyes faded and no longer sparkling. His capacity to love was expansive and radiating from his expression as he calmly led me out. It hurt tenfold to think it was the last time we would hold each other intimately.

"I am worried about you leaving, Eleanor," he said, shaking his head. "I don't understand why you are letting them do this to you. You have so much going for you, Eleanor. You have an incredible life ahead of you. Can't you see that? I wish I could understand what compels you to do this."

I stood silently, the morning sun catching our faces outside on the street. He hugged me, wrapping his arms around me tightly. I could feel him caught in that space between us, caught between right and wrong, saying what was dutiful, what was necessary, yet bursting with the urge to speak the truth.

"I don't want to lose you," he said, squeezing me tight. "You always have me. You know I am here, right? You know that."

I cried, nodding, unable to bring any words that could reflect a response, and with that, I left him standing there as I drove away down the street.

*

When I arrived in Manchester, Mamajee had a full spread of food prepared for the guests. I despised how cheerful she became at seeing her guests, and yet not once did she think of how it had felt for me when I'd fallen down the last hole she'd thrown me in.

Still, she was happy. Wasn't that the main reason I was here? To fulfil her wishes? I watched the banter exchange over the table from the kitchen, the smile on Babajee's face as he discussed politics and the war of independence in Bangladesh. Mamajee had me dressed in a gold saree again; it was the same saree I had worn in her show pony performances before. My hair was tied up in a bun, resting underneath a starry sequinned veil. A strand of hair caught against a sequin and pulled against my head as if it were there to remind me that I deserved pain.

Accept this, my seven-year-old self told me once again. *This is all you need to do, Eleanor.*

Mamajee brought me in through the living room. There were two men sat beside Babajee in the lounge, who immediately rose from their seats upon my arrival into the room.

"This is your uncle; call him Chacha, and bow at his feet for me," Babajee said, grinning and chuckling as if he had asked me to do something of great honour. I bowed down courteously at the rubbery feet before me. The old man's wrinkled hands tapped my head gently with approval at my gesture.

"I suppose you should understand that this gentleman is this young man's uncle, not his father," Babajee explained as I rose from a courteous bow. He nodded slowly as if he had explained this very well and was seeking agreement from the other party.

The old man nodded while stroking his white beard, attaching a wrinkly smile, his teeth red-stained from the chewing of betel nuts. It was only then that I caught a glimpse of the man next to him. The man my parents were happy to choose for me as a suitor. The man my parents would happily have me married to without doubt or a flash of questioning. I realised that it was not at all important to them, who I married. To them, I was now excess baggage that had missed the flight and was now clearly labelled for dumping. I noticed the sharpness of his face, the serious scorn he wore on his brow, his eyes set heavy with a cold, emotionless stare, the lips tight and closed together. He was wearing a suit, standing tall beside Babajee like a commander in the military. Nothing like the man I had met in Matthew, I thought, the kind, compassionate, accepting man, with a face like a sun, smile like a sunbeam and eyes that captured my soul. I missed him already. I missed how clear and content I felt around him, his neat hair and clean shave, his smooth skin. *This feels wrong*, I thought in my head.

Beggars can't be choosers, remember? came the voice from the seven-year-old me.

No, but I shouldn't let them destroy me once again, I fought back internally with these words, but with each reminder of Mamajee's words, I felt as small as an ant making his way up the bathtub, only to be washed away down the drain.

As we sat down, I crouched underneath my veil while my parents continued to talk. I sat silently until Mamajee had me go back upstairs and sit quietly in my room. How alien it felt in this room now. It had changed somewhat now that my sister had moved in. Gone were my clothes, the curtains, the bedding that I had used, the flowered wallpaper that I had spent most of my afternoons making pretty patterns from. It had changed to a plain white embossed paper now. Suraya had crammed her clothes onto a small shelf at the top.

In my boredom, I had decided to pull them down to clear some clutter when a heavy box fell out and landed on the floor with a clunk, the papers strewn out on the floor across the room. I looked at them; it was a pile of photocopies. Then I picked one up to read it. It was one of Babajee's Christmas menus, and on the back were the drawings, drawings that I had created, letters that I had written to Mrs Abbots. A roadmap of where I wanted to be. Smiles came to my face. I felt a tinkle in my throat at the laughter of how much she had believed in me, the help with my exams, the painful letters I had written to her at the upset I'd felt when Mamajee and Babajee had tried to get me married at sixteen.

That was then. Now, sixteen years on, I was feeling that pain again, at my expense, and once again I was reminded that I had a choice. And if I chose it, it didn't have to be this way. I didn't have to marry this person. I could choose to be who I wanted to be.

I picked up the box, put away all of the papers. *I don't have to do this*, I said to myself. *Destiny is not written by anyone; you have a choice. And every decision is made through choice. It is a choice that changes things, changes the course of your life, from the road you walk down, the places you visit, to the people you meet.* And I wasn't going to let anyone write my destiny. I wasn't going to let anyone deny me that right. This wasn't their choice at all, or Allah's choice. Allah had given me the gift of life, the gift of choice, the ability to choose my path. I had to choose the path of my soul, that essence of me that made me alive. That reason for being here was my choice alone.

I pulled down the veil from my head, unravelled the twisted knot in my hair and let it spiral free. I changed into my clothes, packed up my belongings. Then I charged downstairs. Mamajee's face shrank from a large beaming smile to a look of horror at my change of appearance. I walked through the hallway towards her in the kitchen, staring into her face.

"What are you doing?" she said, dismayed.

"I'm leaving," I said plainly.

"You are not going anywhere," she said, trying to stop me by wedging the kitchen door.

"Let go," I said.

"Don't you dare even think you can walk out on me when guests are in the house."

"I am leaving, and you are not going to stop me," I said as I pushed the door open. Babajee peered through the hatch joining the living room and kitchen upon hearing the scuffle as I tried to open the door.

"Hey, what's going on here?" he said.

"Your shameless girl is leaving," Mamajee said, heaving.

I pulled down the door handle, refusing to listen to the insults. I stepped out, tripping on the raised threshold and losing my balance on the floor. The box fell open, with the papers strewn out into the garden. I grabbed them up, some getting wet from the damp lawn.

Then Mamajee launched on top of me, with her full weight pressing me down to the ground.

"Let me go!" I screamed, the sound echoing down the street. Heads raised out from a neighbour's window.

"Everybody is looking. Look at you screaming. What will every-one think of your behaviour?" Mamajee whispered.

"Get off me, get off me!" I shouted and pushed her away. I rose, fuming and terrified at what had just happened. I picked up the box and my bag, shaking with anger.

"You'll regret this. You go and see if you can find someone who would want to be with you. You have nothing."

I stood, appalled and disgusted by her words.

"Oh, Mamajee, you would think that, wouldn't you? After everything you have done to reduce me to something so small and forgettable. What was it? Didn't you say it? 'Dead than divorced'? But don't worry. I would rather be dead in your eyes than be forgot-ten in the eyes of the people who truly love me. And I will tell you something, just so that you can keep your sanity about regret, that I don't regret being divorced, because I have met someone who is twice the man now than you could ever find for me."

"You listen to me, haramzadi. You made a promise."

I ran to the car, slamming the door and locking it, paranoid that she might chase me, as I saw Mamajee drawing nearer to the car door. I then caught a glimpse of Babajee and my brothers now standing in a row in the garden.

I drove out from the street, my eyes blurry from the tears. A sense of liberation and defeat went through my body, tightening my chest. It felt heavy. I agonised at the traffic lights at the junction that led me onto the main road, worrying that my brothers might be following behind me. And then my eyes met what had kept me going all those years, what had led me out of these situations far too many times and what had given me courage and hope: the white house on the hill.

My mind ran through all that had happened on that wedding day. "They are manipulating you," she had said. I knew there was some truth now in that. Just like Matthew, Mrs Abbots was only trying to do right by me. I thought about Mrs Abbots; I thought about what she would say right now. I wondered where she was. How I had let her down too, cutting her out, as I had all the other people who had believed in me along my path, those few who genuinely wanted the best for me. How they heard my inner cry even when I ignored it. The truth is, they believed in me, more than I believed in myself. The traffic lights turned green, and I crossed the main road. I decided I wasn't heading home yet. There was something I had to do. I had to get to those hills. I wanted to see her, thank Mrs Abbots. Open my heart and tell her that whatever had happened, it didn't matter.

I drove out of the town, towards the hills. I had never been that far out from my town before. I didn't know the road name or the street where the house sat, but I never let it out of my sight. I passed through Staningbridge, a small town that sat at the foot of the hill. The house looked closer now, a mile, possibly, from where I lived. As I passed, I could see the whiteness of the brickwork as it shone through the trees. For years I had sat there in my bedroom with Babajee, staring at this house, and now I was almost close enough to it.

When I finally reached the top of the road, I could see the path that led me down to the house. It was a gravel road, the fields surrounding it, fresh and green. I could see Ashcroft below, the house I had lived in and the garden surrounding our property. I felt excited yet anxious to see Mrs Abbots. I parked up and walked up the path and knocked on the grey-painted door and waited patiently. I noticed the paint had peeled on the wood. The windows looked grey and dusty, as if the house had been unkept for a while. It seemed out of character: Mrs Abbots had always seemed so well-dressed and didn't seem the sort to not keep things in good condition.

For a moment I waited, but there was no answer. I knocked again, hoping that she might hear it this time. I turned to face the wind as I watched down below at the hills. There were no cows in this field, I thought. I normally noticed a few from my view. I resolved she wasn't home. *Maybe she is out*, I thought. I walked back to the car, disappointed. I had hoped that I would see her before I left for London. As I approached the car, I saw an old man walking past the hill. He looked local, as if he lived nearby.

"Excuse me," I shouted, waving at him. He stopped to face me. "Do you know the lady who lives here? And would you know when she will be home?"

The man looked quite elderly, and it took some time for him to gather his response between breaths. "Oh, I am not sure, love. I don't think ... I don't think I have seen her for quite some time." The man pondered over it.

"Thank you, sir," I said, letting the man go on his way.

*

That night I drove home, the box resting on the passenger seat. I thought about where Mrs Abbots would be, how I would be able to get in touch with her again, but there was something else on my mind: the other person who I needed to be with, the one other person who had restored my life to some normality. Someone I couldn't wait to see. I wanted to be home again, home with Matthew.

I rang the bell to the flat, and Matthew answered after a brief pause. "Hello?" came his voice from the intercom.

"It's me," I said, feeling a little nervous.

He unlocked the door via the intercom immediately, and I came up to the flat. As I approached the landing, I found him standing at the door to the flat, waiting.

He looked back at me with a pained half smile. "You didn't have to knock," he said calmly. "You have keys, remember?"

"I'm sorry," I said, standing there searching his face. "Can you forgive me?"

He sighed with a look of relief, embracing me in his arms. "There is nothing to forgive. I know what you are going through is difficult," he said softly. "But there is something I want you to do, though," he said, drawing me back to look at me with a serious face.

"Can you forget what your parents want and think about what you want from now on? Can you do that?" he pleaded, holding onto my hands tightly.

I nodded in tears at his small request.

He pulled me towards him again, and I felt the warmth of his chest, encompassed with the feeling of being wanted, and being accepted by someone who truly wanted the best for me.

*

I never told my parents when we decided to get married. I wanted to put my whole self into it this time. This time, when I married, I wasn't going to face hostility, or protest, or obligation, or doing right by others. This time, when I married, I wanted to feel complete. We decided to keep things simple, and our ceremony took place on a sandy beach in the middle of the Indian Ocean.

On the day of our wedding, I woke to a light breakfast of fresh fruit and pastries, sitting in our hotel room with the sea air drifting in from the balcony, the faint sound of waves lapping on the shore, the warm breeze rustling through the trees.

Thoughts passed me often on whether I was doing the right thing, but I let them walk by like people passing in the street. *It's okay.*

You can have an opinion, I said to them. *But you don't own mine.* I could see everything with Matthew, but what was clearer was that decision was my own; it wasn't led by anyone else's thoughts or ideas. I was in control, and nothing could destroy that.

About the only real thought that I couldn't shift was Mrs Abbots. I had tried writing to her. I had sent a card inviting her to the wedding, but I hadn't heard back. I managed to find her number and called the house line, but the line rang dead. I often wondered whether she had just moved on. I was used to not speaking to her. Perhaps she had gone away to China again to teach at the schools there, but I had no way of finding out where she was. Throughout my life, often months and years had passed before we spoke, but it still felt strange that she hadn't responded.

I gazed at the box of love she had returned to me, filled with stones and trinkets from my last wedding. I had brought it with me: she was the only person from my early life who I wanted present on my wedding day. Looking at those stones reminded me of how much I missed her. I thought about her wise words that had led me on the search for love and how she had taught me that love is everywhere and in everything, and as I tied my hair and applied my make-up, I finally saw in me the woman she had made me. I knew she would have been proud of me if she had seen me. I looked back at my reflection now and saw a woman standing calmly, uninterrupted by opinions, inner voices, fear or self-doubt.

"Today will be a day when I will feel beautiful again, Mrs Abbots, just like you inspired me to feel."

When I climbed into the dress I had made from fifteen yards of ivory satin material, I no longer felt like the perpetual mould of my mother and my mother's mother, and their daughters and sisters who made up that world. For once I was me.

Our wedding ceremony was at sunset in front of thirty guests seated outside on a beach. The only people from my side were my three supporting friends, Andrea, Lenna and Sonia, who were for the occasion my bridesmaids.

I walked down an aisle decked with orchids and white flowers to a musician serenading us with the sounds of an acoustic guitar, to where Matthew stood to receive me.

The air was warm, and a gentle breeze lifted my veil as I joined him. Matthew stood at the top, his face a calm sunbeam, the sun, setting behind him, glowing fiery rays from small orange clouds. He stood handsomely in a cream suit. Alongside him was his best man. I smiled when the guitarist strummed "Somewhere over the Rainbow" as I made my way towards him. It reminded me of a time when I had searched the hills with Mrs Abbots, a time when I had prayed I would one day go beyond the hills and fly over them to better places. If only she were here now, I thought, I could finally tell her, finally show her, who I had become.

*

As the guests mingled under the evening stars for our wedding dinner of lobster and seafood, Matthew held me close, his hands warm against the palms of my hands as he locked them gently together. I felt a rush of excitement as he smiled and squeezed them gently.

"This is beautiful, isn't it?" he said, looking around the canopy set on the beach. We sat silently, taking it all in, the flowers and candles flickering against a light breeze, the soft strum of the guitar behind us, the warm sea exhaling and inhaling softly as its waves lapped against the shore and hushed the flames of a glowing beach fire that guests mingled around.

"This is more than beautiful," I said with a calm smile. "This is living a dream," I said, whispering the words softly on his mouth and looking deeply into his eyes. "And I, for one, will not think of waking from it."

CHAPTER FORTY-FOUR

– *Confessions* –

The years flew by, and our lives drifted from moment to moment, one by one, like clouds rolling over the sky.

We bought a house in the suburbs before the children were born, where there were plenty of trees, one of which happened to be a magnolia tree, that I looked out at in our garden. It was the same type of tree that years ago I had gazed at with enviable desire from my bedroom window to escape from the darkness and confinement I felt then. Now though, I opened my window to enjoy the beauty of a new garden and the sun-drenched blossoms of the magnolia, dancing to nature's song.

These are small gifts of life that you only treasure when they have been taken from you.

We had the house painted white on the outside, and on my drives home at night, it reminded me of the house Mrs Abbots lived in, with its brilliant white masonry that could be seen from distances across the hills. I now only hoped that one day perhaps Mrs Abbots would surprise me with a visit or might decide to knock on the door of our white house. It seemed the closest hope of ever meeting her again. In the past, I had called her house, but the phone had rung a dead tone. Sometimes I tempted myself to pick up the phone and call Babajee, to find out where she was, whether he knew anything about her whereabouts, but cutting myself off from the family didn't allow me that right anymore. Moreover, I couldn't bear another argument with either of my parents over the mere mention of her name. I missed her, but it no longer felt appropriate to bring it up. Babajee had been difficult at times to even talk to, even when things were good between us, and now our relationship was severed beyond repair.

I was caught up in my own life now too. In the ten years since Matthew and I married, we had renovated our house, had two lovely boys and were now sending them to school. We both worked full-time at a bank. Often, the long hours took a toll on any personal time we had together.

It was often in those journeys, dropping the boys at school or on the train to work, that I thought I saw her face. I longed for her the most then, reliving those moments on the walks home, when I had spotted puddles shaped like love hearts. Or when I asked my boys to find a heart-shaped pebble on the beach, or sometimes in their smiles, or when they would tell me the highlight of their school day was eating jelly. And even in the shadowy depths of doubt, the jaded story that had now cast over my view of Mrs Abbots, my heart only ached and longed for her more.

*

One Saturday morning I woke to an unexpected call. It was Babajee. At first I ignored it. It was 7 a.m., and I didn't want to wake our boys. I muted the line and put the phone on silent.

I thought it was odd that Babajee would call so early, considering they were a household that woke late and did everything late.

I was lying there with my eyes closed, my arms wrapped over Matthew's chest, when the phone rang again.

"Who is it?" he whispered sleepily.

It seemed inconvenient to both of us, given it was the only day we would get a lie in.

"It's my dad," I whispered back. "Just ignore it; I don't want to speak to him."

We carried on resting, my eyes closed, but with my conscience beating me up about not picking up the phone. I didn't want to speak to Babajee, wasn't sure what I would say anymore. In all the years that had passed between us, he had tried to call. Voicemail after voicemail. Sometimes he tried through Mamajee, who would stubbornly and reluctantly leave a message on behalf of Babajee. "Can you call back? Your dad is really worried about you. Is this how you treat people? Is this what you do to your family? Where are you? What are you doing? Nobody knows. Call back. This is disgusting behaviour."

I blocked them all out, ignored them and distanced myself. I was lessening the noise from my inner demons, protecting myself from any further damage. I didn't want to bring up the past and hear the mental abuse of not doing right by them. I had no interest in being compelled by their reasons. I was forty years old now and still had to fight a war inside whenever they called. It was emotional sabotage with every message, each time sending me back to a dark place, and often, in my head, I was exhausted from reconciling and repairing myself. There were hours spent with Matthew in those dark moments, his counselling, comforting, restoring any confidence left in me. Their messages took me back to a place where I complied with every whim, sending me off course and in the direction of their grand plan. I couldn't let that happen. I refused to let that happen.

It had been a few years now since the last missed call. Even with every problem you face with your family, you suffer inside because the pain comes from a place of love. I still loved them. I loved my mother and father. Sometimes I would miss them when I recalled a childhood memory. Those moments when I felt close to Babajee, when he used to read to me from one of his great literary books, or when Mamajee and I would sit and talk by the fire endlessly about Bangladesh. But these recollections were few and far between now. Those memories were now tarnished by deep-rooted pain, inflicted on me in many examples throughout my life.

I regretted that things weren't different. It ached inside, that their idea of best wasn't the same as mine. It still hurt that Mamajee had wished I was dead in my hour of need and that they still wanted me married, flogged into a situation that wasn't the best for me and was only right by the laws they had subscribed to. That world of theirs, a predefined ideology and structure, entangled in an obscure mess of culture, society and religion. My relationship with them only worked if I conformed to that, their ideas of what was right, conditional and in compliance with their grand plan, and only if I committed to what in their minds was written.

Now, as a mother myself, I knew I wanted more for my children. I wanted to be the best I could, without war and constant interference. My life was peaceful now. I had two lovely boys and a kind and wonderful husband. I wasn't going to let anything compromise or jeopardise that.

I lay convincing myself of all of this in that brief moment, and as I turned my face away from my bedside, where the phone rang, I contemplated all these things again. The voicemail message alert came on. I turned to face the phone. I could feel Matthew beside me, tossing the other way. I sensed he knew that I was giving in. Later, for him, it would mean another counselling session or endless hours of consoling me.

"Honey, maybe leave it. It's probably nothing," he said, turning, his voice groggy and sleepy.

"I don't know. It doesn't feel right. He normally wouldn't call me at this time of the morning," I said, rising up from the bed to look at my phone.

He sighed with an air of resignation.

I dialled the voicemail to hear the message.

"Is it Eleanor?" came Babajee's voice in the message. He sounded weak, his breathing laboured. "Call me, Eleanor. I need to speak to you. I have been trying for many years now, and not once have you returned my call. I am not well, Eleanor. I am not sure how long I will live, and I miss you."

He paused once again, his breathing laboured, struggling to muster the words as he cleared his throat.

"I don't want you to worry about me though," he said, clearing his throat. "Baba's health has not been good for a while. It's you I am concerned about. I want you to come up. Bring the grandchildren; at least let me see them." He paused again, taking slow, deep breaths. "There's … there's something else I need to tell you. I … I can't tell you over the phone. It's important, though; you need to know. You know … before something bad happens. Do you understand? I know you understand. Please, it's urgent. Just come as soon as you can, Eleanor … Just come up, and I can talk to you about it."

I held the phone in my hands, my palms sweaty as the anxiety sucked the air out of me.

Matthew shuffled in the bed, rolling over to face me. "What did he say?"

I sat silently, thinking through his words.

"He …" I paused. "He wants me to see him about something," I said slowly, turning to make eye contact.

He stroked my arm that was resting on the bed. "What do you think it's about?"

"I don't know." I sighed deeply. "It worries me, especially after all these years. Should I go up?" I continued. Finding Matthew's assurance was all I needed. "He wants to see the kids," I added.

I could see his reluctance, as his eyes closed slowly, that pained expression as he seated himself up in bed.

"Well, he hasn't seen them. It's understandable. Do you want to take them?"

"I don't know. I just don't want all the horrible aggro that comes with everything. I'm just … I am happy now … I don't want to know what their opinion is either, on anything."

Matthew nodded, understandingly.

"I don't know what feels right anymore. On the one hand, I feel as though I should go and see what he wants. I … I would regret it, if something happened and I didn't give him his last, dying wish."

"So, do you want us to come?" he asked, supporting me.

I nodded. "I think … I think that would be good if you did." I was hesitating. My protective instincts kicked in. My family would probably harp on about religion, preach about how I should be raising my kids.

"Maybe we should just go today, get it over with." Matthew shrugged.

"I guess so. What? Today?" The thought dawning on me. "It will take a few hours to drive there. Where would we stay?" I contemplated, jittery with nerves. "I'll book a hotel," I continued on, answering my own questions. "We can stay overnight. Let me call him back and see what is going on first."

The phone rang for a while when I called, and my mind wondered anxiously. Why was it taking so long to answer? Could it be that he had ended up in hospital?

After some tries, somebody picked up.

It was Mamajee.

"Hello," she said calmly. I had not heard that voice in a while. It sounded a little rugged.

"Hello," I said after a brief pause. "It's me, Eleanor," I added awkwardly.

Mamajee paused silently.

"Is Babajee there?" I continued, finding it difficult to talk to her.

I heard her put the receiver down on the table, silently, without saying another word. I could hear the television in the background and Babajee's coughing as he approached the telephone. At least I knew he was alive, which calmed me a little.

"Hello," Babajee said, clearing his throat.

"Assalamualaikum, Babajee. It's me, Eleanor."

"Is it Eleanor?" he said. His voice lightened, and it sounded as though he had taken in a fresh gulp of air. "You had me so worried, my dear. All these years, and not once ... not once have you tried to call back. I have tried to call so many times."

I could hear the emotion and relief, and feel the guilt slowly closing in on me.

"So, what's going on?" I said, trying to change the subject.

"When are you coming up? There are things we need to talk about."

"What things, Babajee? Do you think it's easy for me to just drag everyone up just so that you can talk?"

"I know that." He hesitated.

"So then, what is it, Babajee? Tell me."

"I need you to come. I can't tell you like this."

"Well, you are going to have to tell me what is so urgent. Are you well? Is it your health? Are you in some crisis?"

"No," he croaked.

"Then what, Babajee? What?"

"It's not about me."

I paused as I waited for him to breathe.

"It's … it's about that house on the hill. Come, come and meet me there."

*

"I've wanted to know what happened, so I am glad you brought me here," I said, looking out of the window from within the white house. I couldn't bear to look at the details of the house now. I knew now why it was empty, the summer breeze pressing against the window-panes. The passing of time seemed to have collected here as the smell of dust lingered in the faded curtains. The remaining table and chair placed against the side. It was nothing like how I'd imagined Mrs Abbots's house, when, as a child, I'd looked out from my window.

He nodded his head slowly, shifting his feet on the wooden floor as he cumulated his words. "I know," he wheezed, his face looking down at the floor.

There was a long silence as we both took it all in.

"I am sorry," he said, his voice raspy and throaty.

I turned to face him somehow. The man I knew to be my father had vanished, his face melted with the words. I could feel a silky warmth from his voice, as though a weight had been lifted as heavy as a warrior's armour. What had he harboured? What had he been holding on to all these years? I wanted to cry but held back the tears with gritted teeth and anger. I wanted to punish him, return the good that he was trying to give, make him suffer for all he'd had us lose, the damage he had caused from the affair, but what I saw now before me was a tiny, weak old man, holding on to memories filled with pain, suffering and sacrifice, and with it nothing more.

"Here," he said, coughing, looking down from his bag. "She left this for you; she told me to keep it safe for when you came again." Babajee's voice became heavy and laboured, and he sat himself down as he passed over an envelope.

He stared out of the window, his breathing slowing. "She used to write a lot," he said, clearing his throat. "It was how we met. I used to read to her, and we used to exchange poems, that sort of thing. That's how we became friends."

He locked his hands together to comfort them from the chill lingering in the air. He coughed, clearing his throat again. Part of me didn't want to know. It made me angry to think he'd had this relationship with her, and yet any mention of her name, he would tear me apart.

I looked down at the envelope; the colour had stained a brownish tinge as if it had been sealed for decades. It felt thick in the middle.

"Open it." He nodded, peering over his thick brown glasses that took over his face, beckoning me as he rested his hands on his knees.

I tore the flap. Inside there was a small key. "Armoire" was written on it in Mrs Abbots's cursive handwriting.

"Armoire," I repeated. Babajee pointed towards the bedside; a large double-doored cupboard stood to the left of the bed.

It took some shuffling with the lock, and I prised it open with stiffened, cold fingers. A large fur coat, the faint smell of her perfume lingered around the collar as I stroked it, resting my head as I had that very first time I'd met her. I began to choke, recollecting the meeting in the car park that had brought me to her.

Babajee watched from behind me, his breathing heavy and awkward from the faint whine beneath my breath.

"She gave you something else. I believe she placed it on the top shelf."

I turned to face him, shifting my focus from the coat to look at his glinting eyes.

"Up there," he said, pointing at the top shelf through his spectacles.

I fumbled around the shelf with my cold, jittery hands, sliding them over the dusty shelf of the armoire, collecting some of the dust on my fingers before I hit something large and leathery. It was a book. I pulled it down, shifting it slowly towards me until its heaving weight caught in my hands.

"Bring it over," Babajee said with laboured breath.

I sat next to him on a rickety chair, unfolding the first page, the thick cream watercolour paper withered on the ends.

There was a picture of me with a beaming smile through the school gates. It had faded in colour, my hair in pigtails.

"She used to meet me at lunch."

"Did she?" Babajee seemed surprised but said nothing more as I turned the page.

The next page was written in her elegant writing.

So write, write it down. Tell them our destiny wasn't written, that we had a choice, that we don't need to hide behind a name, that if you follow love, you will be blessed with love. The path of love is written in our hearts. Let this be your compass, and your mind be your map that will take your soul through its voyage of discovery.

I remembered these words only in fragments now. They had often been repeated, but I could not make sense of them back then. But here, in this lonely room, I felt close to them; they felt synonymous with my life.

There was a picture of Babajee and Mrs Abbots on the next page, the white house in the backdrop. They were standing in the field, laughing together. A rare expression that I saw in Babajee's face as they stood near a cow, which seemed to be inching nearer to them in the picture. He looked elegant, smartly dressed in tailored trousers and shirt. Her hair was short, bobbed, turned outwards in a sixties hairstyle and pinned on one side. She was slim, her tiny, cinched waist in a pleated dark shirt dress. I recollected now, this was the same picture he had put on his bedroom wall in Bangladesh. The same picture Mamajee had looked at with disdain.

"When was this taken?" I said to Babajee.

Babajee paused, steadied his breathing. "Before you were born."

His face down, he nodded reassuringly to himself.

"Before Mamajee?"

"Yes," he said. "Before I married your mother." His expression wore into the deep hollows of his cheekbones as he rounded his mouth to let some air into his throat.

I turned the page, a picture of a baby on the next page, where Mrs Abbots was holding it with a beaming smile.

"So ..." I hesitated. I couldn't bring myself to say it, but in my heart, I knew. I couldn't bring the words to my lips, what brought me into this world, knowing now what Mamajee had said all along. "It was all my fault that she was here."

He looked at me, the look that begged to not disgrace him any more than he had been, to spare an old man the guilt that he bore for his actions forty years ago.

"I loved her. We met at the factory her father owned. She was the only one who helped me. For a while we were friends. She taught me how to speak English, to read, to dress." He gargled, clearing his throat. "In those days, English people were very racist. I worked long hours in the factory. Jane helped me with things you would never think you would need help with. Like getting a bus or reading food labels to see if it was halal, or working out how to read or send letters. She was a beautiful and giving woman." He nodded as he thought about her, swallowing with a deep breath. "Your mother."

The words went right through me, prickling the hairs on my arms with a rush of heart-torn pain. "My ... mmm." The words couldn't reach my lips any further as a feeling of love and pain rushed through and intensified in my body.

I turned the page. There was a picture of me, one that explained why Mamajee had never had any firstborn pictures. How I had scowled at her for not taking one when I was born, as I had needed it for a class project. It explained why Mamajee used to get mad at me when I'd ask. The anger, the resentment at the mere mention.

"Why, Babajee?" It ached inside; I couldn't explain which emotion.

"How could I? Why? I will tell you why. *Izzat*, honour; it's a disease that most of us are powerless against. She was Catholic, bedeen, non-believer, and her father? Would he have approved? No. Would my family have approved? He rightfully did not want his daughter anywhere near a penniless factory worker who barely spoke English. As for the baby, well, they wanted you adopted, moved away into some English home. Believe me, if they weren't so Catholic, they would have been tempted by another option."

"So, I was a malfunction? Hmm? Is this what you came to tell me? I spent my whole existence being a mistake to you people, and for what, may I ask?"

I felt utterly disgusted and looked away from him to the window. The green hills before me, the steps on which houses nestled between trees, my school in view again. I let a tear run down my cheek as I swallowed the pain.

He brought me back, placed his cold marble hand on top of mine.

"Don't you see? You don't see how precious you were to me? I hid my treasure in my home, not somewhere else. I didn't want you being raised in some English home. You were my past and my future all contained in one."

"Oh, please, Babajee. You and 'MUM'," I shouted with my hands raised, "were selfish! How you dishonoured Mamajee behind her back; how it destroyed me. You simply saved yourselves from the shame of it all and had everyone else pick up the dirty pieces. Hidden treasure? You did nothing to care for it, like everything else that existed around you."

I rose from the chair, its feet scraping the wooden floor with a painful screech, a timbre echoing around the room deep loneliness, closely resembling the mood that lingered inside me.

I headed to the door.

"Where are you going? Wait, I haven't finished." His breathing was exaggerated by noisy phlegm that caught in his throat.

I stopped.

"Sit." He nodded. "Let me finish." He then gargled, steadying his voice. I patiently waited, looking down to the floor.

"I know you can't forgive me. Babajee is selfish, I know, but Jane, she wanted the best for you."

"The best for me? What, by abandoning me?"

"She couldn't keep the baby. It would have been an outrage. Her community … there was no support for unmarried couples." Babajee searched his memory, his eyes glazed, stroking his nimble fingers as he stared into space. "So, I made a plan. I would get married in Bangladesh. That way, you would be looked after." Babajee shook his head again as he continued. "She wasn't happy with that, of course, like any mother, but she knew it was better than any other option." He leaned into himself, gesturing with his head. "There was nothing in her vision but that view from that window over there."

I looked out beyond the hills, my old school, the playground, farther beyond, the glistening slated roof tiles and our house emerging beyond trees and hills. I saw what she had looked out at now, the meadow before the school playground.

"I know she tried, despite the walls that separated you. Really, love is inseparable, and you can't deny the profoundness of what you gave each other."

I shook my head incessantly, refusing to take it in. *What do you want me to say, Babajee? You are telling me this now? Now she is gone?* I thought, shaking my head as he continued flicking through the pages one by one.

There were more memories of Mrs Abbots and me: the days I had sneaked through the school gates and picnicked with her, the notes we had written in code to each other, stuck down on each page. There were tickets to the cinema, a picture of us both at a fashion show that I had sneaked out to, my graduation day that nobody but Mrs Abbots had attended. There were pictures of my wedding day, her in the background, trying to reach for me, and then something that I'd never thought I would see, never really known could exist: pictures of me with my boys, coming back from their school.

"I don't understand. How? How does she have this picture?"

"She moved from here, left it abandoned after you married."

"Why?"

"Why do you think? She moved to London, found a job in a local school as a dinner lady."

"Seems a long way to move for a job like that."

Babajee nodded silently. "She went to more lengths for you than I could ever imagine."

"For me? I haven't spoken to or seen her in years."

He flicked through to the next page.

A picture of my own two boys, aged four and five, smiling at the camera, sitting eating their lunch at school, beaming from ear to ear in the picture. They had been given strawberry jelly, something that Mrs Abbots used to give me as a treat, as I wasn't allowed it at home.

I smiled tearily.

"She didn't have very long," Babajee added. "She tried many times to get through to you, but, er …" He nodded, clearing his throat. "Her house was close to the boys' school."

A sudden rush of recollection, of the rushed school runs, the half-listened-to conversations with my sons, where the boys had explained their day. "Look, Mummy, over there. That's Miss Jane, one of our dinner ladies."

"Oh, really? That's nice. Come now, let's go. We'll be late," I would say hurriedly.

"Who's your favourite teacher?" I would often ask.

"Miss Jane," they would say, giggling. "Miss Jane. She's our dinner lady, and she has a secret."

"A secret? What's her secret?" I would ask.

To which one of my boys had whispered, with an earful of giggles, "Jelly!"

I remembered how I had laughed and reminisced back to my days at school in the playground by the trees, when out of Mrs Abbots's bag came a secret pot of jelly for me. I remembered how she would slip it between the bars of the school gate, where I devilishly ate it, sitting on the root of a tree. I would smile, recollecting those moments.

"Then it got worse." Babajee paused, coughing. "The cancer."

I felt my tears crystallise, fearing what seemed to be on the edge of his lips. I wanted desperately for time to go back, for a chance to talk openly like mother and daughter now. How far we had come, and yet how far she still remained.

"You see, I didn't want to just come here to pass on the news about her death but to tell you the truth. Jane wanted more than anything in the world for you to be safe, looked after, happy, and for you to follow your dreams. When I watched her dying, at her bedside, I found what I had known all the time about her, what I had denied myself the right to, and anyone else. Love, love has no boundaries, Eleanor. You can still continue to love someone, give them everything you need. It has no physical limitations. It penetrates through walls; it radiates in letters, in words, in your voice, in your smiles. It never tires; it never sleeps; it never says no. You can love with every beating of your heart, even if you are locked in the deepest, darkest prison. I lost sight of all of this; I traded all of that for face, obliged myself to something, which, in the end, didn't serve anyone any purpose and tore people apart in the process.

Babajee shook his head in tears, squeezed his eyelids a little as he lowered his gaze to the floor. His wheezing, slow and heavy. "I can't go back in time now; I can't change what happened, but I couldn't pass away and not let you know. We loved you, and the mistake we made was to live in fear of love. We failed at standing up against it all, and because of that, we lost what really mattered – you."

His trembling hands buried his face. In my entire life, I was unable to recollect a time when I had seen Babajee cry. Sometimes his face resembled a rock surface, cold, dark and rugged, impenetrable, void of any emotion. I could see it as he lifted his head from his palms, the reddened eyes, the lines on his face softened now. The withered mouth and loose jaw revealed more of the being inside than I could ever have imagined.

I sat silently, overwhelmed, trying to reconcile his words. In all the years we'd had together, I had never known Babajee to speak so openly. There was a pain at the thought of knowing that all of this had been hidden from me, a deep regret that moments had been taken away from me. I couldn't entertain those thoughts though. It would have meant years of Mrs Abbots's teachings being in vain.

"Every moment is an opportunity to turn it all around," she would say. "You have the power to choose it."

"You can't go back in time, no, but you have the opportunity to rewrite the future, Babajee." Babajee shook his head with resignation.

"I am an old man now," he sighed. "There is nothing left for me."

"There are things you can do, Babajee." I leaned in to make contact with those reddened eyes, that humble face, my elbows resting on my knees as I gathered my words. "Cherish what you have; pick up the pieces that you broke; and repair what needs fixing."

He nodded, silently, his face down to the floor.

"You know who I am talking about, don't you?"

CHAPTER FORTY-FIVE

– *Mamajee Speaks Out* –

Babajee led me in through the front of the house, which felt strange. As children, we always came in through the side entrance; the front of the house was where guests and visitors entered. It was late afternoon by the time we arrived, and the hills in front were darkening. The front of the house had changed a little. Gone were the pale blue wooden windows. A new front door and double-glazed windows had given it a facelift. The crumbling brick wall surrounding the garden had been replaced with a newly rendered wall. Mamajee had lined the paved walkway with rose bushes of various reds and pinks, and scattered beneath them were the remains of marigolds that she had planted before my wedding, with the intention of making garlands for the ceremony.

I could hear the faint sounds of my boys in the living room and the chatter of people through the open window as we waited.

Mamajee opened the door, her smile reduced to a thin line as she saw me.

Babajee led the way to the living room, passing her quietly as she turned and made her way back through the hallway and into the kitchen silently.

I found Matthew sitting on the main couch.

"Are you okay?" he mimed with his lips.

I nodded back, pursing my lips as I watched the boys pushing toy cars around on the main rug. My sister knelt beside them, playing with them.

It looked as though Mamajee had already got into her usual rhythm of entertaining. The coffee table was laid out with teacups and cakes for Matthew, and juices and biscuits for the children.

Suraya looked up, pleased to see me, then rose to where I stood by the door. We embraced in a hug with few or no words. She was older now, her face thinner; it had lost the teenage version I had once known.

She sniffled as she looked at me with a contented smile. As often, with my family, more was said without words; this was one of those moments. I sensed the longing, old wounds, harsh words and thorny ideas that had pressed on her mind and were slowly diminishing with each silent smile, with my very presence.

"Did you want a tea?" she asked, kneeling back down to the coffee table. "Mamajee just made a pot."

"No … thank you," I said, sitting down awkwardly next to Matthew. "I am okay for now."

She nodded, understandingly.

"Where did Mamajee go?" I asked.

"It's prayer time. I guess they have gone upstairs," Suraya said, looking up at the old clock that hung in the same old place.

"It's okay. You can go up," she said reassuringly as she moved to the rug again, where the boys were trying to show her their toy cars.

"Have you been okay?" I said, turning to Matthew, who sat to the left of me.

"We've been fine," he said softly. "Are you okay?" he asked.

I smiled wearily back. I caught a glimpse of my reflection in the gold panel around the fireplace. I looked washed-out, pale, as if the blood had drained from me.

"I think Mamajee may have finished. I just want to speak to her before we leave."

"Sure," he said.

"Will you be okay with the boys for a little longer?" I asked calmly.

"Of course, you go talk to her," he insisted.

I rose from the seat.

"I'll be right back," I said to the boys, who were too occupied with their toys to even look up.

I walked up the hallway; the walls, now painted in ivory white, gave the illusion of an open space, which had once felt dark with the wild rose colour it had been painted in.

I found Mamajee in the room that Babajee and I used to sit in, endlessly looking out of the window, rolling prayer beads. Her head was covered with her white prayer scarf.

"I guess you know now," she said, turning quickly sideways as I stood by the door. "It's not the same now, is it?" she whispered, looking out of the window again. "I used to see that house light turn on, and I could only pray that it never shone."

"Well, you can be happy now," I said, seating myself slowly at the dressing table chair. Part of me knew she had been punished enough, that she didn't deserve that. How could I judge her, given how accepting, how accommodating she had been throughout the years? She had suffered far worse a consequence. Somehow the cards dealt for her seemed now purely in my favour. I hoped that she could somehow see that I knew no different, that all I had wanted was to please her all these years, to prove that I was a good person to her. I only knew now that I had been born not to heal her but to be a test of her strength. I saw her capacity to love now in a different light. All these years, she had quietly stood by her decision, to love and care for another, with everything else she knew about societal expectations against her. And knowing this, I could only hold compassion for her. Perhaps I had to only know who my real mother was upon her passing so that the one who bore the truth could feel in essence the fruits of her endurance.

I stared out of the window with Mamajee, the hills ashen in colour now against an orange-and-vanilla sky. The thoughts slowly hit me: by now the lights would have come on, the thought that the house was empty slowly creeping in on me. I tried hard to block out the pain, and as we sat in the darkened room, I couldn't stop the tears.

I could see Mamajee's eyes glance over at me, the whites of her eyes illuminating from the street lamps turning on outside.

"I wasn't expecting it. I didn't know. 'What have I arrived to?'" she said, looking emptily out of the window. "I thought I had left everything behind to walk into this life, to accept all its flaws. To thin walls and weary windows, to dark skies and smoky rooms. To languages I didn't understand, to people I didn't know, and then I heard something. An undecipherable noise at first, from the corner of the living room. It started with a couple of grunts, and then, there, as I walked over, closer to the corner, there was a baby crying in a crib basket. Delighted, yet intrigued, I picked you up, those beautiful eyes looking back at me with that beaming smile. Who could resist? It gave me instant salvation from where I was.

"'Whose is this baby?' I asked your babajee. I saw that fixed, vacant stare of his, down at the floor. I waited for his response. He turned away as normal, lighting up another cigarette. 'Whose is this baby?' I pressed him again. I could tell he didn't want to answer the question, as though I wasn't worthy of any explanation. His breathing was deep, the smoke lingering in the air as he faced the window. But I waited, patiently. Part of me knew where this was going with the growing silence.

"'Yours,' he said, turning his back to me.

"'What do you mean, mine?' I gasped at the sheer mindlessness of his response.

"Of course, your father hates it when I challenge or question him.

"'She's your baby, and you will treat her like your own,' he said, turning to look at me. His eyes narrowed into mine, those features sharpened, his lips pressed together with an air of insistence that could only arouse fear if you pressed any further.

"'You won't ask any more on this. You bring her up. Look after her.'

"I didn't mind the baby so much; it was the lies, the way he had approached it all. Clinical, detached, lacking any understanding of what he was asking me to do. How it made me feel. It wouldn't have hurt to tell me. To him, I didn't deserve to know. The silence hurt too. What was I getting myself into? The indignation attached to his mistakes. Only a fool would have accepted such a proposition.

"'How is this going to look with the family?' I asked him. 'How am I going to show my face?'

"'Well, you won't need to show your face to them. You won't be speaking to them anymore.'

"I was outraged, the fury inside, pent up.

"'Who is this woman? Who is the mother?' I said angrily.

"I could only think what a cold, selfish and harsh man I had married, and why my parents would have pawned me off to a spineless creature like him.

"If it weren't for you, I would never have existed in your father's life. I realised why I was only here; it was now for one purpose. You. Of course. And these were all things I was powerless to fight. Accept, submit, that it was all written by Allah like this. The grand plan." She sighed, gulping in some air.

"Accept it. It's written. That was the way for me."

"'You better promise me,' I said to him," Mamajee continued, "'that you keep my honour intact. If you want me to call her my own, then you better make sure this never comes out.'

"He said nothing, of course. But his silence was as good as golden.

"For a while, anyhow, I didn't see or hear of her, that woman; you might as well have been mine. I had accepted my fate, with Allah's grace. I was your mother now, and in my head, it didn't take long to feel like one. I bathed you, fed you, made clothes from old sarees for you. Taught you Bangla, to be a Muslim. You were my skin, my blood now. You were the first thing I saw in the morning, and the last thing I saw at night. Yes, I often thought about her. I wondered who she was, why she had abandoned you. Was she still alive? And it didn't take long for the answers to present themselves. It all changed that day when I saw his car driving up the hill."

⋅ She paused, looking onward at the dark sky. She wiped her tears with the end of her scarf, shaking her head in disbelief.

"I wasn't going to let these two people destroy me now – my honour, name, dignity, pride, respect. They would take it all with that shameless act. This was going to stay the way it was written for me. Written for you."

Written, I thought. After all these years, she was still mouthing it off. After all the damage, all the hurt, the pain those words had caused. I listened to my old voice waning inside. *I should be angry right now*, it said. I should scream at her. If thoughts could bleed, the things I would say to her if this day ever came. But the words had dried out in my mouth, my thoughts like scattered leaves being blown around in the wind.

All I saw now was an old woman who had suffered, who had navigated a loveless, barren territory, without expectation for the quality of her own life, without rewards, without asking for love in return.

"How we have all suffered, Mamajee, suffered at the hands of honour, pride, izzat, face, shame, and after all of that, we sit here in the dark with one single question: are we still loved?"

She turned to face me. Her eyes glistened, melting with tear-drops.

"I am sorry." Her voice cracked. Her words crumbled as she spoke. "I am sorry for what you have lost. I don't think any mother makes reckless choices; I know they had to figure out the best for you."

I shook my head in disbelief. "I am not asking for any apology, Mamajee. We all suffered, suffered because we accepted something we didn't believe, accepted something because we chose to believe we didn't have a choice, and the truth of the matter is, in doing so, we sold our souls to the devil. Nothing was ever written, Mamajee. You perpetuated a belief that had been instilled in you and chose that path out of fear. I wasn't looking for an apology, Mamajee. I just wanted you to be happy. I wanted you to feel loved, and you would know that never changed, that wasn't conditional, it didn't have a grand master plan. It wasn't written. All I want now is for you to feel that unconditionally."

She looked down silently, and there were no words exchanged between us for a while. I could hear the boys downstairs, playing, laughing and giggling.

"It's getting dark. I have to get back to London," I whispered with a long breath.

"Eat before you go," Mamajee said hastily.

"No, it's okay. We'll pick something up at a services on the way. I need to get the boys back home before bed."

"Why don't you stay tonight?" She was clutching at anything now. I could hear it in her voice, the softness of her tone. She was trying to make amends, but that was not needed anymore.

"No, that is not necessary, Mamajee." I turned, moved away from the window, heading for the door.

"Wait, just hold on," she said. "There is something … there is something that I have to give you."

She rustled through her wardrobe and opened up a red velvet jewellery case, and from it, she pulled out a large locket on a chain. It was gold and burnished. She took my hand and placed the chain into my palms. "This … this belonged to you," she said a little guiltily.

I felt the shiny, cold metal in my palms. It felt heavy in weight, and smooth as a pebble on one side. There were vines engraved on the front, with the letters M. J. Abbots. My heart felt heavy reading the name, as though it were holding up a dam of tears.

"I am sorry that I took it from you," Mamajee said as I opened the locket. "All those years ago, when you came back that day from helping your babajee. I found it. It fell out of your pocket. I knew he was setting it up so that she could see you, and it hurt. I know now, it was wrong of me to deny you her love, but it seemed, well, I guess, I felt betrayed by you, even though you weren't to know."

All those years, I had wondered what it had been, sitting there in my pocket on our return home in Babajee's car. I remembered how warm I felt inside from her touch, that lady, who, supposedly, now I could call my mother, that lady in the fur coat. I was looking at the gift now with those eyes that were no longer hungry for any other want but the lady herself. How was it that life could be so callous, so cruel, and deny a child of such basic wants? I could only savour the feelings it had brought when she'd given it. Her arms around me, the softness of her coat, the comforting feeling of safety and the exchange of warm words as she parted with that gift. I held it in my hands, opening it with a childlike curiosity and relinquishing the guilt of losing it. Engraved around the sides of the mirror were the words "You are beautiful, and I love you." And on the left side was a faded picture of Mrs Abbots, fair and elegant. I missed her even more now, seeing her there. If only I could bring her back to life.

"Thank you," I said to Mamajee, pressing my lips together to hide the pain. It still felt awkward, as if I were to blame. In her presence, I could not allow myself the right to mourn Mrs Abbots yet, not in the way I wanted to, as it may upset Mamajee, be insensitive to her feelings.

She followed me downstairs to the living room, where Babajee stood by the fireplace, contemplating his words with momentary glances between the boys and me. This was the first time he had seen them, the first time he had met Matthew, the first time the four of us had set foot in that house as a family.

"We are going to go now, Babajee," I said, avoiding his eyes.

"Eat something; stay for a while before you go."

"No, it's okay. I need to get the boys home. It's getting late."

He nodded acceptingly. His frail hands clasped together behind his back yielded more of what he was holding back in other ways, those words caught in a vacuum or a void somewhere that no one could get to easily. Like him, I could easily become a reflection of this. I, too, was holding back now. Amongst the commotion of the boys playing, the television blaring and the clatter of noise in the kitchen, I felt his grief and mine in unison.

"So, we never had a chance to talk," he said, looking down at the floor from the fireplace. "But, er ..." His hesitation now increasingly uncomfortable, it pained me more that he wasn't going to say it, he would deny himself again.

"Babajee, there is nothing you can do to change the past. Yes, that has now been written. All you can do is learn from this; you can make it better by changing the future."

I sensed I only had to say a word to have the weight of those words come flooding out.

"How? There is nothing left now, nothing. Everything has gone; it's destroyed me, you, my reputation, my pride, my honour. There is nothing left at all." He shook his head tearfully. "Allah only knows why it was written this way." His voice grazed against his throat. He cleared it as he looked on.

"You have everything, Babajee. You had everything even when you thought you had nothing. You just chose to think you had nothing, and that became your reality. Nothing was ever written, Babajee. We had a choice; we chose to believe that it was all written, and we chose to accept that we had no choice and to believe in some grand plan, and because of that, we were unable to pave our own destiny, or own future. Yes, I know it's a harder task to pave your own destiny. It is a harder task to make that journey into the unknown, isn't it? That place with unpredictable consequences. But everything has consequences, Babajee. You see, in choosing confinement over freedom, we chose darkness instead of light, and in choosing darkness instead of light, we chose to hate instead of love. And in choosing hate, we only lost the most important part of our being, the ability to love unconditionally. And as you have finally learned, love never has any boundaries. But all is not lost, Babajee; nothing is ever wasted. You can still choose to love."

"I don't understand, my dear. You speak in a tongue different from your old man, my dear. It is hard for me to understand." He shook his head.

"Well, how about just looking in the direction behind you? That woman there, who has stood behind you all these years." Mamajee stood calmly by the door, a pained expression held within it, an air of redemption. "It is never in the truth that hurts, Babajee, it is in the lies that disguise the truth that it hurts. Open your heart and mind, and for once acknowledge Mamajee, as she did for you all those years, unconditionally, and just as that woman I now know as my mother once said, 'You will always be loved if you open your heart to feel it. It will be there for you, as long as you seek it, as long as you will it.' All of this is meaningless without that, Babajee. All of it is meaningless."

Babajee stared on, agreeing silently and considering my words, his chest heavy with laboured breathing.

I looked over at Matthew, who had been sitting on the sofa and trying to decipher the exchange between myself and Babajee silently.

"Shall we go?" I asked him.

"Yes, let's do that. Boys, come, let's get moving," he said, packing up their toys and belongings.

Babajee observed them playing, rustling around to clear up their toys scattered across the rug. "I am glad you brought them here. I have longed to see them, you know. You should make sure you bring them often."

I nodded, refraining from negative thoughts.

"Here," he said, clearing his throat again. "There is something else that I needed to give to you."

He handed me a large brown envelope, his hands trembling a little. "This is yours now, whenever you come up with the boys. She left it for you," he said as I tore open the envelope flap.

Inside was a copy of my birth certificate, some legal papers and a set of keys to the white house.

My parents saw me out as we walked slowly back to the car, the air cooling with the setting sun. Babajee edged nearer to the car to wave to the boys now strapped into their car seats.

"Remember to come and visit, won't you?" he said.

I nodded, closing the door of the car.

As we drove away and bid our goodbyes, I exhaled as if I had been holding my breath for a thousand years. It was only then that a thick cloud of emotion came swirling out, and like the heavy monsoons, I felt the rains pouring down, emptying out from the clouds of doubts.

Matthew rested his hand on mine. "Is everything okay? What happened, darling?"

For a moment I couldn't answer. I couldn't reconcile. The years that had passed by unknowing, the loss, suffering, anger, resentment, bitterness, sacrifice, all entangled in a tender feeling of love and compassion now.

My children sat behind, quietly observing.

We approached the traffic lights of the main junction, the sun setting over the hills where the white house stood alone. Matthew patiently waited, quickly glancing, with one eye on the traffic passing by, his face full of concern for my grief.

"Do you see that white house over there?" I said, still in tears.

He looked over at the hill, nodding. "Yes."

"Can you drive me there?"

*

The boys raced out, freed from the confines of the car. It was safe though, the hills looking out over Ashcroft. I watched as they collected daisies and dandelions, handing them to me and running back down the hill for more. Matthew looked on, the sky around crimson now and the meadow in front darkening with a purple hue. I turned to look at the house before me. All those years of looking at it with wonder had been prevailed with only one thought, that I indeed had only looked on it as a signpost for hope and salvation from all that had been battled. It only felt cold and empty now, looking at it.

"So, are you going to tell me what this is all about? You are worrying me now, honey," Matthew said, putting his arm around me.

I burst into tears uncontrollably, explaining all that had happened in my childhood. How countless times it had been Mrs Abbots watching over me, guiding me. How she had inspired me to forgive, to love and pursue all my dreams and to not give up on the truth, the golden source of who I really was. And now, after all of this, I was standing here looking out on where I had been born, and knowing that she was my mother. We sat perched on a grassy mound, looking down on Ashcroft. I felt relief now: underneath the web of lies and destruction, I could see that it had all been well intended, that I was not unloved, but it was love covered by mountains of ego, culture, face, shame, honour and faith. How shrouded love became because of them.

It all fell into place. I realised now what was important and what wasn't. It wasn't important that my own mother had not raised me fully but that she had instilled the values of love profoundly. This I knew had no boundaries. I could take this anywhere. Love prevails in everything. She had built within me the capacity to love irrespective of circumstance, faith or race. She had taught me to speak what was golden inside, the source of truth, and care less about what people thought and more about what mattered to me. Speaking that truth took courage, but it was worth fighting for, because in taking that journey, I realised how far I'd come in the things that I'd thought I would never overcome. Nothing is ever written. My life was no longer defined by other people's standards. Whether they are your family, your partner, your sister or your children, we may all be connected by love, but as God intended for our souls, we walk that journey alone.

"I love you, Mrs Abbots. I love you, dear mother of love," I whispered out on the wind. I felt the warmth of those words flood inside me as if I had been submerged in a warm bath.

Then I turned, and Matthew's warm hands locked in mine as we looked on at our children playing together. I smiled at him, and his warm eyes looked lovingly back. I could only feel the love now for everyone, for myself and for everything I had fought to become.

We can choose to believe that our life is written and carve our existence page after page, chapter after chapter, through someone else's story, someone else's values, culture and religion, or we can choose to write our own story. One that is to be guided not by the language of fear but by the language of love, the language of our soul. I realised this now, forty years later, looking through the eyes of that four-year-old girl standing at the window with Mamajee, knowing now what she believed then was golden.

"You see, I wasn't born for it all to be written for me. I was born to write it."

****

A Little Message to You...

Dear Reader,

I just want to thank you for reading my book 'Written,' and I hope you enjoyed it. The book started as a journal to help me through my own experiences with domestic violence and cultural pressures such as arranged marriage.

Although it is told through the eyes of Eleanor, this book is something very real and close to me. It helped me work through some difficult and emotional times. When my life was shattered into pieces, it was the fragments of this book that helped me back together. My writing eventually evolved into a book, one that took 14 years to complete, and where a total of 195,000 words of heart-felt emotions were poured into its chapters.

The book was also like a loyal friend to me; it guided me to a better place, where I could make choices about my future and create a reality that allowed me to live a loving, creative and inspirational life.

If you have read 'Written' I would be grateful if you could write a review, as I would love to hear your thoughts and feedback. It also makes a real difference in helping other readers discover my book.

You can also keep in touch with me through my Facebook page, Twitter, Instagram and of course my website.

Thank you!

D. A. Lee

www.dalee.co.uk

click to subscribe

Facebook page

Twitter

Instagram

About the Author

D.A. Lee is a Bangladeshi-born British author, artist and poet, best known for her novel 'Written' published in 2019. Raised in a small town in Lancashire, England, Lee describes the cultural challenges of growing up in a Bengali household whilst navigating a western world.

Lee's novel, whilst fictional, draws on many of her own experiences of growing up in a Muslim family and explores the underworld of cultural expectations, arranged marriages, honour, abuse and domestic violence that often limit women's choices.

Lee first started writing as a form of self-healing through the challenges of home life. The word 'Written' had become a poignant theme throughout the book, a word often expressed culturally to describe the notion of determinism and predestination adopted by most traditional Muslim families as a common explanation for events in life. Lee takes us on a journey through her character Eleanor, a young girl caught between a web of family secrets and lies where she comes into conflict with these values.

Today, Lee is an advocate for women's freedom of choice and encourages women to speak out and seek help if they feel they are in danger.

Acknowledgements

I would like to thank a few people who have made this book possible. Thank you to Michael McConnell for copy editing the book it was great to work with you. To Leonora Bulbeck for your eagle-eyed proofread, it was wonderful to work with you and your input was so valued! To Caroline Barnhil, thank you for your proofread, input and review of the manuscript, I know I will be troubling you again I am sure! To Southbank Photography Ltd for the cover photography and to Tihaami for polishing the cover illustrations, you got it, you knew what I wanted! Also, a big thank you to Panagiotis Lampridis - Book Design Stars, you have been amazing with the book cover and interior design, I know how much effort you have put into getting me here. To my friends and family who have kept on at me to finish, yes, it's here thanks to you! And finally thank you to my wonderful husband for reviewing the book and all the encouragement in helping me get this through to the finish line. Thank you again, I couldn't have got here without you!